Person to Person

Person to Person

THE INTERNATIONAL IMPACT OF THE TELEPHONE

PETER YOUNG

for Pat,
who saw the
beginning of it

with thanks, *Peter Cg*

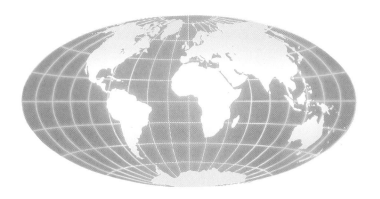

GRANTA EDITIONS

For Patrick Byrne, who encouraged.

'Telephones don't talk, people do.'
Eric Clayton, in a Norfolk accent

© Peter Young 1991

ISBN 0 906782 62 7

Published by Granta Editions
47 Norfolk Street, Cambridge CB1 2LE
Granta Editions is an imprint of The Book Concern Ltd

A CIP catalogue record for this book is available from the British Library.

The author and publisher are grateful to the University of Sussex Library
for the financial support *Person to Person* received as winner of the 1987-88 Ralph Lewis Award.
They would also like to thank British Telecommunications plc
for its support and involvement in the book.

Designed by Jim Reader
Design and production in association with
Book Production Consultants, 47 Norfolk Street, Cambridge

Printed and bound in Singapore by Kyodo Printing Co (S'pore) Pte Ltd

FRONT COVER ILLUSTRATIONS: *Pictor International – London (globe and man); NTT (woman).*
BACK COVER ILLUSTRATION: *BT Museum.*

CONTENTS

AUTHOR'S PREFACE

Planes, boats, trains and motor vehicles continue to attract personal and media interest, drawing crowds to places and events, and inspiring books, radio and TV programmes. That is probably because, as a physical means of communication that moves, each affects all our five senses. Steam buffs, for example, can see, hear, touch, smell, even taste the great days of the iron horse. Nostalgia lives, the romance reaching younger generations.

In comparison, despite its importance in our everyday lives, telecommunications has aroused far less interest. Partly this is because it forms such a large section of the media – the means of sending messages. Except to technicians, the hardware is for the most part uninteresting: racks and boxes of equipment concealed from public view, cables buried under the streets or resting silently on the sea-bed. Occasionally, forms of telecommunications surface as impressive features on the landscape: radio and TV masts, microwave or large satellite dishes. The collectors of telephones, switchboards, relevant stamps and phonecards are also specialists, although they are relatively few in number.

There are degrees of interest in forms of telecommunications, past and present, particularly those which affect people – of all classes – often indirectly. For instance the telegraph enabled: news and financial information to be transmitted rapidly, reducing time-scales from days to minutes; railway trains to reach their destinations quickly and safely, enabling fresh goods to be carried to market and providing people with greater opportunity for taking day trips and living away from the grimy cities in which they worked. The arrival of radio and TV meant that it is now possible for events on the other side of the world to be broadcast live.

In contrast, the telephone is essentially a personal instrument, mainly for one-to-one communication. So many people, so many conversations – each individual and intended to be private. At first the instrument was a curiosity, an invention long desired but without a universally agreed

purpose. Its success depended on the number of subscribers and their ability to reach one another. Not everybody could afford or wanted an instrument. Its availability was restricted by costs, vested interests and suspicious governments. The telephone took longer than other media to make a direct impact on society at large.

There are books about technical and economic aspects of the phone but surprisingly little has been written about its social influence, its impact upon societies and individuals, and the way in which their attitudes to it have changed. Its importance is also evident where it is either absent or not easily accessible, as in many parts of the Third World.

When I started research for this book I knew there was a gap to be filled and that it had to be done on a global scale. I did not realize how big the subject was. The initial scraps of information grew to a mass of material that became difficult to manage and reduce to a publishable manuscript. At the same time there was a frustration in not being able to find answers to all my questions.

My thanks are due to many people, acknowledged elsewhere in the book, who have helped me in so many ways. For making publication possible I am grateful to the University of Sussex Library for the Ralph Lewis Trust Award 1987–8 and to British Telecommunications plc, which has purchased its own edition of my book. The company has been an enlightened sponsor, by no means a censor, in making helpful contributions to the text and illustrations.

It is impossible for one volume to tell the complete story of the telephone in all its fascinating social and historic detail; I trust that this book will encourage others around the world to add to the literature of telecommunications.

Peter Young
April 1991

CHAPTER 1

WORD OF MOUTH

In 1863 a Maryland newspaper reported:

A man about 46 years of age, giving the name of Joshua Coppersmith, has been arrested in New York for attempting to extort funds from ignorant and superstitious people by exhibiting a device which he says will convey the human voice any distance over metallic wires, so that it will be heard by the listener at the other end. He calls the instrument a 'telephone', which is obviously intended to imitate the word 'telegraph' and win the confidence of those who know the success of the latter instrument without understanding the principles on which it is based. Well-informed people know that it is impossible to transmit the human voice over wires as it may be done with dots and dashes and signals of the Morse code, and that, were it possible to do so, the thing would be of no practical value. The authorities who apprehended this criminal are to be congratulated, and it is hoped that his punishment will be prompt and fitting, that it may serve as an example to other conscienceless schemers who enrich themselves at the expense of their fellow creatures.

Yet there is no evidence that Joshua Coppersmith ever existed. He may have been invented by a journalist stuck for a story. Certainly the idea of the telephone existed long before the reality, and an otherwise unknown author, G. Huth, noted in a treatise published in Berlin in 1796 that there was a convenient Greek combination (*tele*, far off, + *phone*, voice or sound) to describe it. In the sixteenth century Mother Shipton, a Yorkshire witch, prophesied:

Around the world thought will fly
In the twinkling of an eye.

In *Simplicissimus* (1669) the German novelist Grimmelshausen opined: 'If only one could have an instrument with which one could miraculously hear what is said at great distance.'

What a difference to society such a device could have made. Had it existed in ancient Greece, the Athenian courier Pheidippides would not have had to run some 150 miles in two days to enlist Spartans against the Persians just landed at Marathon. It could have saved from punishment messengers who brought bad tidings. It could have prevented the tragedy of star-crossed lovers such as Romeo and Juliet. History and life would have been very different with the abolition of distance and the telescoping of time.

Unlike the term 'television', 'half Greek and half Latin', which the *Manchester Guardian* editor C. P. Scott thought boded ill for the device, 'telephone' had a respectable ancestry. A pure Greek compound, echoing classical excellence in art and science, it described various means of conveying sound and meant different things to different people. 'Captain J. N. Tayler's telephone instrument... The chief object of this powerful wind instrument is to convey signals during foggy weather.' So wrote *The Times* in 1844. *The Illustrated London News* called the invention a 'Marine Alarum and Signal Trumpet'. Working on compressed air, it was used as a fog-horn at sea and like a steam whistle on railways.

Early associations were with music. The name 'telephone' was applied in 1828 to a French system for signalling by musical notes and later to 'the Enchanted Lyre' devised by the co-inventor of the telegraph, Charles Wheatstone, for transmitting sound from one room to another, perhaps for a concert. Where the telegraph was unlikely to be used there was the portable telephone: large concave reflectors, made from the recently rediscovered rubber-like substance gutta percha, that were intended to carry a conversation across, say, the inner quadrangle of a building.

More common and also made of gutta percha – the company of that name was incorporated in 1845 – were speaking tubes. 'Small and cheap Railway Conversation Tubes', according to the company, enabled parties 'to converse with ease and pleasure, whilst travelling, notwithstanding the noise of the train. This can be done in so soft a whisper as not to be overheard even by a fellow-traveller. They are portable, and will coil up so as to be placed inside the hat.' In omnibuses too, 'the saving of labour to the lungs of the Conductor is very great, as a message given in a soft tone of voice is distinctly heard by the Driver. In windy weather, and in the noisy streets of London, the Gutta Percha Apparatus is peculiarly valuable.'

In steamships, speaking tubes were a quick means of communication between bridge and engine room. To alert the duty engineer below, the officer of the watch removed the stopper from the mouthpiece at his end of the tube and blew down it. Not surprisingly, sailors soon called it 'the

blower', a term they had hitherto used for a certain type of woman. What was a strumpet became a trumpet.

Similarly, in the theatre speaking tubes were used between stage and flys. They were built into the walls of offices so that partners could converse while seated. In households they were also labour-saving. Summoned by a wire-hung bell, servants often had to make two journeys, one to receive the instruction and one to carry it out. Like their betters, servants too could be saved legwork. Shorter lengths were sometimes inserted in the lids of coffins so that the body could indicate if it was not yet ready for burial.

Words to make the listener blush or giggle could be whispered on lovers' or string telephones, popular among Victorian children, as J. E. Kingsbury, an early authority on the instrument proper, noted in 1882:

A few years ago in the side streets of our great highways numbers of hawkers were selling toy telephones, made of a little tin cylinder with a paper

RIGHT: *Further testimonials for the Medical Man's Midnight Friend raised no qualms about the communication of disease by speaking tube.* (BT Museum)

INSTRUCTIONS
FOR THE MAGNETIC CORD.

Hold the instrument with the open end close to the ear, or if asking a question with the open part of the tube close to the mouth, speaking in a low but clear tone. Keep the magnetic cord quite tight, and care must be taken that it does not come in contact with any object, otherwise the transmission of the message will be prevented.

The instrument being highly magnetised, great care should be taken that it does not come in contact with metallic substances.

TEST.—Place a watch against the open end of the tube, place the other tube against the ear, when the ticking will be distinctly heard at a distance of 50 yards.

Copyright entered at Stationers' Hall.
E. S. & Co., Manufacturers.

ABOVE: *Victorian toys used one instrument as both transmitter and receiver, a principle followed in the earliest electric speaking phones.*

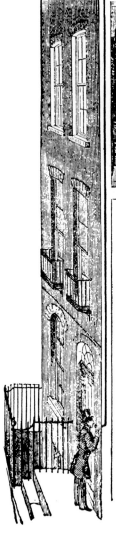

Gutta Percha Speaking Tube.

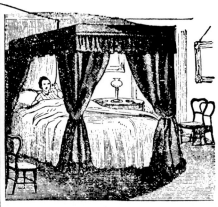

GUTTA PERCHA
SPEAKING TUBE.

Testimonials.

From HENRY ASHTON, Esq., Surgeon.

Walton, near Preston, Dec. 11th, 1850.

I have had Gutta Percha Tubing carried from my front door to my bedroom, for the transmission of communications from my patients *in the night.* I have it brought to my pillow, and am able with the greatest facility to hold any communication with the messenger in the street, without rising to open the window, and incurring exposure to the night air. It gives me great satisfaction in being able to recommend to my medical brethren, an article so cheap and easy of adoption, which will save them from the injurious effects of being exposed to a current of cold air from an open window the moment they rise from their beds.

From Messrs. WALL & TROUNCER,
SURGEONS, &c.

6, Mount-st., Grosvenor Square, Jan. 22, 1851.

We state, with satisfaction, that the Gutta Percha Tubing fitted up by Mr. H. C. Dulley, 18, Wilderness Row, communicating between the street and the bed chamber, answers our expectation as a conductor of sound, and that the necessity of going down stairs, or opening the window to receive messages from our nightly visitors, is thus obviated. It is, therefore, with confidence we recommend all exposed to this inconvenience of our profession to adopt a similar plan.

THE GUTTA PERCHA COMPANY, PATENTEES,
18, WHARF ROAD, CITY ROAD, LONDON.

drumhead, to which was attached a string. These instruments were perfect little telephones, and effective for short distances with a very taut string. In their case the vibrations of the voice were carried from one drumhead to another by the string, a medium suitable enough for a few yards; but for any longer distance some other means must be found to do the necessary work. Electricity was evidently the most suitable means, only awaiting successful application, and many scientific men were patiently working and experimenting to discover what that application was to be.

Among them was Philipp Reis, a schoolmaster near Frankfurt, who started his researches in 1860. His first apparatus incorporated the hollowed-out bung of a beer barrel, a sausage skin, a violin and a knitting-needle. Reception on an improved model was spasmodic and not conducive to understanding or appreciation. According to one witness, 'Reis did obtain articulate sounds, but this was when the instrument worked in a manner which it was not intended it should.' Nevertheless Reis called it a *Telephon*, a minor variant on the word that was to become almost universal. The Germans, though, had their own combination, *Fernsprecher*. The word for an operator later caught the fancy of the English humorist Paul Jennings: '*Fernsprechbeamtin* has already provoked a vision of a placid, fair-haired, semi-mythical Teutonic figure, a kind of Telephone Queen, deep in some German forest – the Far-Speaking Beaming One.'

Achieving what so many had imagined and thought impossible turned out to be a matter of practical perseverance. It was a Scotsman's misunderstanding of a book in German that led to sustained experiments on electric telephony. Knowing little German and not much about electricity, the young Alexander Graham Bell got the impression that Helmholtz, having produced vowel sounds by tuning forks, had sent them over a telegraph wire. He set out to reconstruct Helmholtz's invention, and later, on seeing a French translation of the original German, realized that he had embarked on a new line of experiment.

The credit for successfully applying electricity to the tin-can-and-string principle belongs to Bell, who invented what was first called 'the electric speaking telephone'. There had been speaking telephones that were not electric and electric telephones that could send a note or a noise but not speak. Bell found a way of bringing the two together and, a week after his 29th birthday, on 10 March 1876 in a Boston boarding-house achieved the first electrical transmission of intelligible speech. His first words to his assistant, 'Mr Watson, come here, I want you!', have been interpreted as an order – they spoke formally to one another – or a cry for help – Bell had spilt acid from a battery on his clothes.

The accident was soon forgotten in the joy of success, and Bell himself

Philipp Reis was not forgotten in Germany, where stamps were issued in 1952 to mark 75 years of the telephone and in 1961 for the centenary of his invention.

(Stanley Gibbons Ltd)

quickly saw the telephone as an instrument of love. A woman had given him inspiration and was to share in the rewards. With the $85 from his first public lecture on his invention he bought a silver model of his primitive apparatus for his fiancée, Mabel Hubbard, who, left deaf by scarlet fever when she was four, would never hear the real thing.

Ten years later, in 'The Wonders of Forty Years', Benjamin Franklin Taylor tried to capture some of the impact:

> The far is near. Our feeblest whispers fly
> Where cannon falter, thunders faint and die.
> Your little song the telephone can float
> As free of fetters as a bluebird's note,
> Quick as a player ascending into Heaven.
> Quick as the answer, 'all thy sins forgiven'…
> The Lightning writes it, God's electric clerk;
> The engine bears it, buckling to the work
> Till miles are minutes and the minutes breaths…

In his prospectus addressed 'to the capitalists of the Electric Telephone Company' and dated 'Kensington, March 25, 1878' Bell made the following point about his invention:

> The great advantage it possesses over every other form of electrical apparatus consists in the fact that it requires no skill to operate the instrument. All other telegraphic machines produce signals which require to be translated by experts, and such instruments are therefore extremely limited in their application, but the telephone actually speaks, and for this reason it can be utilized for nearly every purpose for which speech is employed.

The difference was crucial to the application of the two types of instrument. Whereas operating a telegraph system demanded a working knowledge of Morse or some other code, using the phone was simplicity itself. The electric telegraph was an institutional instrument used strategically, quickening the pace of life. It enabled steam trains to run fast safely; news to be transmitted soon after it happened, across land and sea; financial deals to be done – sterling is still called 'cable' on the international money markets. It strengthened the hand of central governments, even reaching some imperial outposts.

Some decades would elapse before the phone had that kind of reach. Meanwhile, it was a different kind of instrument: at hand, personal, immediate. The contrast was crucial to Hong Kong Chinese, who readily appreciated the advantages of cable service but initially regarded the

"The Voice Returned"

THE "Great Blizzard" of 1888 had blocked railway traffic and disrupted mail and telegraph service. Through the drift-piled Boston streets groups of men and women made their way to the public telephone stations, anxiously inquiring whether the long distance lines to New York were still in service.

"People did not want a message, they wanted to talk," runs a contemporary story. "They wanted to find out where the other party was, if he was alive, indeed. **** It was the voice returned, the personal interview that was especially valuable."

A telephone conversation is more than a method of communication—it is a means of projecting personality. Hope, cheer, comfort and reassurance, made intimate and personal by the spoken word, speed over the wires. The "voice returned" is the telephone's great gift to man.

What Great Writers Have Said of the Voice

Classsical poets and prose writers have made frequent reference to the spoken word as a revealer of character and to the voice as a reflection of personality. Among these allusions are:

Poetry	Prose
He ceas'd but left so pleasing in their ear His voice that list'ning still they seemed to hear. —Homer, *The Odyssey*.	The voice is Jacob's voice, but the hands are the hands of Esau. —*Genesis xxvii, 22.*
Mend thy speech a little Lest it mar thy fortune. —Shakespeare, *King Lear*.	On the tongue of such an one they shed a honeyed dew, and from his lips drop gentle words. —Hesiod, *The Theogony*.
Give every man thy ear, but few thy voice. —Shakespeare, *Hamlet*.	The living voice is that which sways the soul. —*Pliny the Younger*.
How sweetly sounds the voice of a good woman. —Middleton, *The Old Law*.	For one word a man is often deemed to be wise, and for one word he is often deemed to be foolish. We ought to be careful indeed what we say. —*Confucius*.
For it stirs the blood of an old man's heart And it makes the pulses fly To catch the thrill of a happy voice And the light of a pleasant eye. —Willis, *Saturday Afternoon*.	Out of the abundance of the heart the mouth speaketh. —*Matthew xi. 34.* He who has truth at his heart need never fear the want of persuasion on his tongue. —Ruskin, *Stones of Venice*.

To thousands of the people whom she serves, the telephone operator is only a **Voice**.

Yet so completely has she mastered the fine art of making her voice project her personality that it cannot but carry to the listening ear some hint of the spirit which makes her the highly valued public servant she is.

Hundreds of times a day her voice carries over the wires its message of efficient and courteous service to the public which never sees her but which knows that, whatever the emergency, it may depend upon her unwavering devotion to duty.

Within 12 years of its invention in Boston, the phone had become essential to the inhabitants of its home town, as Telephone Almanacs *recalled in October 1925.* (AT&T Archives)

phone as an intrusion into private property, necessitating the presence of an installer and possibly a repairman in the office. The notion of it in the home was unthinkable.

Users in general might have to strain through interference and poor reception, but facts, feelings and much of a personality could be conveyed. Yet there was no general agreement on its role in society. Early on in the USA it was considered as a way of broadcasting information and music. According to New England newspaper prophecies of early 1877: 'By a judicious distribution of instruments, a whole parish might hear its minister preach on a stormy Sunday, without his leaving his study', and 'When some future President is inaugurated, may not his words be caught by a telephonic ear, and be repeated to listening audiences all over the land?'

Soon more mundane possibilities became evident: 'Mrs Smith is lonely of an afternoon, and the central office man having, by her request, joined her wire with Mrs Brown's, the two spend an hour very enjoyably in cutting up Mrs Robinson.' One anonymous prophet envisaged 'a cacophone devised as an instrument of torture, to be used, perhaps, as a means of punishment for the worst class of criminals' and 'a faithful antiphone of some sort, whose function it should be to take the life out of every intruding sound'. An instrument of torture would in time be easier to achieve than peace and quiet. Ambrose Bierce's sardonic definition was 'An invention of the devil which abrograates some of the advantages of making a disagreeable person keep his distance.' Hell's bells?

Its use reflected the character of nations, societies and individuals, at first limited in number. In many places its progress would be patchy and slow, deliberately. The phone was not to change ways of life as abruptly or profoundly as the generalizations of Marshall McLuhan, a philosopher not a historian of the media, later led some people to believe. Although man had long wanted to speak across a distance, there was not going to be a universal and immediate rush to seize the opportunity.

CHAPTER 2

THIS LITTLE INSTRUMENT

After giving a few lectures to Boston scientific groups in the spring of 1876, Bell was not interested in demonstrating his invention at the large Centennial Exposition in Philadelphia that summer. His financial backer, Gardiner Hubbard, urged him to, but it was only the tearful pleas of Hubbard's daughter Mabel that convinced him. At first it hardly seemed worth it; his exhibit was largely ignored by the crowds. The judges too would have passed it by had not the Emperor of Brazil, who had met Bell at the Boston School for the Deaf, drawn their attention to his simple apparatus by listening to his recital of Hamlet's soliloquy 'To be, or not to be'. The Emperor exclaimed 'My God, it talks!' and it received a merit award.

In a two-volume official report and other accounts of the Centennial, however, the phone was not mentioned, whereas items such as the printing telegraph and threshing machines received lavish illustrated coverage. Fifty years later, John J. Carty, who started as a boy phone-operator and became vice-president of American Telephone and Telegraph Company, the giant organization that grew out of Bell's invention, told a Boston Chamber of Commerce meeting:

> Nobody would put a telephone in the house. It was a nuisance. Nobody wanted it in a business office. It was difficult to get anybody to invest a dollar in the telephone business.

Well-to-do Philadelphians were to shun the new invention demonstrated in their city almost as severely as if they had been rural Amish sticking to the old ways. The country at large was in the depths of a depression.

Feeling that technical development had come to a dead end, Bell's partner, Watson, consulted a medium for inspiration but nothing came. Equally pessimistic during the winter of 1876–7, Hubbard offered all rights in the phone for $100,000 to the great telegraph company, Western Union.

The president refused the offer with the rhetorical question: 'What use could this company make of an electrical toy?' His attitude echoed that towards electricity itself in the eighteenth century.

Not until 4 April 1877 was the first permanent line installed, a private 3-mile link between the small Boston electrical factory where Watson made the first instrument and the home of its proprietor, Charles Williams. Soon after, the first business phones were rented, the decision not to sell taken by Hubbard, a lawyer who knew the advantages of leasing shoemaking machines. Yet, when hucksters sold many brands of snake oil, why should the public take the new gadget on trust? It had to be heard to be believed.

To publicize their invention, Bell and Watson staged a series of double acts, with Watson some miles away bellowing and singing to the audience in the lecture hall. The favourite song with audiences was *Do Not Trust Him, Gentle Lady* but, lively though the demonstrations were, they left an air of suspicion. According to the Providence *Press*, 'It is indeed difficult, hearing the sounds out of the mysterious box, to wholly resist the notion that the powers of darkness are somehow in league with it.' The *Advertiser* remarked that 'the weirdness and novelty were something never before felt in Boston' and even in sophisticated New York the *Herald* regarded the phone as 'almost supernatural'.

Nevertheless, in July 1877 the Bell Telephone Company was formed and, two days before Bell married her, he turned over to Mabel Hubbard all but 10 of his shares so that she had a holding of 1,497. Can there have been a more generous and rewarding wedding present in modern times? In early August they sailed for Britain on an extended honeymoon, during which he intended to show his home country to his new bride and promote the phone.

The first public exhibition in England of a working phone was made not by Bell but with a pair of his instruments by William Preece, electrician to the Post Office, to a British Association meeting in Plymouth in September 1877. Early in October, Bell was to demonstrate to a Congress of the Sanitary Institute in Leamington Spa but was prevented by ill-health. He did, however, address among others the Society of Telegraph Engineers and demonstrate to Queen Victoria, who found the instrument 'most extraordinary' and had a private connection made between Osborne House, her summer home on the Isle of Wight, and Osborne Cottage, the home of Sir Thomas Biddulph, with whom she conversed on 14 January 1878. The Queen noted in her journal: 'It is rather faint, and one must hold the tube close to one's ear.' Nevertheless, one was installed at Windsor Castle later that year and at Buckingham Palace in 1879.

On 24 January 1878 there was a demonstration at Crystal Palace, the home of the Great Exhibition, entitled *Wire a Thousand Yards in Length*, and on 22 May the first London theatrical use of the idea, at the Gaiety Theatre, in *The Telephone Harp*. Shakespearian and other actors imaginatively played upon this instrument to convey scenes from Stratford-upon-Avon to the Gaiety. *Punch* ran cartoons on the possibilities of the novelty, and in *HMS Pinafore*, originally intended to be *HMS Semaphore*, Gilbert and Sullivan included a lyric lamenting its lack:

> He'll hear no tone,
> Of the maiden he loves so well!
> No Telephone
> Communicates with his cell!

In January 1879 a new farce by H. Saville Clark, *Tale of a Telephone*, was staged at the Theatre Royal, Drury Lane.

The instruments were first offered to the British public in a circular issued by Bell's local agent, the energetic American Colonel W. H. Reynolds, in October 1877, the advertised cost being £25 for a pair of phones on a short circuit, or £5 per annum rent, £35 for a pair on a long circuit, or £10 per annum rent. G. H. Lewes, with whom the novelist George Eliot lived from 1854 until his death in 1878, recorded in his diary: 'Thursday, 21st March... We went to the Telephone office to have the Telephone explained and demonstrated. Chat with Kate Field and Col. Reynolds.'

Kate Field, an American journalist who was a great phone publicist, gave details of the visit in the *New York Tribune* of 22 December 1880, the day on which George Eliot died. She reported the novelist as saying: 'It is very wonderful, very useful. What marvellous inventions you Americans have!' George Eliot 'for an hour tested its capacity' and in a letter to Charles Ritter on 22 May 1878 thanking him for news of her friends M. and Mme D'Albert Durade in Geneva, wrote 'If telephonic converse were possible for us, we could say many things to each other.'

Such enthusiasm did not exist in official circles. W. H. Preece, who in 1877 had recommended that the Post Office 'enter into arrangements with Professor Bell as early as possible, paying him for its use a royalty upon each apparatus', as assistant engineer-in-chief testified in 1879 to a House of Commons committee:

> I fancy the descriptions we get of its use in America are a little exaggerated, though there are conditions in America which necessitate the use of such instruments more than here. Here we have a superabundance of messengers, errand boys and things of that kind... The absence of servants has compelled

Americans to adopt communication systems for domestic purposes. Few have worked at the telephone much more than I have. I have one in my office, but more for show. If I want to send a message – I use a sounder or employ a boy to take it.

There was similar resistance to new technology in the French capital, where the Pneumatique was shooting messages under the city by compressed air.

Opinion within the British Post Office on the future of the phone was divided. Losses on inland telegraphs, acquired from the private companies in 1870, were still mounting, and if the phone that so fascinated some engineers developed successfully it would be a threat to telegraph revenues. At the same time the Treasury, the real power because it controlled the money supply, was putting pressure on the Post Office to cut costs and not get involved in an expensive technical innovation. The risk was that private enterprise would succeed with the phone, which would reduce telegraph income in the short term and in the longer term create something that would be more expensive to buy out than had been the telegraph companies. What the dogs in the Treasury manger wanted was a private-enterprise phone service that did not work. Its potential in business, administration and social life was not envisaged, let alone grasped.

At this period a shift in the national attitude was evident. Gone was the mid-century confidence of the Victorians who had organized and managed the workshop of the world. Britain now faced competition from new nation-states such as Germany and the USA, and the economy was sluggish. 'Above all', commented *The Electrician*, there was 'the phlegmatic indifference to everything new which is characteristic of us as a nation'. It had not been so when the main railway network was laid down between 1830 and 1850 in a mania of modernity, when flamboyant promoters raised capital, fortunes were made and lost, and steam trains affected the pace and way of life of most classes in society.

The phone was to spread much less rapidly, in a geographical and social sense. It was not to throw up any colourful characters like those produced by other media. Among those developing and producing equipment or operating services there were to be no equivalents of powerful Press barons like Northcliffe and Beaverbrook, or of the legendary film moguls, immigrant Eastern European Jews who blossomed larger than life in the Southern California sun. In the USA, where there was a labour shortage, this advance in technology was an opportunity to be seized, another time-saving device that speeded up business, enabling more Gilded Age money to be made more quickly. Against a dismal background of government restrictions, public indifference and hindrance, in Britain the phone took a long time to become more than a curiosity.

James Clerk Maxwell, the physicist whose work on electromagnetism was to be so important for communications systems, wrote in 1878:

> When at last this little instrument appeared, consisting, as it does, of parts every one of which is familiar to us, and capable of being put together by an amateur, the disappointment arising from its humble appearance was only partially relieved on finding that it was really able to talk.

So simple was it that Dr Mayo's 14-year-old son Charlie, going on nothing but pictures and descriptions, was reputed to have produced instruments for linking his father's office over a drugstore in Rochester, Minnesota, with the family farmhouse. They worked so well that the phone company threatened an infringement of patent.

By the end of 1879, in the first six weeks of his employment in the way-leave department of the Edison Telephone Company in London, where his job was to persuade property owners to allow the company to erect rooftop poles or other structures for overhead wires, George Bernard Shaw had secured one consent. For this he was paid half a crown ($12\frac{1}{2}$p) commission, 'in practice unremunerative' as 'my private expenses meanwhile have amounted to two guineas' (£2.10) and 'I entered my duties in obedience to pressing pecuniary demands'.

To encourage the practice of using the phone, then called 'telephonetics', Magnus Volk, the Brighton engineer who was the first person in that town to be connected, advertised in a local newspaper in 1882 that intending subscribers should apply to him for a three-month installation free of charge. That same year the Hull Merchants Exchange could muster only 28 votes out of a possible 600 in favour of an installation, a decision that was not reversed until four years later. In November 1885 the instrument was still such a novelty in Cambridge that George Darwin and his wife, who had the number 10, used it at one of their dinner parties to entertain their guests, among whom were Charles Villiers Stanford, the composer, and later professor of music in the university, and his wife. 'We amused them', wrote Mrs Darwin, 'by talking to Ida [her sister-in-law on number 17] on the telephone. They had never seen one.' Yet six years before an Arabian emir had shown an English traveller, Wilfred Scawen Blunt, 'his latest toy'.

Installation was not simple. Leave was granted to Dr A. Macalister so that his rooms in St John's College, Cambridge, could be connected to the exchange on 28 May 1886. That year Oxford got its first exchange. Doubtless the Darwins employed servants, who for the annual cost of a phone did much more. In London the Bell Company charged £20, the Edison Company £12, which was the going provincial rate. For this outlay one could call a limited number of subscribers whereas a servant was a maid of all work, including perhaps answering the phone, much as she would answer the door. The fact that the maid accepted calls emphasized the low status of the instrument, and the practice endured until the perpetual 1920s of Jeeves and Bertie Wooster. In most places, phone companies sought business rather than domestic users, a distinction recognized in Basle, where private citizens had to pay a basic cost of 150 Swiss francs and public institutions 100 francs per annum. It was noted that the people of Basle 'warm only very slowly to something that costs them money before they can enjoy its purpose'.

In the UK, public authorities seemed to conspire against the efforts of private enterprise. Jealous of the companies' success, the new Liberal government sought an interpretation in the High Court of the Post Office's rights under the Telegraph Act 1869. The government contended that 'telephone' was a 'telegraph' within the meaning of the Act, to which the companies rejoined that it was impossible an Act could include what was not merely unborn but unconceived at the time it was passed. Logic might appear to be topsy-turvy, but there was no doubt that the government had a monopoly of communication by electric signals and, against popular expectation, the 1880 verdict was in its favour. A similar judgement had been handed down in Switzerland in 1878. Instead of using its victory to provide its own service, the Post Office, under Treasury direction, employed it as a bargaining weapon in its licensing of the companies, from which it extracted 10 per cent of income.

Local authorities also objected to the advance of the phone. In Brighton, when Magnus Volk set up the first pair of wires, to a friend's home nearby, it had to cross a road. A busybody reported the eyesore to the council and Volk was asked to remove it. His reply was to erect another pair, this time connecting two councillors' homes. Both pairs stayed. Elsewhere, some rating surveyors found them a legitimate new source of revenue. Obtaining way-leaves often involved considerable negotiation, and the refusal of some property owners not only caused expense by forcing companies to take circuitous routes but also denied some districts the advantages of phone communications.

The earliest systems were point-to-point, confirming existing relationships. After Bell visited *HMS Vernon*, a naval training establishment at Portsmouth, a clever mechanic, Isaac Tall, made a number of instruments, and a cable was laid across the mud to the house of Captain Arthur, commanding the Torpedo School. Awakened early by the phone, the captain discovered that it was his coxswain ringing up to chat with a maid, a practice that immediately ceased.

Limited in scope, point-to-point systems nevertheless did open up new possibilities. An early one was improved safety in mines, especially in emergencies. Instant voice communications were cheaper than telegraph signals, more effective than code-ringing on bells, and safer than using boy messengers. First users in British Columbia and Nova Scotia were collieries. In Cornwall an inspector of mines established a link from the office to a china-clay mine and on to a doctor's house. An enlightened legislature in Pennsylvania enacted a law in 1877 requiring several hundred anthracite mines to have oral communication from underground to the surface, but in the UK such provision was at the discretion of individual coal owners.

Parts of a business could be brought closer together. Early in 1880 Messrs Butt, timber merchants of Littlehampton and Brighton, had their offices connected over the 22 miles and conversations were held as if under one roof. To make the point, a chess match was played between the clubs of Chichester and Brighton, by kind permission of the postmaster-general. When Joseph Lloyd, miller and merchant of the Little City of St Asaph in the Vale of Clwyd, established a link between his office and mill, the bishop made the inaugural call in Welsh.

Bell's native Scotland was not left behind. By the spring of 1878 'this wonderful instrument' gave some residents of remote Easdale in Argyllshire the opportunity 'of holding converse with parties at Oban, 16 miles distant, which they were able to do, at first rather stiffly, but, after a little experience, with great satisfaction, speaking and singing being distinctly heard, and any change of voice being quite recognizable. The entertainment was exceedingly interesting.' Henry Dyer, a young graduate of the University of Glasgow invited to help found the Imperial College of Engineering, introduced the telephone to Japan in 1877, when he installed London-made instruments to connect his office at the college with the public works department. Soon instruments were being made locally. Japanese was the first foreign language to be used on the phone. During the Centennial Exposition Bell had a Japanese student, Issawa, in his classes at Boston University, who asked: 'Mr Bell, will this thing talk Japanese?' A demonstration to Issawa, verified by two of his countrymen from Harvard, was convincing.

The first exchanges, an idea taken over from the telegraph service, were for private subscribers with a common interest. In the USA the first switchboard was opened in Boston on 17 May 1877 by Edwin Thomas Holmes, who ran an electrical burglar-alarm business. His six subscribers, among them banks, used the exchange as a telephone system by day and it served as an alarm at night. Soon after, the proprietor of a drugstore in Hartford, Connecticut, had a subscription list mainly of doctors and a livery stable.

Professions and trades that had to respond to demands quickly were more eager to subscribe than those for whom an emergency was rare or unknown. Doctors, who were also to be early users of motor cars, were quick to subscribe, whereas lawyers were content to live with delay. The value of speedy communication was demonstrated in January 1878, when the Hartford doctors and livery stable were urgently required to attend a railway accident at Tariffville. That month the first public exchange, serving 21 subscribers, opened in New Haven, Connecticut. It was manned by George Willard Coy, assisted by a boy, Louis Herrick Frost, and their first experimental shout was 'Ahoy, ahoy'. 'Hello' came later.

Initially, the opening of exchanges depended on local enterprise and not on the importance of the place. Thus Denver, Colorado, a town of plank sidewalks swarming with silver miners and prospectors and yet without electric light, had an exchange established on 24 February 1879, before New York City and Washington DC, through the enterprise of Frederick O. Vaille, in his late twenties. A 31-year-old banker, Hugh Baker, was responsible for Canada's first exchange, and the first in the British Empire, opened at Hamilton, Ontario, in July 1878. Operators in Bell Canada answered 'Well' or 'Are you there?' until 1895, when somebody suggested 'Number, please', which was not standardized until 1925.

In the UK, The Glasgow Medical Telephone Exchange was established early in 1879, offering an unlimited number of calls for £12 per annum. On 10 May 1879 Arnold White, Edison's UK agent, in a letter to *The Times* argued that

> Metropolitan interests are too vast and too complicated to be dealt with from a single centre. Telephony in London must decentralize to be efficient. It would be impossible, as it would be useless, to include the stockbroker in the same exchange as the insurance office or the produce merchant. An exchange in Mark Lane might include all the grain interests indigenous to that locality. Or, were the amount of business too great for efficiency, further subdivision might become necessary.

The first UK public exchange was opened by the (Bell) Telephone Company at 36 Coleman Street in the City in August 1879 with fewer than ten subscribers. They were served by four operating staff, two of whom were seated to receive instructions, which were passed to two others, probably boys, who made the required connections with double-ended cords. The rival Edison Company quickly responded to the challenge and early in September established its own exchange close by in Lombard Street. It had ten subscribers, among them the Pullman Car Association, the Equitable Insurance Company of the US, Messrs Kingsbury advertising agents, and *The Times*, which was number 10.

The Times commented in a leader:

> There is no limit whatever to the number of points between which communication can be established, and scarcely a moment's delay in bringing them into connexion with one another...At the present moment there are ten favoured spots at which this privilege can be obtained; but there may just as easily be ten hundred or ten thousand, and, doubtless, before long there will be.

By the spring of 1880 the Edison Company had five exchanges and nearly 200 subscribers. Australia opened its first exchange (in Melbourne) in 1880; France, Germany, with eight subscribers in Berlin, and New Zealand (at Christchurch) in 1881; Hong Kong and South Africa (at Port Elizabeth) in 1882.

The introduction of exchanges changed the whole character of the phone service. As J. E. Kingsbury, a contemporary observer, noted: 'The great use of the telephone was to be not merely for communication but for intercommunication.' All sorts of people not connected by their trade, profession, social group or anything else were in potential contact with one another, without the ceremony of introduction. As technical improvements were introduced it would become progressively easier to make contact. No more skill or social grace was needed than simply asking for the appropriate number. It would take many years for that simple notion, with all its implications, to spread through society. Meanwhile, users had to put up with the inconveniences of independent and unconnected systems.

The idea of what a few tried to popularize as a 'telepheme', thought to be a less clumsy expression than 'telephonic message', was catching on but there was still a widely held view that it was an intermediate instrument. In the USA a Western Union official had foreseen its application as transmitting speech between telegraph operators, not eliminating them. Kingsbury testified to 'the great advantage of having been saved frequent journeys to or from the City' by summoning a messenger.

Looking back in 1916, he recalled:

> The expectations were that the principal business firms would become exchange subscribers. It was not contemplated that the service would become general.

In the USA the advent of the phone coincided with the 'robber barons', who, after the Civil War, built their giant corporations and formed trusts. Like the *zaibatsu*, the well-established trading companies of Japan, they were able to put the telephone to greater use than the corner store or livery stable. When they were doing deals it enabled them to raise money quickly, and there was no written record for the trust-busters to use as evidence. In the building of their symbols of corporate success, the skyscrapers, phone wires were a quicker, surer and safer method of communication than hand signals, shouts and whistles.

This new method of communication was the basis of the modern office, which could be physically separate from the factory. Head office, in a smart quarter of town, could have its own character, unrelated to the less appealing aspects of the business elsewhere. This became evident in Chicago, where the commercial centre was razed by fire in 1871, creating an opportunity to rebuild the business capital of the Middle West. It also happened to be the base of the major phone manufacturing companies. The new technologies in communications and the load-bearing steel frame, exploited by architects such as Louis Sullivan and Burnham & Root, came together in the creation and operation of high-rise buildings such as corporate headquarters and department stores.

Among British businessmen there was a much more cautious approach. In September 1878 'a line of private wire' was established between the head office of the Bank of England in Threadneedle Street and its Western Branch, followed in December 1881 by a wire between head office and the Law Courts Branch. Looking back in 1905 on his brief period with the Edison Company, George Bernard Shaw observed in *The Irrational Knot* that the phone was 'of such stentorian efficiency that it bellowed your most private communications all over the house instead of whispering them with some sort of discretion. This was not what the British stockbroker wanted.' The Baltic Exchange carried out a six months' trial of the Bell (you had to shout and could hardly hear) and Edison (in which you spoke and were deafened) systems in 1879–80, during which members complained of the inefficiencies, and it was suggested by the Bell Company that the instrument should be moved from the subscription room to the luncheon room or some other quiet place where it could get a fair trial without too much background noise.

Doubtless transactions were quicker but the faster pace of life was not always welcome. The phone could become a tyrant, an insistent instrument. Before its own phone installation was made, *The Times* commented:

It is a common complaint that the conditions of modern life, and especially of mercantile life, have been rendered well-nigh intolerable by the telegraph; and the addition of the telephone must inevitably 'more embroil the fray'. In old times a man of business could arrange his affairs for the day after the delivery of the morning post, and the perpetual arrival of telegrams has served to add new stings to existence. The case will surely be much worse with the verbal communications than with the written ones. The despatch of a telegram gives some little trouble, and therefore almost requires to be justified by some sort of occasion. With the new instrument hanging over his desk, the merchant or the banker will be liable to perpetual interruptions from telephonists, who will begin with some such phrase as, 'Oh, by the bye.' But there are limits to human endurance, and those who are threatened by such an evil will probably discover some means of keeping it within reasonable bounds.

During Bell's visit to Norway in 1880, a bank manager who had taken part in the first demonstration commented: 'Gentlemen, this is a very amusing toy, but it will never have any practical significance.' When a salesman canvassed Saint John, New Brunswick, it took him a fortnight to land one new subscriber. Since a service would need at least two subscribers, the solitary enthusiast was dropped. Another prospect wanted nothing to do with such an antique device: 'Why they had those things in China 2,000 years ago! Goodbye, young man.' Three weeks of canvassing in the Canadian capital, Ottawa, produced no interest. Even when the Hamilton–Toronto long-distance line was completed at the end of 1881, subscribers had to be persuaded to use it with two days of free calling.

No such doubts presented themselves to the bankers of Berne, Switzerland, who took the initiative in 1881 in establishing a local system. Within nine months it started operating with 144 subscribers. In Britain it was the legal profession that gained the earliest benefit, especially the patent lawyers involved in the claims and counter-claims of competing suppliers, which continued long after the merger of the Bell and Edison companies. It was not to be the engineers who made the apparatus or the enthusiasts who promoted it that were to make fortunes. These were to be accumulated by shrewd users who sat back, gathered commercially valuable information, and took swift action to profit thereby. What couriers and the pigeon post had done for Nathan Rothschild early in the century was now being done by the ornate telephones his successors had installed at New Court in the City.

Writing in 1882, Kingsbury presented an optimistic view:

In England its use is now rapidly extending. A resident in the suburbs, having his house connected with the Telephone Exchange, has had his letters read to him from his office, dictated his replies to a shorthand writer at the City, communicated with his broker, solicitor, or banker, and all without leaving his bedroom; sermons delivered in church have been heard by invalids when reclining on their sofas; operas performed in the crowded theatre have been listened to in the quiet library; dancing has been carried on to music which I have myself played more than ten miles away.

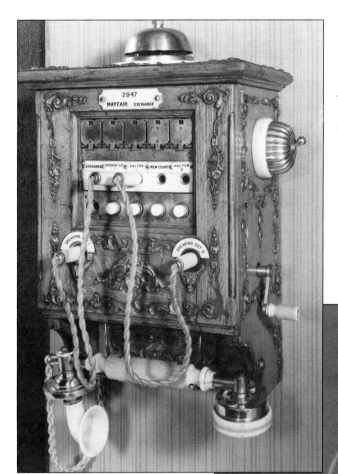

This small switchboard in the London home of the Rothschild family gave connections to New Court in the City of London and to Halton House, the family mansion in the Vale of Aylesbury. The two lines to Halton were possibly for the house and the cottage/stables, which kept separate accounts. (BT Museum)

In the nineteenth century N. M. Rothschild & Sons were reputed for the superiority of their private communications network. Ivory and gilt telephones at New Court in the City of London ornately kept up the tradition. (BT Museum)

In 1883 Albert Robida imagined the twentieth-century videophone, but over a century later it had not become a common service.

(Bundespostmuseum, Frankfurt)

We are often told that the telephone is in its infancy. It would perhaps be now more correct to say, it is in its childhood... I have conversed between London and Norwich, a distance by wire of about 140 miles... Although at present it is used for comparatively short distances, it is not hazarding too much to suggest that it cannot be far in the future before London is connected with Birmingham and Manchester, or Edinburgh and Glasgow, and when it may be possible to speak from Land's End to a friend in John o'Groats.

It was in 1882 that Bell, who was born in Edinburgh and had intended his patent to be filed first in England, took out US citizenship. By then he no longer took any active part in the phone business, apart from testifying in law suits to defend his original patents, the basic one of which mentioned neither 'telephone' nor 'speech'. They were the most valuable patents ever issued and cost over $5 million (£1 million) to protect. He had succeeded during 1880 in transmitting sound on a ray of light over a distance of 213 metres and patented what he called the photophone, or what a French scientist said ought to be called a radiophone, probably the first invention to which the prefix 'radio' was applied. After President Garfield was shot in 1881, Bell devised an electrical method of locating bullets in the human body, initially unsuccessful because of the steel springs in Garfield's bed, but after the President's death he perfected an electric probe for surgical use. His main interests now, though, were in continuing work for the deaf and in the development of flying machines. Forty years later, his wife wrote to a friend: 'I verily believe that the reason Dr Bell did not follow up his invention of the photophone and the reason he took up aviation instead was that I could not hear what went on over the radiophone but that I could see the flying machine.'

Having clearly foreseen the growth of communications, he left it to other talents to provide the service his one great invention had made possible. His basic model was improved and added to, for example by the Revd J. Hunnings of York, who constructed a better transmitter by using oven-made engine coke, and by Lars Magnus Ericsson of Sweden, who in 1884 invented the handset by arranging a transmitter and receiver at opposite ends of a six-inch broom handle.

How instruments were used in society depended upon circumstances. Most of the blame for the inadequate service in the UK was laid at the door of the Post Office, as for example in *The Spectator* of 6 September 1884:

> The New Yorker of means is understood to be no more able to do without his telephone than the Englishman without his Penny Post. As we are the most letter-writing country in the world... it is most probable that had it not been for the hateful effects of state monopoly we should have been the most wire-speaking country in the world.

Letters in London were delivered within two or three hours of posting and there were several deliveries a day, from before breakfast till after dinner.

Englishmen could perhaps take some consolation from across the Channel, where the French were an anti-phone nation. The instrument did not fit into the formal social structure and was looked upon as a one-way device, like a summoning bell or a means of broadcasting, not as something to encourage spontaneous dialogue between people. *Aller au téléphone* was to become the popular term for making a call in the sense of going to the lavatory, another one-way process.

CHAPTER 3

GETTING THE CALL

Official opposition and discouragement led to telephone timidity. Installing one could be a momentous decision. In mid-1886 the board of the Refuge Friend in Deed Life Assurance and Sick Fund Friendly Society resolved unanimously 'that a telephone be put on to chief office' in Manchester. A single line was by far the most common form of installation and then not necessarily in a prominent place. One firm of stockbrokers had it installed in the partners' lavatory, away from clerks who might make personal calls. In some offices it was the responsibility of a clerk, acting like a messenger or telegraph operator, to take messages and give them to seniors.

Similarly, the original exchange operators were boys. When the first exchange in Norwich opened, in March 1883, its 32 subscribers were looked after by a 15-year-old grammar-school boy, John Manning, from 8.30 a.m. to 6 p.m. on weekdays and from 8.30 to 10 a.m. on Sundays. During meal breaks his superintendent, Fred Heath, took over. Doubtless the boy, recruited more for being a cathedral chorister than for his education, had other jobs to do, like sweeping the office, tending the fire, running errands, and using his initiative. Once, after several days of gales, he heard groaning and creaking above the operating room. Clambering through a trapdoor in the roof, he saw heavy snow on the overhead wires, which he promptly knocked off to prevent further damage. Lads sometimes had to go out and, with a well-aimed stick, part a pair of overhead wires entangled by a gust of wind. At night, wind whistling through the wires could be 'decidedly spooky'.

In Christchurch, New Zealand, the first operator was a young man. For two years from 1881 he worked alone every day from 9 a.m. to 5 p.m., at first handling 30 subscribers and eventually 200. He got an assistant only when a judge refused to exempt him from jury service, and when the assistant arrived the operating hours were extended. Another conscientious operator was Charlie Tilley, who, when fire quickly spread through the

timber buildings of the small town of Vancouver in 1886, fled with the switchboard in his arms. When it was back in business in his father's rebuilt bookstore, in the evenings he entertained subscribers with his guitar and some friends 'broadcasting' hits such as 'The Old Folks At Home', 'Solomon Levi' and 'God Save The Queen'.

Subscribers expected service and were not slow to complain if it was lacking. When it came to rewards though the lads could wait, as a New Jersey operator recalls:

> It was the custom of some of our big men to telephone from New York to the Bayonne operator and say 'Tell Barney to meet me on the 11.30.' The business then was for the operator to shout out through the window across to the station cabman: 'Hey, Barney, meet Mr A on the 11.30.' Subscribers making such requests invariably added, 'I'll fix you up for this some time.' Fixing, however, never took place.

No wonder the boys did not always treat the new instrument with due seriousness. When leaping around like monkeys to make connections, they enjoyed pranks like swapping over numbers and cutting off subscribers. Recalling his fellow boy operators in Boston, John J. Carty declared:

> They were not old enough to be talked to like men and they were not young enough to be spanked like children. I shall never forget the noise that was made by those young fellows. My colleagues of that time were what I think the ethnologists would rank but a little lower than the wild Indian!

With the simple switchboards then in use, they had to call across the room to make a connection. A Swiss visitor to a Paris exchange in 1883 wrote: 'We couldn't believe our ears... one would believe that one had stumbled on to a battlefield, so loud were the cries of the telephone operators.'

OPPOSITE: *British boy operators, in Sunderland in 1883, were not as smartly dressed as their uniformed German male counterparts, in Berlin in 1881* (ABOVE).

(BT Museum/Siemens Museum)

There were slack periods and places. The first exchange in Dublin had about five subscribers, who even for Irishmen must have found the conversational possibilities limited, which enabled the boy to go and play out in the courtyard. When he had the cheek to ask for 'a rise' he was promptly asked whether he meant 'over the bannisters'. In Scranton, Pennsylvania, six boys left the switchboard to celebrate St Patrick's Day and on returning found their jobs had been taken by women. It was a sharp example of a change spread over a few years. By the late 1880s daytime operation of switchboards on both sides of the Atlantic was mainly in the hands of girls. In London, an exception was 'at some of the City exchanges which are situated in positions rendering the employment of girls undesirable'. Night operators were also men, certainly during the Victorian period.

The new instrument seemed made more for women than men. In *The Birth and Babyhood of the Telephone*, Thomas A. Watson pointed out:

> A curious effect of the telephone I noticed at that time was its power to paralyze the tongues of men otherwise fluent enough by nature and profession. I remember a prominent lawyer who, when he heard my voice in the telephone making some such profound remark to him as 'How do you do?' could only reply, after a long pause, 'Rig a jig-jig and away we go.'

Mark Twain was quick to see comic possibilities. In *A Telephone Conversation*, an 1880 sketch that has not dated, he details one overheard end of women's chat about domestic trivia, social gossip and the inevitable delay in saying goodbye.

The first woman operator, Miss Emma Nutt, began work in Boston on 1 September 1878. As 'telephonists' – the word quickly became established in the early 1880s – women had much to recommend them. 'The female voice is always clearer', remarked the *Pall Mall Gazette* in 1884. With it went a docile manner, manual dexterity, and a reliable attitude, all of which were comparatively cheap. Nevertheless, it was a new occupation for women at a time when opportunities outside domestic service were confined largely to becoming a teacher, a milliner or a shop assistant, and it had its own appeal. It was respectable, calling for young ladies of good breeding who would be distanced from a possibly irate and profane public, such as men in saloons and billiard halls, yet who performed a service of growing importance to society. It called for an agreeable manner; a memory for individual names, numbers and quirks; and some knowledge of what was happening in the world around her.

Applicants for jobs with Bell Canada had to be 18, have current references from three people including their clergyman, be tall enough for their arms to reach all the lines on the high switchboards, and slim enough to fit into the narrow space of an operator's position. Those with consumptive coughs were not accepted. They had to know which line a subscriber was on and, if it was a multi-party line, how many rings to call a particular subscriber. Numbers were not introduced until 1884 but long after that subscribers persisted in the personal approach, giving names only. To the president of the telephone company it all looked easy. Watching the operators in Toronto, he was amazed to see 'the languid air and leisurely manner' with which they replied to callers and made connections. Their manner was graceful but it reminded him of 'my grandmother playing the harp rather than a lot of women paid to do a certain job of work'. In November 1881 *The Globe* came out against the hardship of their now having to work on Sundays 'depriving the young women... of their weekly rest'.

Working conditions in exchanges were reasonable, especially in the Netherlands. Operators, dressed in white pinafores, and wearing slippers to minimize noise, began their day by dusting their positions. During the quieter periods needlework was allowed, in the afternoons knitting, and after 6 p.m. embroidery and sewing. Some of the young ladies, aged between 18 and 23, managed to crochet a bedspread in three months. There were not many other occupations in which it was possible to start setting up one's home in company time.

Improvements in switchboards took some of the strain out of the job. The multiple board meant that an operator could handle more subscribers and make faster connections but it also relieved her of having to shout across a busy room like her boy predecessors. She had to be able to stretch to reach some of her lines, which could tear the sleeves of her dress or shirtwaist. Hence the advent of the multiple switchboard led to the fashion for the knitted jersey, 'a waist that would stretch'.

The following comment was made in the *Pall Mall Gazette* in 1883:

Here, indeed, is an occupation to which no 'heavy father' could object; and the result is that a higher class of young women can be obtained for the secluded career of a telephonist as compared with that which follows the more barmaid-like occupation of a telegraph clerk.

The work could nevertheless be physically and temperamentally demanding, with no time for personal pursuits, as a visitor to the Melbourne exchange – called The Palace of Winged Words by *The Australasian Sketcher* in 1881 – wrote in 1887 in *Town and Country Journal*:

The operators stand up when attending to subscribers' calls, chairs being, however, provided for the leisure moments of the fair and nimble-fingered

Not so much a headset, more a heavy harness, worn by a Canadian operator. (Courtesy Bell Canada Telephone Historical Collection)

battalion of operators… From 10 a.m. to noon and 2 p.m. to 4 p.m. are the busiest portions of the day…

Place yourself in the middle of the room and gaze upon the delicate hands in magic confusion playing as it were upon metal switches, plugs and switching cords. There is no shouting or even excitement – no apoplectic strain into the machine's mouth. The young ladies rarely turn their heads. There is a soft sighing murmur in the room: and one could easily imagine the spare forms to be automatic figures; and yet that little pouting delicate mouth is wrestling with the pangs, groans and tempers of 100 subscribers, that number being attended to by one lady operator, 'sectionized' all over the city and the suburbs. A telephone tells a person's character as surely as a sea voyage. A woman is quick to wrath when crossed in her inquiries, snaps bitterly, but has it all over in a moment; while a man in a passion switches off as if crazy.

At moments like this an operator could become aware of her heavy headset. One of the early types weighed $6\frac{1}{2}$ pounds.

Ahead of her she could see secure employment, with perhaps a percentage for recruiting new subscribers, a chance of promotion to supervisor, and there were opportunities for meeting people inside and outside the office. A Chicago operator remembers:

> A subscriber would request us to awake him with a call at a certain time in the morning. Upon leaving his office, he would request us to make a note of the calls coming in for him during the next hour, as he was leaving the office and would return at the end of that time; or, if he were going home and someone was anxious to reach him, the call was put through to his residence.

Often an operator got to know her subscribers so well that, after the first call of the day, she made all the regular connections without being asked. Such help could lead to a ring of another kind.

Women requested a call to wake them from a nap or to remind them to take a cake from the oven. More adventurously, when they were out to tea or the like they would leave babies near the phone with the receiver off in the hope that if the baby woke its cries would be heard by the operator, who would call the mother. Personal service like this could be remembered at Christmas time, when gifts of chocolates, flowers, perfume, hankies, poultry and other food, sometimes as an act of contrition, might be left for exchange staff or individual operators. Virginia fruit-farmers brought in barrels of apples, and one enthusiastic Louisiana plantation owner told his favourite operator that he was going to present her with a barrel of sugar. She politely declined the offer.

During the Klondike gold rush operators in Fairbanks grubstaked many a prospector. When he struck it rich a miner would often dump a poke of nuggets out on the switchboard and invite the operator to pick one or two. Miss Lillian W. Camp, an operator on Montreal's first exchange, recalled:

> My relations with subscribers were always of a pleasant nature, and sometimes in the evenings when there was very little to do, we would talk with them on the line. I remember one subscriber used to sing to us. We would all get on the line to listen. One of his songs was entitled 'Although I Listen to Thy Voice Thy Face I Never See'.

The respectability of being a telephone operator was demonstrated in Japan, a nation emerging from seven centuries of military feudalism. Within a decade of the Meiji Restoration of 1868 the power and wealth of the samurai were diminished. Yet it was socially acceptable for their daughters to take up the new occupation when the public telephone service opened in Tokyo in 1889. It was a genteel way of bringing an

The new instrument helped old professions, like that of a geisha, to follow their calling. (NTT)

income to an impoverished middle-class family, and the beginning of a social revolution in that women were embarking on their own career. Not since the seventeenth century, when geishas began to emerge as professional female entertainers for the rising class of urban merchants, had there been such opportunities for women. Geishas of course found the telephone convenient for making appointments with their patrons.

In Germany, Crown Princess Louise, daughter of Kaiser Wilhelm I, championed the cause of women being allowed to work in exchanges. She had fought in the 1860s for the rights of women to work outside the home as railway telegraphists. Now her opponent was Postmaster-General Stephan, and she needed all her power and influence. After initial trials in 1887, women began permanently in 1890. They had to be between 18 and 30 and in good health. Until the introduction of multiple switchboards they had to work standing up. Because the authorities did not want them dressing competitively, and because lace, ribbons and jewellery could get in the way, uniforms were prescribed. In France, after the government takeover in 1889 – scarcely a centennial revolutionary act – operators were subject to bizarre regulations, among them a list of people they could not marry. There was always the danger that they might pass on confidential information to foreigners, to people handling money, and to guardians of law and order such as policemen and mayors.

One thing operators were encouraged to study was their directory, at most a small booklet, so that they could offer a personal service to subscribers. In Milan they were fined for every wrong connection. Sometimes, as in Lowell, Massachusetts, subscribers wanted to keep the service personal and resisted the idea of being known as a number. During a measles epidemic in 1880 a local physician, Dr Parker, recommended the use of numbers because he feared that, if the town's four experienced operators caught the disease, relief staff would take too long to become familiar with the expanded system. Most users preferred to ask for names rather than numbers, which could also be misheard.

Subtle differences in phrasing were important. At a New York conference on switchboards held by American Bell in 1887, one complaint aired was that on receiving no reply operators often told callers 'They won't answer', which implied a stubborn refusal rather than the absence of the other party. Unanimously it was agreed that in future operators should say 'don't' not 'won't'. They were also instructed to give short rather than long rings 'to excite the curiosity of the subscriber'. Business subscribers were to be discouraged from having their numbers printed on their cards. The word 'Telephone' was sufficient to show that they could be contacted. 'The book' was the proper place of reference.

Originally, it was common to group subscribers alphabetically under their trades and professions, not only for the benefit of users but also as publicity for the phone company. It was an advance on listing subscribers in the order in which they applied for service. Gradually directories became simply alphabetical and addresses were added. In 1886 a return to the original idea was made with the publication in Chicago of the first business guide in the form of yellow pages. As the service grew so did the size of directories, from a few sheets to substantial books. In 1897 the $1\frac{1}{4}$-inch thick national phone directory, which listed all subscribers who could make toll calls to one another, was the last of its kind in the USA. Of course it was possible to be 'ex-directory', but that did not necessarily prevent you from being included since all numbers could be listed, even if all names were not. For example, in the London directory of 1899–1900, Kensington 471 was listed between Benson J. W. and Benson Robert & Co.

Most calls were local, for social and technical reasons. Even when subscribers topped up the sal ammoniac in the Leclanché battery that up to at least 1894 provided their speaking current, transmission was weak and it was necessary to shout. Thomas Watson remembered it as 'the telephone epoch when they used to say that all the farmers waiting in a country grocery would rush out and hold their horses when they saw anyone preparing to use the telephone'. There was often noise on the line, described by the *Colorado Magazine* as: 'All kinds of humming and singing noises, singing not like an anthem, but more like the suppressed wailing of lost spirits...' It added: 'Subscribers soon found when the transmitter got on such a tantrum that temporary peace could be obtained by pounding on the instrument.' In dry climates such as Colorado, keeping the ground rod damp was often a problem. Each instrument had to be earthed via plumbing or damp ground. Often, when a subscriber complained about the sound level, the operator advised throwing a pail of water on the ground rod to restore audible speech.

Customers would get so angry that they would sometimes tear the phone from its moorings, or attack it with an axe, and throw what was left into the street. For proprietors of small phone companies, losing one subscriber was as great a cause for concern as the lost sheep in the biblical parable. When a proprietor in Denver could not dissuade a subscriber from having his installation removed, he took it away at night, returning to his office via back alleys. New installations were paraded down the main street in broad daylight. People also peered into phone offices to see what was going on. With the type of circuits in use, conversations could frequently be overheard. The companies could not guarantee privacy. Because subscribers' lines were suitable only for local connections, when the long-distance service started commercially in the USA in the mid-1880s, calls had to be made from the company's office.

Watson improvised the first soundproof booth in 1877 out of bed blankets to prevent his Boston landlady overhearing his small-hours' shouts to Bell in New York. By the end of the century in the USA, pay phones were common in places frequented by the public, especially drugstores. Some early booths were impressively built, of oak, soundproof, with a writing desk, rug and silk curtains. Sometimes they were mistaken for elevators. Before folding doors were introduced, the double doors of a booth could get stuck, forcing users to fight their way out. In the UK up to 1884 the spread of pay phones was hampered by Post Office restrictions on access to the phone by non-subscribers. 'Call office suites' were installed about 1882 for members of the Stock Exchange and Baltic Exchange in London and the Wool Exchange in Bradford.

The first exchange in Norwich had a call room for use by subscribers, and occasionally prospective customers made demonstration calls that were not charged and thus did not break the terms of the licence. When the restrictions were relaxed in 1884, the Post Office introduced 'silence cabinets' and the National Telephone Company, which was to become the leading private company, opened call offices. Initially payments were in stamps bearing the portrait of the company chairman. In 1889 the first coin-operated call box was installed, in the Hartford Bank lobby at Hartford, Connecticut. Subscribers paying for phones at home complained when they were asked to pay for the use of a public phone.

Call offices made the instrument available to a wider public, who were able to appreciate its advantages and limitations. Onlookers at railway stations and in shops perhaps saw a man talking over the phone suddenly drop the receiver and describe with gestures the dimensions or shape of some article he was discussing. Practical experience made people realize that it was an everyday instrument to be used without hazard. Just as there had been fears that perching birds would be electrocuted when telegraph messages were sent through the wires so similar consequences were imagined for people in direct phone contact. Benjamin Franklin's kite had brought down lightning from the clouds, so what would phone lines do during a thunderstorm? Fears that Alpine storms might damage his house were very real to the Austrian who delayed the introduction of the service to Innsbruck by four years until 1893. To such sceptics it could be pointed out that, as well as

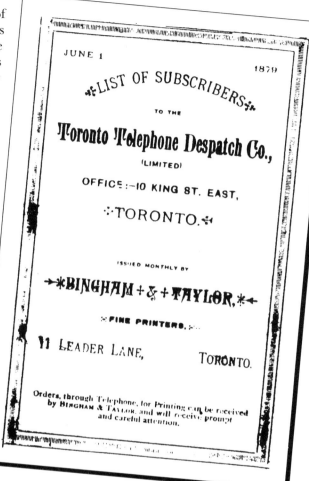

The first directory in book form for Toronto (actual size) included subscribers' occupations and addresses, but in 1879 there were not yet phone numbers.

(Bell Canada Telephone Historical Collection)

being able to bring down lightning from the clouds, science could also arrest it and send it to earth, leaving the listener unharmed. Nevertheless, not all phone systems were protected and some people, including operators, did suffer shocks.

Less easily dispelled were doubts about damage to hearing, which seemed to emanate mainly from France. In 1889 Professor Lannois of the Lyons Medical School presented a paper to the Fourth International Congress on Otology, *Le téléphone et les affections de l'oreille*, advising sparing use of the instrument by those whose hearing was sound and an absolute abstention by anybody with existing defects. On 24 August 1889 *The Lancet* reported from Paris the case of an intelligent man who, from constant use of the phone, had got into a state of nervous excitement, with ringing in the ears and vertiginous sensations. Happily, 'complete rest was sufficient to remove these troubles'. Offering career advice in 1896, *The Girl's Own Paper* quoted another French medical authority:

> Naturally, the constant use of the telephone is injurious, creating what M. Gelle calls 'aural over-pressure'. The working of the telegraphic apparatus, and constant attendance amidst the jar and noise of machinery, likewise tend to overstrain the ear and to induce nervous excitability, giddiness and neuralgic pains. But how long the delicate nerves may be exposed to this over-pressure without inducing any of these evil results we are unable to tell you. Only it is well, when choosing a vocation in life, to look beyond the present into such possible eventualities; and if of a nervous temperament, and at all subject to headache and neuralgic pains, it would be well to choose some other calling.

After a hard day with a tight headset and poor lines some operators felt that their ears were like cauliflowers and found a build-up of wax, but 'telephone ear' was scarcely a serious malady. In the USA it was on a par with 'lawn tennis leg'.

Unlike the speaking tube, the phone could keep infection at a distance. In Cape Town many of the installations were a direct result of the smallpox epidemic that broke out in 1882. For example, the municipal headquarters, the Town House, was connected to Rentskie's farm at Paarden Island, where the isolation hospital was situated, enabling relatives to talk to the sick without infringing quarantine regulations.

Some Montreal citizens thought otherwise. During the 1885 epidemic rumours began to circulate that smallpox was carried by people's breath through the phone. So serious was the epidemic, which was to claim three thousand victims, that compulsory vaccination was introduced. To many, this meant injecting 'cow's blood' into people's veins. Armed with torches and clubs, a mob attacked City Hall and a drugstore, breaking windows and starting fires. A regiment of militia arrived in time to head them off from the exchange, being guarded by employees with axe handles. A number of indoor systems were installed in London in 1887, when there was a scarlatina outbreak. *The Lancet* observed that sick-room phones 'should be so made as to communicate the faintest whispering sound, so as to require no sort of effort on the part of the speaker, and they should be provided with mouth-and-ear pieces so light as to admit of their being held by a weak and trembling hand to mouth and ear during the conversation'.

Early on, the use of the phone in diagnosis had been foreseen. Letters in *The Lancet* in 1878 pointed to its advantages over the stethoscope in listening to lung and heart sounds, especially when combined with the phonograph so that sound vibrations could be made visible to the eye, an early method of electrocardiography. A medical paper published in Richmond, Virginia, discussed the diagnosis of stone in the bladder. There was also the case of a US family doctor who received a midnight call on a case of suspected croup. 'Lift the child to the telephone,' he commanded, 'and let me hear it cough.' On hearing the sound he declared 'That's not croup', and prescribed two grains of turpeth mineral, so saving himself a 2-mile ride through a driving storm and ensuring a decent night's sleep for everybody. But in Britain the instrument could 'be a doubtful addition to one's advantage or repose' according to a *Lancet* editorial of 1883. It feared that 'when people can open up a conversation with us for a penny, they will be apt to abuse the privilege', and that there might be 'a dozen telephone consultations in one day, or conversations that might be thought to supersede a consultation'.

The possibility of providing medical help more quickly was an obvious benefit, as Arnold Bennett mentioned in *Clayhanger*, published in 1910 but set in the late 1880s:

> Dr Heve… went himself to the new Telephone Exchange and ordered a nurse from the Pirehill Infirmary Nursing Home. And the dramatic thing was that within two hours and a half the nurse had arrived.

Medicines could be more quickly prescribed, a fact noted by *The Australasian Sketcher* in 1881:

> One or two doctors have already learned to appreciate the telephone, and are kept 'switched' on to the chemists they respectively employ all night. In more than one case this has been found of considerable benefit, and much suffering and inconvenience have been avoided… Your doctor might send

Overhead wires, such as these New Zealand 'Lemon trees', could dominate the scene.

(Telecom Corporation of New Zealand)

you a black draught instead of a Gregory's powder, but it would be your own fault for not telling him your symptoms correctly.

Too close a link between chemist and doctor though was akin to 'medical touting', a danger of which 'Surgeon' warned in *The Lancet* of 16 January 1886:

> I was surprised to see in a chemist's shop in a first-class watering-place on the south coast a large placard, stating: 'Dr A can be communicated with from here by telephone.' There was another doctor in practice nearly opposite the shop. The telephone man, I found out, resided a little more than a quarter of a mile away; therefore the object was plain. Is not this, with all the interested recommendations of the chemist to Dr A being the best doctor, etc., very unprofessional?

Phone installations could themselves be a hazard, especially when overhead wires and supports were brought down, as in the bad English winters of 1886 and 1887. At risk were the public below and the linesmen who had to restore the service as quickly as possible. Yet they received little recognition for their labours. It was not until 1904 that the outdoor staff in Norwich, courtesy of public subscription, went on a day's outing to Yarmouth, something already enjoyed by train drivers and conductors, policemen, cabmen, and railway servants. In New Zealand the many-armed poles carrying urban wires to the local exchange were nicknamed 'Lemon trees' after Dr Charles Lemon, then head of the Post and Telegraph Department, but they looked much more threatening. When citizens were deploring 'great big unsightly ships' masts', Bell workmen chose 2 a.m. as the time to raise a 40-foot pole bearing 70 wires in Quebec City, but they reckoned without the vigilantes. 'Fortunately the police and a number of citizens were on the grounds to repel any attempt', reported the local *Daily Telegraph*. In Toronto, as the number of wires increased, poles grew taller and the growing mass of material overhead loomed as a public menace:

> The streets in the central part of the city should be cleared as soon as possible, as it is on these crowded thoroughfares that the nuisance of poles and wires is felt to be the greatest. It is there that the greatest danger from fire exists. The buildings are high and cannot be reached by the ladders of the firemen until after the network of wires in front of them is cut through. This means loss of time and consequently loss of property and possibly loss of life.

In Colorado, where high winds, sleet and snow drove down the Rockies, poles were put in only 17 feet apart but, even so, they were broken off like

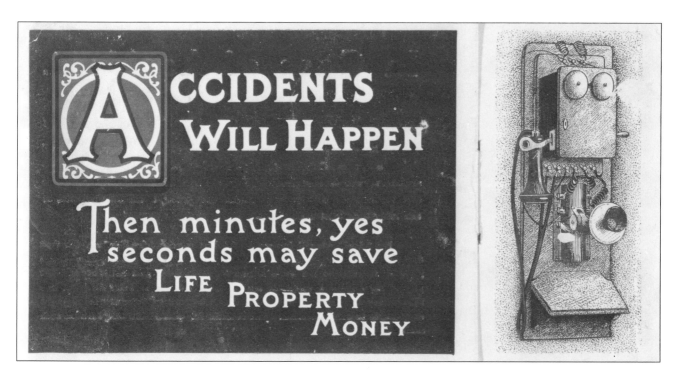

matchsticks. Out on the range cattle found them convenient scratching posts and brought them down by constantly rubbing their sides on them. In town they performed an unforeseen role, noted by a Denver detective:

> Trees were so scarce in those days, we had difficulty finding a suitable place for hanging horse thieves or crooked gamblers. So it wasn't long before several of the new telephone poles in town were festooned with the carcases of those that the community didn't want around any more.

Fire was a risk gas companies were able to exploit in their battle against electric light, so successfully that users had to pay higher insurance premiums. Electrical apparatus was new and untried, and in use tended to deteriorate. Insulation could be improved, for example in switchboards. In 1907 the early and ageing exchange of Antwerp, the main commercial centre of Belgium, was completely burnt out. Not to be disturbed at night, subscribers – certainly in Paris – left the phone off the hook, which kept call lights on the board burning and increased the risk.

Conversely, the outbreak of a fire could be notified more quickly. The phone was quicker than the telegraph and more accurate as a source of

The image of the phone as an emergency instrument, promoted here by Britain's private phone company, was to be an enduring one.

(BT Museum)

information than observations from some high point. Its advantage was appreciated by Mr W. Tallett, an electrician, who in 1877 made and installed the first instruments in Oxford, to connect the volunteer fire brigade with the brigade engineer's home and later the police station. On 28 December 1882, the chief of police of Los Angeles ordered the discontinuance of the custom of firing five shots as a fire alarm. The announcement added: 'Telephones are numerous all over the city and will never be refused as an alarm of fire.' In pioneer days, when most Los Angeles men went armed, such a succession of pistol shots started a local fusillade and summoned crowds of neighbours, who hurriedly organized bucket brigades. Later, the shots were a signal for two rival volunteer fire companies to race madly for the scene. After the custom was abandoned, alarms were phoned to police headquarters, where a bell or whistle was sounded. At Ridgetown, Ontario, when fires were reported the operator had to dash out the side door of the phone office, run up the hill to the Town Hall, find the alarm in the back of the building and pull the lever with all her might to alert the citizens.

Some of the UK private companies thought it public-spirited to install their apparatus free of charge in provincial fire stations. An 1881 offer to Preston corporation was accepted on condition that the company pay a shilling (5p) a year for the privilege and that the free instrument remain for evermore. The offer was withdrawn. Later in the decade local authorities were able to install street fire points, like those placed in Nottingham in 1887, enabling the public to speak directly to the fire station.

Such promptness was not always welcomed, even by the Post Office. In Leicester in 1889 a fire in one firm's premises was reported by another but the Post Office refused to pass on the call on the grounds that the fire had not originated in the renter's premises and that the use of his phone was restricted to his own affairs. The Post Office later claimed that the line was out of order for the crucial 15 minutes. With the delay in summoning help, the damage was extensive. The town council, the chamber of commerce and the local trade protection society, which thought it had a good case for reduction in the phone rental, protested to the postmaster-general, who loftily relented in his reply that 'while the use of the telephone is restricted to the renter's own private and business affairs, my department will be glad to allow its being used to convey information concerning the outbreak of fires or rioting'. Still dissatisfied with the service, The Leicestershire Trade Protection Society approached the National Telephone Company on 'what improved accommodation it could offer the town and traders'. It was not difficult to recruit subscribers.

The phone was first installed in a police station in Washington DC in 1878. Two years later Chicago installed them on policemen's beats and, by a system of regular reporting, the central police station knew who was where. It was claimed that the initial cost of the installation was comparatively small, that fewer police could be employed, and that they could be made more effective. Scotland Yard did not have a similar faith. In 1881 it encouraged the public to ring the metropolitan force on anything important but soon stopped the experiment because the calls were trivial – though they could have been useful during the latter part of 1888, when Jack the Ripper was roaming Whitechapel, knife handy. That the telephone had a security value was appreciated by Bell Canada, which in the January 1885 issue of its Quebec directory offered among its special services: 'Subscribers employing nightwatchmen can arrange with the company to have the central office signalled at stated hours during the night, a record of which signals will be kept in the office, and a copy delivered to the subscriber daily, thus testing the vigilance of the watchman.'

Sherlock Holmes, as depicted in The Strand Magazine *of January 1925, used the phone far less than his fictional successors.*

(City of Westminster: Sherlock Holmes Collection, Marylebone Library)

In the UK, provincial police forces did not rush into employing the new weapon against crime. By 1893 the Hertfordshire Police were said to have had links completed between their large towns but constables were inclined to ignore calls. The chief constable of Reading had a phone installed in his house in 1897, the year that the major stations in Berkshire were equipped, yet the communication between him and his clerks was by speaking tube. Sherlock Holmes, Conan Doyle's great detective, rang Dr Watson in 221B Baker Street in *The Adventure of the Retired Colourman* in the summer of 1898. Soon after, Conan Doyle's brother-in-law, E. W. Hornung, equipped his hero, Raffles, the amateur cracksman. Mostly though the guardians of law and order relied on the telegram for urgent communications. Anybody was accessible that way, whereas phone subscribers were few.

Nor was the instrument crucial to improving physical communications, only convenient. On 21 May 1877 Bell's phone was given a trial in the Pennsylvania Railroad Company shops at Altoona. The demonstration was a success and the company became the first railroad to install a telephone, expanding its network by 1910 to 13,000 phones. In the UK, although railway companies were among the first subscribers to local exchanges, they only gradually adopted the new method of communication for their own services, largely because of their existing investment in the telegraph. Early phone installations in signal boxes eased track communications. From a loud-speaking phone, manufacturers claimed, a signalman could receive instant orders without having to move to another part of his box or having his attention divided between the dial of the telegraph instrument and the row of levers.

In ships, phones were a replacement for speaking tubes, connecting various stations on board. A particular application was in the firing of torpedoes. In the mid-1890s Germany began to equip its warships with all-metal phones that were watertight, had soundproof earpieces, and could be used hands-free. Loud-speaking versions were also in demand. More interesting was the novel use in diving operations. On 12 May 1882 the *Journal of the Society of Arts* reported:

> In raising the vessel *La Provence*, which sank in the Bosphorus, the telephone was added to the diver's dress, thus greatly facilitating the communications. One of the glasses of the helmet is replaced by a copper plate, in which a telephone is inserted, so that the diver has only to turn his head slightly in order to receive his instructions, and report what he sees. Besides, in case of danger or accident, lives may now be saved which would otherwise have been sacrificed.

One advantage was that instructions could be more precise and fuller than was possible with a number of jerks on a cord. It was also more effective than communicating by speaking tube. By 1886 there was an Admiralty paper on the subject and in 1900 the Channel Squadron had on trial four £37 diving helmets with phones, manufactured by Siebe Gorman. The first phone message from a submerged submarine to land was sent on 6 January 1898 by Simon Lake, a submarine inventor, from the bottom of the Patapsco River to the mayor of Baltimore in his office. Calls were then made to Washington DC and New York.

In the four years from 1893 reports were published of the Royal Commission appointed to inquire 'what Lighthouses and Light-Vessels it is desirable to connect with the Telegraphic System of the United Kingdom by Electrical Communication'. By the turn of the century undersea cables had been laid to connect Fastnet Rock and Tuskar Rock off the south coast of Ireland to the mainland. Their lighthouse keepers were able to report storm warnings, vessels in distress, and casualties at sea more quickly. At the same time interest was growing in communication by coastguards, and in coastal defence based on war signal stations.

The first recorded use of the phone in war was at the end of 1877 on the North West Frontier between Peshawar and Sargasha during the Jowaki operations. Lieutenant G. R. R. Savage, inspector of signalling at Roorkee, assisted by Sergeant Martin and some sepoy artisans, made the phones in the regimental workshops, along with some heliographs. So successful was the first use that they were employed again in 1879 in the siege of Sherpur during the Second Afghan War, more instruments being used than then existed in the City of London. When they were introduced in 1881 into Siam, an absolute monarchy, they were only available to the military, the service not becoming public until 1886.

They were used in the field in the Egyptian War of 1882, probably by telegraph personnel because the military staff were not in general keen on the invention. During the 1884–5 Sudan campaign, in the Suakin expedition against the 'Fuzzy-wuzzies', ships' phones were used on land for short-distance tactical purposes, all that current technology would permit. For instance, the Royal Engineers used them from 1878 in mining operations. Not until 1896 was the first military-pattern switchboard produced and even then the written was preferred to the spoken word.

General Sir A. Alison put the prevailing view to General Fielding on 27 August 1886:

> There are certain objections to telephones, one is that though you can talk through a telephone quicker than you can write out, and then send off, a telegram, you cannot communicate by telephone keeping a copy or record of what is sent (a very important point) much, if at all, quicker...
>
> Then again the man holding the cups of a telephone and receiving a message has his hands fully employed. He cannot take down the message he receives, but must call it out, to be taken down by a second man (involving two men) or repeat it at its close by memory only. A good telegraph clerk will take a message down (keeping a record of it while doing so) and be sending off another sometimes at the same moment.
>
> Then the constant ringing of the bell is a decided nuisance. You could not have telephone operators at work within two or three feet of clerks engaged in their ordinary work of writing or calculating in the same way as you have telegraph operators in our present Hd Qrs office. It would worry everyone to death. A special room would be required.

By 1895, for reconnaissance, phones were installed in British balloons connected to wagons on the ground.

In the USA, General William J. Palmer, who founded Colorado Springs and developed railroads, had firm opinions about the role of the instrument in his business life. He gave strict orders to the phone company that he was not to be called unless he had given written permission. At first he refused to give the instrument house room. On one occasion, when he had relented, he was expecting a call from some eastern financiers. He told the phone company that he would accept calls only between 9 and 10 a.m. on either 29 or 30 March. It was not possible for the financiers to call before 31 March and the company refused to put them through. Although the US army did not use the phone in the field until the Spanish–American War of 1898, it was quicker to pick up the habit.

General Alison's views reflected attitudes within the British government, which made very little use of the instrument. Single lines were first installed in the House of Commons in 1883, one at the Members' cloakroom in the entrance and the other in the waiting hall of the upper committee rooms. Little was done to bring the new facility to the attention of MPs, one of whom remarked that the 'one at the entrance is visible to the naked eye when you pass'. The Hon. Alexander Macdonnell claimed that he had had a phone installed in his rooms in Half Moon Street at a time when he could ring only five other subscribers because 'I had recently been appointed a clerk in the House of Lords, which also had a telephone, and I used to ring up each morning to see if there was any work to do and if there was not I stayed away.' In the latter part of the 1880s the 3rd Marquess of Salisbury, then Prime Minister, had a private installation at Hatfield House, which he enjoyed testing with nursery rhymes. Visitors used to more serious pronouncements heard his unmistakable voice intoning 'Hey diddle diddle, The cat and the fiddle.' Private installations of this type were usually based on the estate office, with connections to the farms, timber yard or whatever else was important in the business administration. Such an installation did not necessarily mean that the house itself was connected to the public network or that it was on the phone at all.

From the early 1880s Windsor Castle had had at least two internal lines and a link to Frogmore House almost three-quarters of a mile away, but when connection to the new Windsor exchange was offered in 1894 it was declined. It was probably established about 1896, when Buckingham Palace was also listed in a directory – that installation was most likely at an entrance. The Norfolk Estate Office in Sussex had a phone installed just before the end of the century but for about twenty years there was not one in Arundel Castle. Until the early 1920s the Duke of Norfolk's sisters used to go down to the estate office when they wanted to phone their friends.

If you were a nobody, you did not have a phone; having one did not make you a somebody. There were a few Oxbridge dons who were fascinated by the novelty of it but those colleges that condescended to adopt it usually had a solitary installation in the porter's lodge. The phone was something answered by the bailiff, the butler or some other servant, who had their distinctions among themselves just as they were distinguished from milord and lady. Nor did they always take to the new ways. The domestics at Coborn House, Bow, the home of George Cohen, the founder of the 600 Group of engineering companies, were frightened of 'the infernal machine' and on one occasion, when Richard the coachman asked cook to speak on it, she declined to do so until she had tidied herself.

Household management began to be a little easier from the mid-1880s, as one lady recorded in 1884:

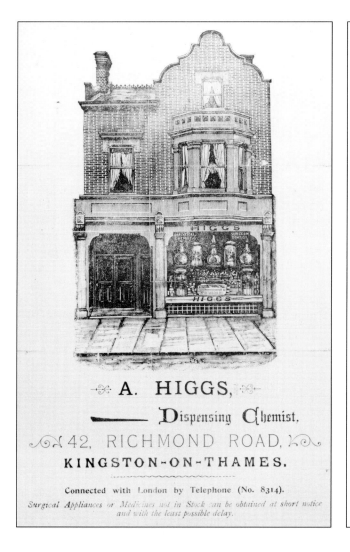

A. HIGGS,

Dispensing Chemist.

42, RICHMOND ROAD,

KINGSTON-ON-THAMES.

Connected with London by Telephone (No. 8314).

Surgical Appliances or Medicines not in Stock can be obtained at short notice and with the least possible delay.

Scene : 42, Richmond Road, Kingston-on-Thames.

Act I.—Mr. Higgs' Pharmacy.

Customer : I have read in your circulars, Mr. Higgs, that you are the only chemist in Kingston or neighbourhood connected with London by Telephone. I must confess my ignorance, but will you explain to me what the Telephone is ?

Mr. Higgs : Certainly, the Telephone is quite modern, and I think I may safely say only a small proportion of the people understand them. I make it a rule when I hear of anything advantageous to my business to get it.

Customer : I quite think that. I know you are an up-to-date Chemist. Your establishment alone shows that ; I have never seen a Chemist's so well arranged and equipped as yours, I also find your charges the lowest and quality the best.

Act II.—Telephone Room, rear of Pharmacy.

Mr. Higgs :—This is the instrument

I can speak from here to London, Brighton, Manchester, and almost every town in England, and be heard as distinctly as you hear me speaking to you. I will now speak to London. I first ask the operator to connect the wire from my instrument to that of the person I wish to speak to, when my bell here rings, that signals the gentleman I asked for is waiting.
The bell now ringing, place the receiver to your ear.

Customer :—*Much surprised*—Well ! ! ! If I hadn't heard this myself I should not have credited it. Do you really mean the gentleman I hear speaking is in London !

Mr. Higgs : Yes, close to Shoreditch. He is the principal of the firm which manufacture the "Chemical Food" I sell a large quantity of.

Customer : *Hesitating.* It sounds as if he is only in your shop.

Mr. Higgs : Indeed, I have heard that same remark passed before, but he is positively in London.

Customer : It is simply marvellous. I conclude you find the Telephone most useful ?

Mr. Higgs : Assuredly so, by being in communication with the principal Merchants, I can buy my stock to great advantage, as you are aware, goods bought well are half sold ; another advantage and not the least, in cases of urgent necessity or accident, any out-of-the-way Medicine or Surgical Instrument can be obtained at short notice, and no extra expense incurred.

Many of the Doctors here know this convenience, and it is no rare occurrence for one to call and order a Trained Nurse or a Surgical Appliance, which I am often able to supply about an hour afterwards.

Customer : Thank you very much for your interesting explanation.

Mr. Higgs : If you know any of your friends who would like to see and hear for themselves, I shall be pleased to show them.

In the morning, after consulting our cook, I put down in a book all the things we require; I go to the telephone and ring up No 7033, which is the number of Mr Whiteley's universal establishment. I enquire the price of different things, and order what I want. Should they not have everything I require, which is next to an impossibility, I ring up No 3080, or No 3069, the Army and Navy Stores, where I have deposit accounts. We always order milk, butter, eggs and cream from the Aylesbury Dairy Company, No 7042, and vegetables, fruit and flowers from Messrs Bott and Son, High-Street, Kensington, No

Like doctors, pharmacists appreciated the advantages of instant communications. (BT Museum)

8535, who are exceptionally civil, and despatch the things ordered without a moment's delay.

This rapid method of ordering was also of value to shops, especially those stocking perishable goods, like Warrin & Craik, court florists, of 43 Jermyn Street. In 1885 Timothy Eaton, who introduced new ideas in merchandising such as only selling for cash at fixed clearly marked prices, installed his first phone in his new larger Toronto store. It was not until the next decade, however, that the larger UK stores really began to take the instrument seriously, Peter Robinson installing it in 1892 and Swan & Edgar in 1894. By 1893 Cole Brothers of Sheffield were an advanced retailer in that they were 'to a large extent lighted by electricity, had a passenger lift upon the most approved principle, and were on the telephone'. About 1893 A. Higgs produced a circular in the form of a two-act dialogue announcing that he was the only chemist in Kingston-on-Thames or neighbourhood connected with London by phone. Hence 'surgical appliances or medicines not in stock can be obtained at short notice and with the least possible delay'. A. Higgs did not mention it but privacy was also an advantage for customers who ordered in this way. A contemporary American trade card depicted a woman asking about 'Dr Richards Laxocomfits'.

The ease of being able to call – most convenient when there was rain or a pea-souper – may have made a minor contribution to the decline of the hackney-carriage and hansom-cab trade, which reached its peak in London in 1888, and was losing fares to the new omnibuses. In 1894 the president of the cabmen's union attributed part of the decline to the fact that City men no longer had to take cabs to go and talk with their business contacts. In 1888 a US railway official bemoaned his loss of custom:

There is no doubt that the telephone is affecting short-distance travel within a hundred miles. Manufacturers who used to communicate with their stores and offices in the cities by messengers or by some member of the firm going to and fro frequently now find they can do business as well and with a saving in time by using the telephone.

CHAPTER 4

ANOTHER WORLD

Going out for entertainment was unnecessary. From the earliest days the instrument was used for transmitting music. For example, Michele Patocchi, an enthusiastic Swiss telegraph official, arranged on 19 June 1878 a reception of Donizetti's *Don Pasquale* in a room near the Teatro Sociale in Bellinzona. On his birthday in 1883 Sir Arthur Sullivan invited the Prince of Wales to his Kensington home to hear his most recent opera, *Iolanthe*, transmitted from the Savoy Theatre, having paid the cast himself. At the 1881 International Exhibition of Electricity in Paris the General Telephone Society relayed opera to a room in the Industrial Palace

TÉLÉPHONES ET PHONOGRAPHES

A L'EXPOSITION UNIVERSELLE

Before radio, phone lines enabled visitors to the Paris exhibition of 1889 to listen for a few minutes to performances at the Opéra or the Comédie Française.

(Collection Historique, France Télécom)

In France a regular Théâtrophone service was developed for phone subscribers. Among them was Marcel Proust, who had a standing order to be connected whenever 'Parsifal' or 'Pelleas' was performed. Listening to a complete opera was both expensive and tiring on the arm, and the reception far from ideal, but Proust enjoyed it. (PTT-Museum Bern)

for the benefit of music lovers. One of the listeners was Theodore Puskas, who that year obtained exclusive rights to develop the phone in Hungary. In 1893 he established a broadcasting service, Telephon Hirmondo, an idea for which there was a bright future according to Arthur Mee in an 1898 *Strand Magazine* article:

> The Pleasure Telephone… will democratize many of the social luxuries of the rich. Those who object to the environment of the stage will be able to enjoy the theatre at home, and the fashionable concert will be looked forward to as eagerly by the poor as by their wealthy neighbours. The humblest cottage will be in immediate contact with the city, and the 'private wire' will make all classes kin… it would be possible with its aid for one man's voice to be heard simultaneously by the whole six million inhabitants of London. All that is necessary is a central office, from which the whole of London – if not the whole of England – might be supplied with a constant flow of news and pleasure all day long… The preacher of Buda-Pesth no longer reckons his hearers by the state of the pews, but by the number of telephone subscribers. It may be objected, perhaps, that religious worship by telephone is not calculated to inspire reverence or inculcate virtue; but, at any rate, the system is an inestimable boon to the aged and infirm, the patients in hospitals, and the women who are unable to leave their houses. A single hospital in Buda-Pesth has over thirty installations, which carry brightness and cheer into the lives of the lonely sick.

At that time the Buda-Pesth News and Entertainment Telephone had 6,000 subscribers.

The Théâtrophone transmitted musical performances from Paris theatres to hotels, clubs and other places. Such possibilities had been demonstrated in 1892 at Crystal Palace near London, where a concert room was connected with the Lyric Theatre in London, then staging the comic opera *The Mountebanks*, and with theatres in Birmingham, Liverpool and Manchester. One clergyman, probably not wanting to be seen in a theatre, attended Crystal Palace every evening until he had heard the opera through in ten-minute excerpts. In six months nearly 60,000 people visited the demonstration. Judging from a sketch, *Telephonic Theatre-Goers*, written by F. Anstey, the humorous novelist on the staff of *Punch*, listeners heard various sounds at the same sitting and imagined others.

Nevertheless, the demonstration attracted enough attention for the Electrophone Company to be founded in 1894 with a capital of £20,000 to provide a regular service of this kind. It was welcomed by the National Telephone Company as a means of increasing interest in the instrument and using evening capacity on its lines, but the initial response was poor.

Always fascinated by the phone, Strindberg kept names and numbers on the wall of the Stockholm flat where he spent the last four years of his life (1908–1912). (Nordic Museum)

Just 47 subscribers were recruited in the first year and after ten years the total was only 600 in spite of all the promotion. For example, in 1896 visitors to the Palmarium at Olympia had been able to go 'round the London theatres in 15 minutes'.

There was not an immediate affinity between the phone and the stage. Indeed, neither Shaw (who had worked for the Edison Company) in his early plays, nor Oscar Wilde used the instrument as a dramatic device. The creator of the music hall, Charles Morton, personally shunned it. Ibsen, who wrote his last play in 1899, did not employ it. William Archer in his 1907 introduction to his own and Edmund Gosse's translation of *Hedda Gabler* (1890) noted that Ibsen seemed to have set the play some 30 years earlier: 'The electric cars, telephones and other conspicuous factors in the life of the modern capital are notably absent from the play. There is no electric light in Secretary Falk's villa'. D. W. Griffith in his 1915 silent film *Ghosts* updated the drama by giving Mrs Alving a contemporary Bell model on a small cupboard by her armchair.

The one major dramatist to grasp the possibilities was Strindberg, a keen scientist who experimented among other things with electricity. When in Sweden, he lived in Stockholm, by early 1886 the telephone capital of the world. No other city, including New York and London, had either more instruments or a higher density of them. Strindberg was responsible for the earliest reference in a significant play, when the captain says to the doctor in the third act of *The Father* (1887): 'Shut up! I don't want to talk to you. I don't want to hear you echoing everything they say in there like one of those damned telephones!' After his restless moves about the Continent during the 1890s, on his return to Stockholm in 1899 he had one installed in his new apartment (his number was 2946), and it occurs in several of his plays though, like so much else, as a malign influence. In *The Dance of Death* Part I (1900), Alice tells Kurt that she and her husband have to maintain contact through a telegraph apparatus, an important device in the play, 'because the telephone operators eavesdropped on our conversations'. Elis, the protagonist in *Easter* (1900), hears only his own voice when he answers the ring: 'Hello. There's no answer. Hello. It answers with my own voice. Who is there? How strange. I hear my own words like an echo.' Later in the second act the mad Eleonora says: 'Listen – the telephone wires are humming. That means the newspaper has come out; and now people are telephoning: "Have you read – ?" "Yes, I've read –" "Isn't it dreadful?"' In both *A Dream Play* (1901) and *The Ghost Sonata* (1907), characters go into kiosks on stage, although we do not hear their words. *Storm* (1907) has actual phone conversations.

The phone, always serving one purpose as well as another, also improved the pleasures of those who wanted to go out. An early call-girl system was established in Melbourne from 1891 when leading brothels in the city joined the network. At least Australian businessmen and politicians were able to ring for appointments instead of sending messages or knocking on the door. There was immediate replacement for the term 'knocking-shop'. More respectably, to increase the number of its subscribers and make itself too big for the Post Office to take over, in the 1890s the National Telephone Company commissioned musical numbers that were played in UK dance halls. First heard in December 1894 was *The Telephone Galop*, a lively tune with bursts of ringing.

Betting, especially on credit instead of in cash, was made easier. Under the pre-phone Suppression of Betting-houses Act anyone who owned or used 'any office, house, room or other place' to which people 'resorted' for the purpose of betting was liable to a fine of £100 or, in default, to imprisonment for up to six months in the common gaol or house of correction, with or without hard labour. The interesting legal point was 'What constituted a place?' The question was settled in the High Court in 1894 (*The Queen* vs. *Brown*), when it was held that the word 'resorting' must be construed in the ordinary sense of physically resorting, and a telephone was not a place like a club or racecourse enclosure. The verdict displeased the Anti-Gambling League and favoured the rich over the poor punter.

Racing results were part of the unofficial news service early phone operators were expected to provide. Sometimes they voluntarily called subscribers with news flashes, a service thought useful in rural areas such as Iowa:

> Once we received the news that Queen Victoria was dead and another time that President Cleveland had been shot and the information was spread over the community by telephone. Both of these reports were false rumours.

Newspapers were quick to see the advantages for transmitting news. The first news despatch by phone was from Salem, Massachusetts, to the *Boston Globe*, a distance of 16 miles, on 12 February 1877. In 1879 *The Times* was ready to experiment in having its parliamentary reports phoned from the House of Commons, a procedure that enabled it to take copy up to an hour later than previously. News of the bombardment of Alexandria by British warships in 1882 was the first important announcement to be phoned from Reuters' head office in London to the Press Association for onward distribution to the UK press.

In the provinces newspapers were often among the first subscribers. In Hull *The Eastern Morning News* and in Arundel the *West Sussex Gazette* both had the number 1. Some staid editors, such as Mudford of the London

Music was both performed over the phone and, in this tempo, used to stimulate demand.
(Eric Clayton)

Evening Standard, refused to have the instrument in the office or at home but they were soon to be overtaken. Getting the latest news, however trivial, and beating rivals with a scoop were the way of the aggressive popular Press such as the halfpenny *Daily Mail* launched by Alfred Harmsworth, the future Lord Northcliffe, in 1896. Technical novelties such as the phone, the motor car and the aeroplane fascinated him and he was quick to see their potential, exploiting them as much as possible.

It was the telegraph that made the greatest change to the speed of news reporting, a fact recognized by its frequent and enduring appearance in newspaper titles. The new instrument received less recognition. In the UK *The Telephone* was the title of three short-lived popular publications that appeared between 1878 and 1885; the only masthead that endured, for almost a century, was the weekly *Smethwick Telephone,* started in 1884. In the USA, few of almost a score of mainly small-town titles – from Arkansas to Maine and Iowa to Texas – survived into the twentieth century. Of particular interest was a succession of Oklahoma newspapers – *The Tahlequah Telephone, Cherokee Telephone, The Arrow-Telephone* – that furthered the cause of the Cherokee nation until publication ceased in 1896.

Journalists jealous of rivals resorted to tapping sources of information to stay ahead of the game. They were not the only ones. Reports from private informers were money to competitors in business, evidence in divorce cases, and material for blackmail. We have no means of knowing when this kind of information-gathering started and how widespread it was. The authorities were not above listening in and keeping quiet about it. Government and private agents could argue that they were on the track of spies and New York City police that they were checking on the working of Catholic charities. When it came to the phone, the privacy of the confessional did not apply, even to priests, who worked closely with ward bosses in organizing the immigrant Irish vote. Nevertheless, the risk of being overheard did not deter users.

One thing that held back development was users' insistence on maintaining a flat inclusive rate of charging. On that basis there was no incentive to install extra lines (the London accountants Cooper Brothers, for example, had one line into a dark and stuffy box in which it was necessary to stand), existing lines became congested and were too often engaged, and large users were getting a cut-price service that was either uneconomic to the operating companies or subsidized by small users. Large users were usually powerful individuals or firms that could use their influence to maintain the *status quo,* disregarding the fact that there was a greater potential benefit in enlarging their circle of communications. On 9 May 1892 the National Telephone Company general manager addressed a meeting of Sheffield subscribers on the abolition of the fixed rate and the

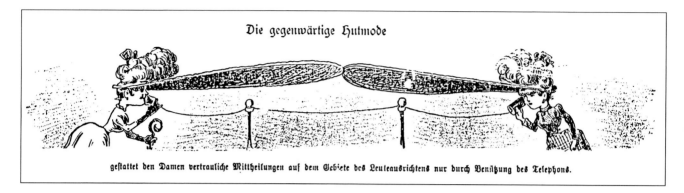

Die gegenwärtige Hutmode

gestattet den Damen vertrauliche Mittheilungen auf dem Gebiete des Leuteausrichtens nur durch Benützung des Telephons.

The extravagant 1890 fashion in hats allowed the confidential exchange of gossip between Viennese ladies only via the phone. (Austrian PTT)

introduction of a measured rate service. His proposal met with such hostility that it was withdrawn.

New York came to grips with the problem, introducing a measured rate in June 1894. The following year the system gained three thousand subscribers, equal to the total gain of the previous six years. The first country to introduce a charging structure based on a separate rental and call charge was Switzerland, on 1 January 1896. Again, the number of subscribers increased rapidly. That year a basic unit for charging for phone calls – three minutes – was laid down at a conference in Budapest of the Swiss-based International Telegraph Union. In the UK a message rate system was started by the Post Office in 1900.

Early phone installations were metropolitan and middle class, largely for business and professional use in major cities and towns. Sigmund Freud, for example, had one as early as 1895 in his flat in the Berggasse in Vienna and doubtless found it useful in making appointments with members of the Viennese bourgeoisie. In 1890 the Hong Kong directory, published monthly in the newspapers, listed only 65 subscribers. Few residences appeared and of these many were doctors'. Government interest was slight, only three establishments being listed: the Central Police Station, Government House, and the Government Civil Hospital.

In a small way the new means of communication helped to increase population movement from country to town. Mainly used in private by individuals, it had less immediate impact on society than public physical services such as railways and steamships, the existence of which could open up new horizons almost overnight for rich and poor alike. Phone networks were a creeping nervous system, the value of which was only gradually appreciated by society at large in different countries.

In Britain a Conservative postmaster-general told the House of Commons in 1887: 'Having regard to the cheap and swift means of communication which at present exist by means of the telegraph between

TELEPHONIC COMMUNICATION BETWEEN
LONDON AND PARIS.

ON and after Wednesday next the 1st proximo, Telephonic Communication between LONDON and PARIS will be open to the Public. CALL OFFICES have been established at:

THE GENERAL POST OFFICE WEST } OPEN ALWAYS.
(BATH STREET)

AND

THE THREADNEEDLE STREET BRANCH POST OFFICE { Open on Week-days from 8.0 a.m. to 8.0 p.m.
(STOCK EXCHANGE)

As soon as possible a Call Office will be established at

THE WEST STRAND TELEGRAPH OFFICE { OPEN ALWAYS.
(CHARING CROSS)

The charge will be **8s**. for a conversation of **3** minutes. Not more than two consecutive conversations can be allowed except when no other applicant is waiting at any of the offices to use the Telephone. In making appointments for conversations, correspondents should bear in mind that Paris time is about 10 minutes in advance of London time.

Persons desiring to speak to Paris direct from their own houses or offices in London can be provided with the necessary connection by wire with the General Post Office West, on terms to be ascertained on application to the Secretary, General Post Office, E.C.

The wires provided for this purpose can be used also for the purpose of sending telegrams for transmission within the United Kingdom or abroad, or to call a Messenger for the Express Delivery of a Letter or Parcel.

GENERAL POST OFFICE,
26th March, 1891.

By Order of the Postmaster-General.

(4747) 100 3/91

Printed for H M Majesty's Stationery Office by W. P. Griffith & Sons, Lim., Prujean Sq., Old Bailey, London, E.C.

An inauspicious date, 1 April, was chosen for the opening of the London–Paris service in 1891.
(BT Museum)

the principal towns in the UK... it is extremely doubtful whether there would be much public advantage in establishing telephonic communication generally between those towns'. Then the only place in Britain that could be called from London was Brighton, the link having been established in 1884. In the ensuing years there was agitation for a state monopoly to improve the situation but nothing resulted from the various pressures. The first telephone society, formed in 1889, was more technical than political. In 1891 a line to Paris was established from London, a three-minute call costing eight shillings (40p), and it was also possible to call Birmingham and Merseyside. The first link between Britain and Ireland, an undersea cable between Scotland and Northern Ireland, was opened by Lord Kelvin in 1893, and thus Dublin could talk to London on a roundabout route. By 1892 New York was in touch with Chicago, 723 miles away. From 1894 long-distance calls were timed on a two-handled contraption called a Calculagraph instead of on a stop watch. Some operators had been expected to keep an eye on no fewer than eight watches.

A Liberal postmaster-general told the House of Commons in 1895:

Gas and water were necessities for every inhabitant of the Country. Telephones were not and never would be. It was no use trying to persuade themselves that the use of the telephone could be enjoyed by the large masses of the people in their daily life.

The following year the Post Office took over the trunk lines from the private companies, but long-distance calls were only a small percentage of the total because the telegraph was cheaper and speech could not always be heard distinctly. In the UK the phone had found various uses but not yet a role in society.

Attitudes in the New and the Old World were markedly different. In 1889 Robert Louis Stevenson, an immigrant to the USA, complained to an editor that the telephone invaded 'our bed and board... our business and bosoms... bleating like a deserted infant'. In more humorous mood Mark Twain wrote in the *New York World* in 1890: 'It is my heart-warm and world-embracing Christmas hope and aspiration that all of us – the high, the low, the poor, the rich, the admired, the despised – may eventually be gathered together in a heaven of everlasting rest and peace and bliss – except the inventor of the telephone.' He later explained to Bell's father-in-law that he had nothing personal against Bell, only the phone system of Hartford, Connecticut, 'the very worst on the face of the earth'. He had already used it anachronistically ('Hello, Central! Is this you, Camelot?') in *A Connecticut Yankee in King Arthur's Court*.

The newly formed People's Party at its July 1892 convention in Omaha, Nebraska, called among other things for the nationalization of phone systems, but the party was short-lived. Popular sentiment was for profiting by the phone. In small towns, doctors, lawyers, dentists, merchants of all kinds, undertakers, livery stable operators put funds – sometimes regarding it as 'taking a flier' – into companies newly created to provide a service. They were also ready to invest in companies making phone apparatus. Yet advanced as the USA was, in 1897 the year that *The Telephone Girl* opened at the Casino Theatre in New York after a run in Islington, London, the White House had only one telephone and, across the street, the State Department two, one of them for the livery stable. There had been a phone in the White House since the presidency of Rutherford B. Hayes (1877–81) but Benjamin Harrison (1889–93) said it was beneath the President's dignity to answer it. By 1899 there were one million US phones.

In the UK, there were many people, including those to whom the cost did not matter, and places that managed without it. The Clothworkers' Company, one of the 'Great Twelve' Livery Companies of the City of London, originally welcomed the idea, having an instrument installed at its Mincing Lane hall by 1 January 1882. Soon there was a dispute with the United Telephone Company about 'the great nuisance and public danger' of overhead wires. In 1885 the Clerk wrote that 'I do not find your system any facility', and in the autumn it was removed, not to be renewed until 1904.

Aesthetes such as William Morris and Ruskin seem to have had no time for it. J. M. Barrie, who loved new gadgets so long as they remained novelties but quickly tired of them when they became common, had a phone installed at 133 Gloucester Road, Kensington, in 1898 and got rid of it two years later because he hated it so. A writer for whom it was a scientific romance was H. G. Wells, who had one installed in the house built to his specifications at Sandgate, near Folkestone, in 1900. Curiously, he was to say little about it in his speculations yet its role would expand in the new century.

CHAPTER 5

MAKING THE BUSINESS CONNECTION

As the century turned, the British were using the phone in the Boer War defensively, for deploying besieged troops and using scarce ammunition to greatest advantage. At Kimberley a 157-foot conning tower was improvised from the headgear of the De Beers mine. In the defence of Mafeking, Baden-Powell led his small garrison by having his office connected to every fort and post, calmly taking a call from a Boer who had seized a fort 800 yards away.

Better information secured the Boer victory at Spion Kop. Messages hand-delivered to British gunners were slow, and, under heavy fire, signalling by heliograph and flag was dangerous. Phones were not used as mobile weapons in the field, an omission rectified in later conflicts. The strategy was to take over existing installations, reinforce them where necessary, as in Johannesburg and Pretoria, and establish other static lines of communication in key points such as blockhouses. Originally built beside railways as part of the defence against guerrillas, many of the blockhouses were equipped with phones, mainly imported. Almost two thousand instruments and about nine thousand miles of wire were used, providing a system surpassing that of the civil government. At the end of the war it was dismantled by the army and most of the blockhouses sold for their corrugated iron. When the *Rand Daily Mail* started in Johannesburg in the autumn of 1902 under the editorship of Edgar Wallace it was no better off for communications than a blockhouse had been. The paper had one phone on the partition of the editor's office and it was answered by whomever happened to be passing.

For the British, the instrument was at war too on the home front. A patriotic song of the time, 'Ring Up Britain', or 'John Bull's Telephone', written, composed and sung by the music-hall artist F. V. St Clair, extolled Mother England, looked down on Little Englanders and the French, took heart from the new king and the support of 'each Colonial Son' for 'the dear old Motherland'. There were also skirmishes in the phone business,

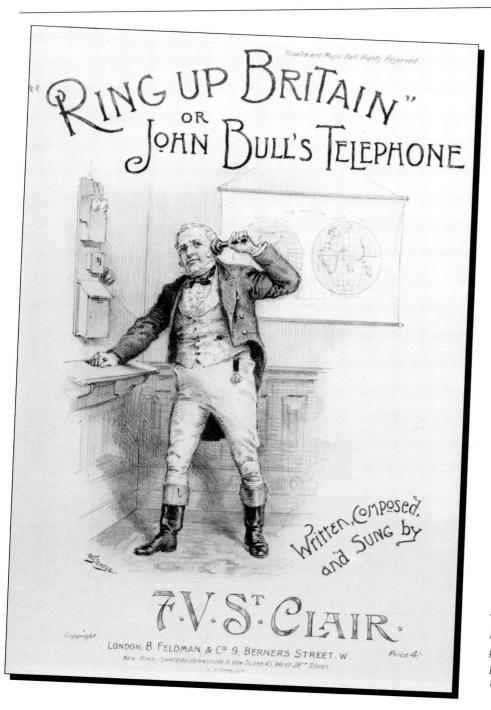

The chorus command to 'Ring up the British Public, John' was an exaggeration. Not many of them had phones in the early years of the twentieth century. (BT Museum)

with ill-fated attempts by municipal enterprises to establish services. Most were underpriced short-lived undertakings. The only survivor was Hull, which became the Andorra of the British system. It differed from other municipal systems in having free intercommunication with its local rival, the assets of which it bought in 1914. Duplication was to nobody's advantage.

In areas with direct competition, as in Michigan, two phones and two directories were necessary to reach all subscribers. Bell and independent companies often exhibited a class difference, with the older, established businesses and families being committed to Bell. New money was more likely to be at home with an upstart independent company. In places such as Minneapolis phone wires could form as definite a social dividing line as railway tracks.

There was also the widening transatlantic divide in usage, with major European countries lagging behind the USA. In France, Gigi's grandmother thought the phone was of real use only to important businessmen or to women who had something to hide. In 1902, commenting on the London County Council's complaints about the inadequacy and high rates of the service in the capital, *The Times* argued:

> When all is said and done the telephone is not an affair of the million. It is a convenience for the well-to-do and a trade appliance for persons who can very well afford to pay for it. For people who use it constantly it is an immense economy, even at the highest rates ever charged by the telephone company. For those who use it merely to save themselves trouble or add to the diversions of life it is a luxury. An overwhelming majority of the population do not use it and are not likely to use it at all, except perhaps to the extent of an occasional message from a public station.

Street kiosks were introduced from at least 1904, to the annoyance of some local councils, which argued that they were unsightly and caused congestion in the streets. The number of call offices on premises also increased, with separate signs to direct the attention of users, mainly men. A local call could be made for a penny, a charge disputed by some on the grounds that it was a *public* call office. Whether a coin had been put in could be a matter of dispute with the operator, her disbelief occasionally leading to vandalism by the caller.

From 1907 both the National Telephone Company and the Post Office stopped any more flat-rate contracts, a move that aroused protests from chambers of commerce. In reply, it was pointed out that almost a quarter of calls in London were ineffective because lines were engaged, that payment in proportion to the service rendered was a sound business principle, and

Kiosks helped popularize the phone but their size and appearance did not always make them welcome pieces of street furniture. This Edwardian example, surely worth preserving, has vanished like the pea-soup fog in which it stood. (BT Museum)

that the phone business was one of message-carrying and not instrument-hiring. Phasing out the flat rate was an incentive to install more lines.

For the businessman installing a private branch exchange there were progressively lower tariffs for additional lines and phones, encouraging an organization to put a number of departments in touch with the outside world. This in turn put extra demands on the inadequate public network, complaints from businessmen about getting through increased, and unfavourable comparisons were made with the service abroad, particularly in the USA. There, at the turn of the century, Ma Bell had set out to woo the American public, to make the phone a daily part of everybody's life. At the other extreme was Turkey, where the situation in 1909 was summarized as follows:

> Before the establishment of the Constitution the importation of telephones into this country was prohibited. The government now have under consideration the laying down of an exchange telephone system. In the meantime, a small private governmental exchange with about 17 stations is working.

As phone services expanded so there was more employment for the New Woman. In the UK the National opened an operator training school in London in 1899, followed by provincial centres, and by 1902 in the USA the Bell System employed equal numbers of men and women. In Australia after three years' service a telephonist could earn more than a country

Trainee Australian switchboard operators being given lessons in voice production. (Telecom Australia)

Some operators' chairs were designed to accommodate the bustle.

(BT Museum)

schoolteacher, enabling her to enjoy her independence and feel that she had some status in society. The chances were that she was from a well-to-do family, possibly one that had been hit by the economic depression and land crash of 1893, and well-educated. It was an occupation for young ladies, preferably single. Australia, Britain, Norway, Sweden and Switzerland, among others, did not employ married operators. Employed when single, girls were expected to resign on marriage, when a gratuity might be paid. Germany made an exception for childless widows under 30, while France and Belgium were more enlightened in employing married women, but they were less reliable in their attendance, taking two to three times as much sick leave. Young ladies were not put at risk by night work.

Some felt there was still no word suitable for the status of the new occupation. An 'operator' could mean all sorts of things and 'Hello girl', 'Switch' and 'Central' were flippant or impersonal. Around 1909 the *New York Herald* tried briefly to popularize the more delicate term 'phoniste' on the analogy of 'artiste' and 'pianiste' as 'simple, dignified and swell' but nothing came of it. An entertainment lecturer described her as 'the fairy of the magic wire, who puts us in touch with our distant friends... the dispatcher of the talk trains'. In a private installation she could be the mistress and spy of the boss.

In the UK the National stipulated that candidates for the job, of good education and address, should be between 16 and 25, of a minimum height in their stockinged feet of 5 feet 3 inches. Florence J. Minter, the metropolitan examining matron, noted that

> 75 per cent of the applicants give their height as that, and we have long since found the usefulness of a proper apparatus for measuring the questionable candidates in this respect. The unbelieving way in which a number of girls glare at this apparatus when its record is decidedly against them is amusing... We naturally do not reject a growing girl when she is otherwise suitable for the sake of half an inch, but we do find the impossibility of short operators reaching the board in some new exchanges.

Operators trained in the public service were wanted by industry and commerce for their office switchboards. The world's biggest retailer, Sears Roebuck, installed an internal system in 1905. By 1906 it was reckoned that there were more trained operators employed on private branch exchanges in New York than there were in the service of the New York Telephone Company. In less progressive offices, boards were manned by the worst of all operators, a boy whose time was divided among the switchboard, running messages and licking stamps. More reliable were blind operators, people glad to make use of their senses of hearing and touch in operating

boards and taking messages on shorthand typewriters. It was one of their few prospects for interesting employment.

Not all public service operators worked in large, airy exchanges with comfortable dining- and sitting-rooms. Some worked in adapted rooms over post offices, in the corners of shops, and in private houses. The exchange at Palmers Green, over a North London painting and decorating shop, was so small that when an inspector called the room went dark. It was also infested with mice. Such sites often provided vantage points from which the passing scene could be observed and information relayed to subscribers. If the exchange was in a backroom, an operator who had time to listen in could pick up gossip and pass on information that way. It was reckoned that in the provinces there were about 8 or 9 calls per line per day, against 15 in London. In the backwoods you might have to be a maid of all work, nipping round the back of the exchange to screw up a loose terminal or reconnect a wire, using a hairpin to make a quick repair. At Windsor exchange, which kept a private list of numbers for King Edward VII, instant connections were expected.

Whatever the problems, however inept or obtuse the subscriber, however much indicators on the board might bob up and down signalling a subscriber's impatience, the operator was instructed to maintain an even disposition. She had to 'cultivate her voice'. The Post Office, which in 1908 adopted from the Bell System its standard replies with their liberal use of

'Please' and 'Thank you', warned its operators against using 'uncouth and abrupt expressions'.

In the National training schools monitors pretended to be subscribers, adopting various attitudes to test reactions. Girls had to repress their laughter at the thought of a man in a call office unable to get his bent penny in and hold back tears when a pretended cross subscriber became all too real. One problem was the small man appearing great at a distance. In Iowa a subscriber deprived of service for using abusive language took his case to the Court of Appeals and won. The court decided that phone companies were in business to supply a service and that dictating the kind of language to be used was *ultra vires*. At the other extreme, in East Prussia, a respected citizen after being kept waiting for some time ventured to remonstrate mildly with 'my dear girl'. For this 'insulting expression' to the operator, a government official, he was served with a notice of police proceedings. That sort of situation was unlikely to occur among the frugal and tight-lipped Swiss, who had a low calling rate, an average of only two calls per subscriber per day.

Telephonists in many countries tried to encourage subscribers to visit their exchange so that they could see for themselves what went on in connecting and ticketing calls and looking after subscribers, and how there was little time for reading novels, sipping tea and knitting. A visit from a subscriber gave them a chance to size up the person that went with the voice and perhaps tame a lion, or lioness, with a smile. Ladies in society could claim that they never hurried to the phone but young ladies in exchanges frequently had to. It could be a life of extremes, exemplified by two occasions in the Toronto exchange. In 1900, 133 business firms were asked to dispense with service for two hours so that the operators could watch the parade of soldiers home from the Boer War. The following year, when news of Queen Victoria's death came in, the operators were all rushed back on duty without any lunch because there was a flood of calls to deal with. Moreover, to see whether she was needed for 9 o'clock, each girl had to call in every morning at 8.30. So she had to be up and dressed and ready to leave for work even on her mornings off. Unable to afford a phone at home, she usually went to a pay station. In compensation, she was paid 10 cents for the call, whether needed for duty or not.

A travelling lecturer in the USA did his bit to make people understand:

We are always in a hurry when we telephone. (Take out watch and count $3\frac{1}{2}$ seconds.) That is the average time it takes the girl to answer. We have no right to expect instantaneous service from her. We do not expect it from trolleys, or the railways, or the stores, or the Post Office, or the express companies. We sit down in the waiting-room of a ferry and contentedly squander 30

"TELEPHONE MANNERS."

[*Reproduced by the courtesy of the* DAILY MIRROR.

THE Postmaster-General has issued orders to telephone operators in his employ to be polite to subscribers. We should esteem it a favour if he would also teach manners to the subscribers themselves. Many telephone users are not only rude to the telephone employees, but inconsiderate to those whom they call up, often keeping people waiting many minutes while they find themselves. There is too much of the "hold-the-line-he'll-be-here-in-a-minute" nuisance.—(*Daily Mirror*.)

Strip cartoonists, as in this British newspaper of 1908, found the behaviour of operators and subscribers a ready-made subject. (BT Museum)

precious minutes – 1,800 seconds. We will stand in line for opera tickets in the worst winter storm and never dream of blaming Mr Gatticasazza. But when we go to a telephone, every second is a precious pearl. Why doesn't she drop that novel and attend this line? Why, oh why, is electricity so slow?

An entire page in Spanish and English in the Tampa, Florida, 1908 directory gave pointed suggestions on 'How to Get Good Service', among them:

Treat the Operator quite considerately. Kind words improve service.
Do not mistake mechanical trouble for service trouble. Report all trouble to the Trouble Clerk.
Do not call during a thunderstorm, as the company will not be liable for any injuries received.

Operators remained polite to keep their jobs but they grew less docile as employees. In the UK some joined the Women's Trade Union League formed in 1904, out of which grew in 1905 the National Association of Telephone Operators to fight under the leadership of Mary MacArthur for continuity of employment or ample compensation when the National was taken over by the Post Office at the end of 1911. Deterioration of operators' working conditions in France led to strikes in 1906–9, something unheard of in the public service. In Australia in 1912, when a four-hour longer working week of 37 hours was ordered, the Sydney operators – a predominantly young group – held their first mass meeting, at which there was an undercurrent of strike talk. At the same time in the USA, where women were scarcely more union-minded than the employers, Caroline Crawford in her report *Hello Girls of Boston* stated that the work required 'constant employment of the muscles of the eye in different directions [and] constant use of the optic nerve'. The ear 'is obliged... to distinguish between a number of different voices, to ascertain at once, so as to avoid repetition, the number asked for, no matter how indistinctly or ill-pronounced the number may be; this necessitates constant alertness of the auditory nerve; while the vocal organs are scarcely less constantly in use in answering calls and such conversations as may be necessary.' Her conclusion was that exchange work involved a tremendous strain upon the mental constitution as well as upon the nervous system, made worse by the offensive tests or listening-in of supervisors, often officious college graduates. The message promoted to the public was: 'The Bell telephone relieves anxieties'.

This was a view of the inside taken by an outsider:

Operating is in itself an excellent method of physiculture. It is not at all like cramping, chest-contracting work that so many girls are required to do. It throws back the head, broadens the chest and strengthens arms and wrists.

No mention of serge skirts becoming shiny from all the movement. To prevent it, girls sometimes wore black sateen aprons tied on backwards. Sweets could be secreted in the large pocket.

Alfred Barnard writing in *Every Woman's Encyclopaedia* on 'How to Become a Telephone Operator' had a similar rosy view in the UK:

> The work of the telephone operator is healthy, and the action of stretching her arms up above her head, and to the right and left of her, develops the chest and arms, and turns thin and weedy girls, after a few months' work in the operating room, into strong ones. There are no anaemic, unhealthy-looking girls in the operating rooms.

A more sober view was taken in a 1911 report by a committee of doctors who studied operating conditions. The doctors recommended not employing women who were 'markedly anaemic' although a 'moderate and ordinary form of anaemia' could be tolerated during the two-year probationary period, when it would either be cured or become worse 'before a permanent engagement is entered upon'. More important than any physical weakness though was 'an unstable nervous equilibrium'. Serving a public 'whose methods, manner, and temper are always diverse and sometimes unpleasant', an operator was subject to nervous strain that could not be removed. In fact, physical aspects of the job, such as having to jump up and down and stretch while wearing fairly heavy equipment, could make it worse. Recommended improvements included a reduction in working hours and ending split shifts, but the Post Office did not rush to implement them. Outside, damage such as cut wires was often put down to suffragettes.

A woman, Margot Asquith, a great talker with a vivid turn of phrase, was probably responsible for the installation of the phone in 10 Downing Street. She was sad to leave her home in Cavendish Square and move into the Prime Minister's 'lodgings' on 5 May 1908. To make the place more comfortable, the Board of Works had among other things installed phones. Mildly lit, they helped the lost Margot to retrace her steps through the rambling building. That same year the Board of Works also installed switchboards in both Houses of Parliament. Like its department the Post Office, Edwardian government became conscious of the phone. To help improve administration, the first pre-planned installations were made, as at the War Office, when it moved from Pall Mall to a new building in Whitehall in 1906 and a 400-line switchboard was installed.

The instrument was also starting to become a part of everyday business and social life. From 1905 it was used to inform Emma, Queen Mother of the Netherlands, about conditions on the beach at Scheveningen, where she liked to take a daily walk. It was the Hotel Netherland in New York that claimed the first installation of room phones, in 1894. In 1904 the Savoy Hotel, London, advertised its residential suites as having 'to each sitting room a telephone connecting with a Central Exchange in the hotel'. The following year it advertised in journals such as *The Sphere, The Queen* and *Lady's Pictorial* with a full-page colour painting of 'The Telephone Girl' saying 'The Savoy? Yes, delightful! I always like dining there, better than anywhere else.' In late 1910, advertisements boasted that 100 new instruments had been added to the hotel. Not everybody had to have the instrument and the hotel's index of guests ensured that it was removed from the room of at least one woman who disliked it, before she arrived. In July 1912 'The Clubman' noted in *The Sketch*:

> Another luxurious change foreseen by the retiring manager of the Savoy [Gustave] is that it will be possible to telephone in comfort from an armchair in a lounge or palm-garden instead of being cooped up, standing in a box, like a prisoner *en route* to a police-court. But before this change takes place, some inventor must find a way of deadening the voice of the man or lady at the telephone, for a man talking business to his partner in the City, or a lady discussing family matters with her relatives do not want their share of the conversation to reach whoever occupies the next armchair. The telephone, like the bathroom, is just emerging from its first stage of being a useful nuisance into that of being a necessary luxury.

Callers asking for the King at Claridge's in Mayfair were often asked which monarch they had in mind. In New York City the Hotel Astor exchange was busier than that of many towns.

Not only did hotels make money from their installations – the Hotel Astor about $50,000 a year – they also saved on messengers. Hotel thieves spotted the opportunities. In 1912 one Charles Alexander, 34, was convicted of stealing luggage from London hotels. His *modus operandi* was to wait in a lobby for a newly arrived guest to go out after checking in his bags. A phone message would then be left for the absent guest, asking him to keep an urgent appointment elsewhere. This was followed by a call from the 'guest', asking whether there were any messages. On receiving his bogus one, the 'guest' would ask the porter to give his bag to the man being sent round shortly. The thief or an accomplice would then collect the bag.

Being on the phone was a mark of distinction and people remarked on establishments that were not. About 1905 Harrods started a phone order office, open day and night, with orders received after business hours being despatched by mail or the company's green and gold vans early the next day. The innovation succeeded, public call offices were installed in 1908, and much was made of the new number, Western 1, with 60 lines. This was ready for competition with Selfridge's new store opened in Oxford Street on 15 March 1909. While working at Marshall Field's department store in Chicago, Gordon Selfridge at his own expense visited New York to study methods there and on his return suggested, among other things, a house phone system.

Having seen the advantages firsthand, he wanted the National to incorporate a public exchange in his London venture. Declining 'most apologetically', they offered him the consolation of a special number, Gerrard 1, which he claimed 'was worth £1,000 spot cash for its publicity value alone'. The theme was taken up by a revue actress, 'Teddy' Gerard, in a song 'Naughty, naughty one Gerard'.

Selfridge claimed that the installation with its 60 exchange lines and some 450 extensions provided 'communication between every counter and every part of the British Isles'. The National reckoned it was 'the most popular item of the many displayed' and in its journal gave an account of the public reaction:

A bold innovation was instituted by the firm when they allotted a position for this right out in the open store, in the very centre of the handsome building just completed. A rail serves to separate the operators from the public, and the novel sight of a telephone switchboard operated in the open attracted at all times a crowd of onlookers standing six to eight deep throughout each day of the inaugural week. So great was the pressure upon the opening day that the rail and its supports were thrown down, and it became necessary to build a barricade of heavy carpet rolls standing upon end, round the switchboard, thereby permitting an adequate view, while preserving the necessary facilities for handling calls. Many onlookers were noted as having stood through periods varying from 30 minutes to one hour, altogether fascinated by telephone operating, any comments they felt impelled to make being made in subdued whispers... The restaurant is equipped with 54 jacks, in any one of which the plug of a pay-station telephone can be readily inserted. The whole scheme indicates in an extremely practical way what an important field for development lies in the direction of shopping by telephone and telephoning by shopping... To gauge the public appreciation of counter pay-stations it is only necessary to shake the coin boxes at Selfridge's.

In 1912, as part of a free exhibition of 'the most interesting scientific discoveries of modern times', the store displayed a Telewriter, which over a phone line received a message in the sender's actual handwriting.

Phones speeded up service and boosted turnover. American Bell published a dozen promotional postcards, one entitled 'The Convenience of Marketing by Bell Telephone'. Wanamaker's in Philadelphia headed its list of instructions to sales staff: TELEPHONE MESSAGES MUST RECEIVE INSTANT ATTENTION. Harrods increased phoned orders threefold. The Army and Navy Stores, which also sold household phones, had a similar installation. Following the trend, John Barker in Kensington and D. H. Evans in Oxford Street extended theirs. The National promoted the idea with one of its postcards, and in the provinces traders started putting phone numbers in their advertisements. A Kingston-on-Thames draper got the message. His 1906 number was 243 but in the 1912 directory he had a bold entry: 'Kingston 1 (Pvte Bch Ex) Frank Bentall Sixty Separate Depts.' He had the number painted large on the lift tower, visible for miles around.

Although local trade was stimulated there were problems in calling long-distance. In 1906 a Norwich tailoring firm complained in a letter to the *Eastern Daily Press*: 'We use the telephone between our London office and Norwich, sometimes several times a day, and it is a matter of great inconvenience to be kept waiting an hour and three-quarters to two and a half hours'. That same year a wealthy brewer in Sherbrooke, Quebec, made a 1,100-mile call to Des Moines, Iowa, to buy a trotting horse and issue shipping instructions. His call was front-page news under banner headlines. The Scotten-Dillon Company of Detroit called one of its products, a chewing or smoking tobacco, Long Distance. Presumably that referred to the gap between mouth and spittoon. At the time there was only one circuit between Montreal and Toronto, the two largest cities in Canada. At best it took 10 minutes for a caller to be connected and to complete a three-minute conversation. With only about five conversations an hour possible, delays were almost inevitable but there was insufficient demand for a second circuit.

The idea of the phone as a business necessity was catching on. Edward Holden, managing director of the Midland Bank, noted in his diary for 15 November 1904: 'Saw Mr William Walker of the Post Office Telephone Branch and had an interview with a view of having installed in this building a separate exchange.' By 26 October 1911 inefficiency had become a matter of urgency:

> I saw the chief of the Trunk Department of the Post Office Telephone Service, and complained very strongly of the delay and inconvenience caused to me by the telephone at The Grange. He promised to look personally into the matter.

By that year an internal system existed for the governors and senior officials of the Bank of England and before the First World War the nine instruments and small switchboards were replaced by a more extensive arrangement. Yet there were parts of the Edwardian City, still largely a place of small family firms dealing personally, where the phone was anathema. The stockbroker Walter de Zoete adamantly refused to use it and had it banished to the basement.

A 1912 board minute of Pilkington Brothers records:

> Telephone. Partners not to be unreasonably troubled. Someone of good education needed in telephone room to take confidential and partners' messages. Question of having a girl for this was discussed.

The instrument was not always welcome. When it was first installed in Arthur & Company, a Glasgow textile wholesaler, a shawl salesman refused to answer it as the work of the devil. Not all business and professional people who used the phone at work wanted it at home, regarding it either as unnecessary or an intrusion into their private lives.

This lukewarm attitude was more evident in Hong Kong, a colonial port where the rhythm of life was governed by the arrival and departure of ships and the time it took for mail to and from the UK. Comings and goings were predictable and an untoward occurrence to disturb the expatriate placidity unlikely. If an urgent message was necessary then chit coolies were readily available. They were fast, reliable, and cheaper than a phone. Ladies of the sleepy colony were more fortunate than their sisters back home in the number of servants they could afford to employ.

A completely opposite view was taken by E. H. Harriman, a wealthy American broker, who had 100 phones in his mansion, 60 of them on long-distance lines. In his 1910 *History of The Telephone* Herbert Casson observed:

> What the brush is to the artist, what the chisel is to the sculptor, the telephone was to Harriman. He built his fortune with it. It was in his library, his bathroom, his private car, his camp in the Oregon wilderness. No transaction was too large or too involved to be settled over its wires... 'He is a slave to the telephone' wrote a magazine writer. 'Nonsense' replied Harriman. 'It is a slave to me.'

Financiers revelled in it. They could deal instantly in stocks and bonds over an ever-expanding territory. More money could be raised more quickly as telephone wires became tentacles of Wall Street. J. P. Morgan reckoned that his partner George W. Perkins could raise 'twenty million in twenty minutes'; and Morgan himself averted a financial panic in 1907 by promptly extending $25 million credit to other banks, the operations of which reached out from New York to Chicago and St Louis. Economic growth developed as a national phenomenon, to reach its first peak in the

A Telephone, "No. 84, Godalming," has been placed in Verites. Boys who wish to use it must obtain a signed order for each message. It is proposed to charge 6d. a quarter to each boy as part payment of the rent, and an account of charges for calls will be sent in with other items in the quarterly accounts. You are requested not to call up anyone in Verites during school hours, unless the need is urgent.

A. H. TOD.

VERITES.	VERITES.
TELEPHONE ORDER.	*Telephone Order.*
Name of Caller :	*Name of Caller :*
———————————	———————————
For Call to (full name):	*For Call to (full name):*
———————————	———————————
At Office : ————————	*At Office* ————————
Date ————————	*Date* ————————
	Signed ————————

In the summer of 1913 the arrival of the phone in Verites, one of the boarding-houses at the English boys' public school Charterhouse, signalled the beginning of the end of the obligatory weekly letter home. Instead of writing boys could send a message. Little more than a year later tragic messages began to arrive. Altogether, 687 Carthusians lost their lives in the First World War.

(The Headmaster, Charterhouse)

late 1920s. Yet, as communications spread and economic power was distributed, the influence of the Eastern Establishment would diminish. New industrial and commercial centres would arise on the communications network, first on the West Coast and then, in the latter part of the twentieth century, down in the Sunbelt States.

Meanwhile, in a humbler way, people with the phone could become messengers for others. Corner candy stores in American cities were working-class social centres with a booth or two where messages could be left by pre-arrangement or with a friendly owner. In an emergency, a contact could be made, perhaps involving somebody being fetched, by a boy, from a six-floor walk-up tenement a block away. In the small village of Wainstalls, West Yorkshire, the only phone was in the spinning mill and the office manager was frequently woken up at home by people wanting the doctor. Whatever the hour or weather he would dress, more or less, and make the five-minute walk to the office to call the doctor, who would make the two-mile journey uphill on horseback. The office manager was also in touch with the world at large. On 6 May 1910 he sent a note on the back of an envelope, 'The King is dead', to his family. They were the first people in the district to know. Conversely, damage to lines could deprive people of news. In March 1909 a sleet storm cut off Washington DC from the rest of the USA, and it missed out on President Taft's inauguration.

The newspaper proprietor most associated with phones was Northcliffe. He had them in every room, sometimes more than one, at home or when travelling. When he took over *The Times* in 1908 he was also reputed to have acquired the telephonist as a mistress. On the Continent he would reserve a line so that he could talk to London when he wanted. From his magnificent home at Sutton Place, near Guildford, Surrey (later the home of the oil millionaire J. Paul Getty, who had a pay phone installed in the hall), Northcliffe kept in touch with his newspapers. 'I've been able, without moving from this room, to speak to 20 people already today and tell them what I want doing,' he said to one of his employees, Tom Clarke, on their first meeting on New Year's Day 1912. He insisted on all his staff being 'telephone-conscious' and asserted that 'People who don't hear properly on the telephone are a danger to my business'. On 10 September 1909 a speech by Lord Rosebery in Glasgow was transmitted at very short notice to the *Evening News* in London. Two rooms in Carmelite House were set aside with reception facilities for 12 reporters. Within 10 minutes of the speech ending, copies of the paper were on sale with most of Lord Rosebery's words. Leader-writers had to be prepared to phone in articles from home to meet a sudden situation. The popular press was also helped by news pictures wired from Paris and Berlin. To impress visitors, Northcliffe had a dummy phone in his office with a foot-operated button to make it ring. He would answer and pretend to be talking to the Prime Minister or some other important figure but, as he was not that good an actor, his own staff at least saw through his boyish ploy.

Reporters of racing results had to resort to all sorts of ploys because the racing authorities, fearing that attendances would fall if punters could get results within minutes and that fraud would increase, would not allow phoning from the course. Course officials had to be cultivated, tick-tack signals and telescopes used to convey the winning numbers to reporters waiting off-course at the end of a line. To fox Exchange Telegraph reporters, officials at Leicester and Derby in November 1904 deliberately hoisted wrong numbers, an action that upset bookies, newspapers and punters. The Jockey Club disapproved but the practice did not immediately cease. There was also rivalry between Press agencies, which got up to all sorts of tricks to be first with the results, regardless of expense. Gradually the parties learned to work together for the common interest, and by 1914 rapid communication of results from courses was a recognized practice that offered far less scope for betting on a certainty.

Inside information was also sought by spies and intelligence agencies, notably the FBI, formed in 1908, and a year later in the UK the Secret Service Bureau. Most of their information was gained through informers, observation, and the interception of mail: a mixture of not always reliable sources. With international tensions rising, there was a growing market for intelligence, even that of doubtful value. In 1908 Baden-Powell, for instance, fell for a bogus plan for the German invasion of Britain, when 'spies stationed in England were to cut all telephone and telegraph wires… and thus to interrupt communications and create confusion.' There was an occasional triumph. In 1914, waiting for the declaration of war, the head of counter-espionage, Captain Kell, stayed in his office, surrounded by phones. From them, with 12 hours' notice of the declaration, he issued orders for the police to arrest a German network of 22 spies.

CHAPTER 6

YOUR PARTY'S ON THE LINE

Edwardian subscribers to the Electrophone service could still be numbered in hundreds. In 1907 grand opera from Covent Garden and London church services were relayed to the royal family at Sandringham, Norfolk, but they did not set the fashion. The Houses of Parliament were opposed to broadcasting equipment. Nor would Westminster Abbey allow it, leaving stay-at-home congregations to churches like St Martin-in-the-Fields, St Mary le Bow, St James's in Piccadilly, and the City Temple. Transmitters in churches were made to look like Bibles. Among theatres and concert halls connected were the Alhambra, Apollo, Drury Lane, Duke of York's, Empire, Gaiety, Garrick, Lyric, Palace, Pavilion, Prince of Wales, Savoy, Shaftesbury, Tivoli, Queen's Hall, and Royal Albert Hall. In 1913, to celebrate the Entente Cordiale, Electrophone and Théâtrophone exchanged transmissions, with *Faust* coming from the Paris Opéra and *Tosca* from Covent Garden. Sometimes other users required the trunk lines and *Faust* gave way to an excerpt from a West End theatre performance. Subscribers reached a maximum of about two thousand and it remained a minority pastime. Rome introduced a news service, Araldo Telefonico, in 1909.

The instrument helped in theatre bookings, as the *Daily Mail* recorded in September 1910:

> So great is the demand for seats at the Coliseum, where Mme Sarah Bernhardt is now appearing, that the telephone authorities are connecting the box-office with four new lines. On Tuesday there were 2,030 calls impossible to connect.

When Oswald Stoll opened the Coliseum in 1904 he had a central information bureau for enquiries and messages. Doctors and others expecting urgent calls during a performance could leave their names and seat numbers. District Messengers, smart lads in blue uniforms with silver

Personal listening in the early years of the twentieth century was for the few on the phone. In the latter years personal stereo was to make it mobile for the many. (BT Museum)

Both ends of a movie conversation could be shown on a split screen, as in the 1901 short Are You There? (BFI Stills/Williamson Kinematograph Company)

buttons and pill-box caps, could be summoned from their booth to deliver and receive messages.

Among the lower classes, the instrument was popularized by songs such as 'I'll Tell Tilly on the Telephone' (1907) and 'Kitty The Telephone Girl' (1912). It was also a dramatic device and a comic prop in short silent films, then a novel attraction in penny arcades. In a two-minute 1901 British comedy, *Are You There?*, a young man and his girl converse on a split screen. The father takes the receiver from his daughter's hand, unbeknown to the young man, who sits back awaiting his girl's arrival. Instead the father comes in and beats him with an umbrella. Endless visual jokes were based on getting an earful at the receiver, as when a termagant at the transmitter caused a blast of steam at the other end.

New plots were opened up for thriller writers. In 1902 the *Chicago Tribune* ran a short story about an anarchist arranging a bomb to be detonated on call. The police raced against time to trace and catch him, finally detaching the bomb seconds before he was due to ring. Using the phone as a remote control device for criminal purposes such as arson was to remain more in the realm of fiction than fact. More real was the problem of thieves posing as inspectors to gain access to private residences.

Edgar Wallace, a journalist who made frequent but brief use of the telephone, made it the basis of his first book, *The Four Just Men* (1904). The Foreign Secretary, a frightened man threatened with death, was in a locked room in 44 Downing Street surrounded by police. Nevertheless, he was killed at the appointed hour. As a publicity stunt, £500 was offered for the correct answer as to how he had been killed. Solutions poured in and the delay in awarding prizes prompted suggestions of fraud. Wallace, unable to pay, had to be bailed out by Harmsworth. The fictional Foreign Secretary had been electrocuted by a high voltage wire attached to his phone, the shock being too much for his weak heart. In 1910 Wallace wrote a comic phone sketch, *Hello, Exchange*, that went into a West End revue. Another journalist, E. C. Bentley, made use of the phone in *Trent's Last Case* (1913) to provide an alibi for the victim. It also led to the minor crime of breaking insulators on poles. In 1913 a paper was read to the Institute of Post Office Electrical Engineers on 'Procedure at Stone-Throwing Prosecutions in Police Courts of England and Wales'.

Even in the USA replacement of street alarm systems by phone boxes for police and fire use was slow, even after the San Francisco earthquake of 1906, when the whole system was disrupted. An idea advanced but not adopted was that each patrolman should have a phone number. In Cardiff, Wales, a subscriber tried to communicate with a constable by giving the exchange the number on his helmet. The British police were still not taking up the instrument. Buckinghamshire Constabulary had its divisional stations connected in 1901 but the superintendents were allowed to make only two calls a day. In 1904 a sergeant in a station not yet connected was asked to speak from a house opposite to a man five miles away. He believed it was impossible but, after discussions with his wife and the reassurance of a neighbour, decided to do so. Having put on a collar and tie, he was accompanied to the house by his family. When he shouted into the receiver 'I'm here', everybody recoiled. He did not lower his voice throughout the conversation and afterwards averred that the invention would never succeed because it would be the ruination of people's throats. Scotland Yard did not install private lines to its divisions until 1903 and outside lines to the public until 1905. Perhaps the benefits of the instrument were appreciated by Harry Smale, who retired from the Metropolitan Police in 1908 to become a private detective, a calling in which quick information was vital. With other colleagues, in 1913 he formed The British Detectives Association.

An argument against the phone in emergencies such as fires was that people were too agitated to use it. There was the added risk of more malicious calls being made. Exchanges themselves were still subject to fires, as at London Wall in 1902 and 1905, when there was also a fire in the Bank exchange. Overhead, bare tram and trolley-bus wires were another hazard.

If a phone wire fell across them, somebody could be electrocuted or a fire started so tram companies fitted insulated guard strips. Starting, stopping and running of trams could impair speech quality on the line. There were complaints that when a tram was in a certain position there was enough current for a false call to a switchboard, that the noise of the tram – and even the sound of the conductors collecting fares – could be overheard. Growth of electrical transport in the streets thus helped campaigns to put phone wires underground, where they were safe and less prone to interference.

Gradually people came to appreciate the advantages of the phone over an alarm, providing prompt detailed information on the severity of an incident. A writer in the *Daily Chronicle* in 1907 reckoned that 'dangerous fires in London had been reduced to about 1 per cent and annual deaths from scarlet fever from 5,000 to 500', largely through getting urgent cases into proper hospitals. A sick child in Bray, Berkshire, had to have her temperature phoned to her doctor twice daily between visits in case an urgent operation was necessary. Her father used a hotel phone, one of four in the village. When the world-famous Mayo Clinic opened in 1914, it had the first intercommunicating system in the USA, enabling doctors to talk to each other directly, to the operator, or to a person outside at will.

In 1907, with the consent of the vice-chancellor, an Oxford undergraduate ill in Birmingham took the ten-minute *viva voce* part of his examination over a trunk line. 'A Master of Arts of the University was with the undergraduate during the time he was using the telephone, so that no question could arise as to the fairness of the examination.'

Occasionally telephonists became heroines. On 27 August 1908, 68-year old Mrs Sally Rooke was at the switchboard in her home in Folsom, New Mexico, a village on the banks of the Dry Cimarron stream. During the evening it began to rain and at 10 p.m. she took a call from a canyon 10 miles up the valley. She was told that after a cloudburst a tremendous volume of water was rushing down. Realizing the danger, she began to call householders in its path, steadfastly refusing to leave her post until she had warned more ranchers down the Cimarron. She was swept away with her home and her body was not found until seven months later on a ranch eight miles below the village. More than 4,000 people, most of them phone employees, contributed to the granite monument over her grave inscribed: 'With heroic devotion she glorified her calling by sacrificing her own life that others might live'.

The worst disaster in British mining history, involving the death of 439 miners in Senghenydd, a South Wales village, on 14 October 1913, was possibly caused by an old method of signalling. Sparks from an electric bell might have ignited the gas that exploded and turned the colliery into a mass crematorium. Following a similar explosion at Bedwas Colliery the previous year, where it was proved beyond reasonable doubt that the cause was a sparking bell, attention was focused on safe and reliable communications in mines. The month after the Senghenydd disaster *Scientific American* carried a report on the subject that praised the use of iron box mine phones, compulsory in some US states, and oxygen helmets incorporating a throat transmitter for rescue operations.

Railways too were extending the use of the phone, not so much in administration as in operations such as traffic control over busy sections of line. On Hallowe'en 1907 a system for preventing collisions in fog was demonstrated on the South-Eastern and Chatham Railway. It reproduced the state of the signals on the line in the cab of the engine driver, who while held up could also talk to the signalman. In 1910 on the London to Brighton line an experiment in phoning from a moving train to a signal box was successful. Fifty years later the Railophone idea was mentioned in a *Times* article on 'Forgotten Inventions'. Theodore Vail, president of the Bell System, travelled around his empire in a private rail car, which at a stopover was connected to the local phone service.

To the motorist the phone was essential, putting him in touch with hotel accommodation, spare parts, petrol, messages to home and friends. Les Collins worked in Gadsdon's, a garage midway between London and Brighton:

We were called out for breakdowns on the road. Until immediately after the Great War there was no garage between us and Brighton, a distance of almost 25 miles. People found it very convenient to know our number. Many of our customers also lived in large houses on estates in the surrounding countryside. They needed their chauffeured cars and their house lighting plants maintained. Whenever there was a fault it had to be attended to urgently and we were in a position to do both. We also used the phone – it was a wall model in the proprietor's office – to ring up suppliers. We were the biggest cycle place in the area and there were no delivery vans. We used to ring up suppliers like Brown Brothers and the East London Rubber Company and they'd put what we wanted on the train. We could get, say, cycle tyres from Croydon in two to three hours. We'd collect them from the station just round the corner.

The Automobile Association began to cater for its members in a similar way, installing in 1912 the first of the phone boxes for its patrols.

Meanwhile there had been several technical advances making the phone easier to use and more effective. Desk sets were more convenient than a box on the wall. A common battery at an exchange, first used in 1894 at

Lexington, Massachusetts, provided centrally the electric current on which speech was carried. It relieved subscribers of maintaining their own wet batteries, which could leak, leaving dried crystals on walls and discolouring wallpaper. Topping up a Leclanché cell with sal ammoniac could be a messy business, and complete renewal was a job for a repair man.

The first UK common battery installation for public use was opened at Bristol in 1900, and in 1906 the Post Office installed a coin-operated call box at Ludgate Circus in the City. The previous year 50 dial telephones in Fall River, Massachusetts, had been equipped with coin boxes. From 1908, when loading coils in cables were inserted in the Liverpool–Manchester trunk route, the distances over which clear and audible speech could be transmitted were increased. In 1913 a start was made on such a cable between London and Birmingham. The convenience of the phone for the delivery of telegrams had been appreciated both by the Bell System and by the Post Office, which in 1910 carried out successful experiments in the London area. The telegram followed the phone message, for confirmation. Even so, some business houses were wary of the new practice because messages had to be written down, there might be mistakes, and damage could have been done before confirmation was received.

Greater public use of the phone at a time when spitting was a nuisance and consumption – 'the phthisic' – a killer, led to fears about catching diseases. In 1870 Bell had emigrated to Canada with his parents for fear that, like his two brothers, he should die of consumption, and now his invention was being regarded as a means of spreading it. In 1900 *The Lancet* carried a report from its Paris correspondent that the Under-Secretary of State, 'with a view to avoid transmission of infectious diseases', had ordered that all public phones be disinfected daily with a strong solution of carbolic acid. French doctors treated the announcement with 'a certain amount of scepticism', not about the diagnosis of the danger but about the efficacy of the remedy. 'They take exception to the choice of a disinfectant, for carbolic acid has an abominable smell and is of very feeble microbicidal power.' American doctors were also concerned. 'Does the public telephone transmit disease?' asked W. G. Bissell in the *Buffalo Medical Journal* in 1902. R. S. Stanley dealt with the 'dangers of infection which lurk in the telephone' in the *Memphis Medical Monthly* in 1904, returning to the subject in the *Charlotte Medical Journal* the following year. In 1905 the annual report of the medical officer of health for the City of London contained an account of an investigation by Dr E. E. Klein, who concluded:

> that there is no real risk in the use of the telephone at public call offices and that the alarm that has been raised has no foundation in fact. It is satisfactory to be assured that the use of so valuable a means of communication is without

any attendant danger and that the only precaution advisable is the obvious commonsense one of keeping the mouthpieces clean.

Fears were not allayed. In 1906 'Call Office Attendant' wrote to *The Lancet* warning of the 'growing danger arising from the use of the common mouthpiece by promiscuous callers at public telephones'. He quoted the case of a man 'evidently advanced in consumption having a violent cough with expectoration [who] used the instrument and afterwards I found the mouthpiece damp with, I presume, his congealed breath'. That was not all. 'Later in the week a lady called up her medical attendant from the call office and from the conversation which ensued, I gathered that her children were suffering from measles. I also had a case in which from the conversation heard there is no doubt that the user came from a house infected with chicken pox.'

In 1907 *The Lancet* itself declared that 'the public telephone call office seems to be singularly well designed for the capture and growth of pathogenic organisms'. Call boxes were like hothouses for the breeding of disease, being 'usually closed, and padded, and kept almost airtight; sunshine and fresh air seldom can reach the interior while, of course, no attempt is made to keep them aired or ventilated, because any provision for securing ventilation is calculated to make difficult the hearing of the message. External sounds must be kept out, the box must be sealed against them, and when this plan succeeds it must succeed also in excluding with equal efficacy external purifying agencies.' Soundproofing created 'a bacteriological box' in which various organisms were carefully 'nursed' and the 'imprisoned air' became infected. 'Caller after caller thus may either infect or receive infection.' The journal offered as a remedy that 'the interior should be air-swept regularly or automatically disinfected'.

Another solution was offered by William H. Young of Hampstead, who invented in 1908 a 2/6d (12½p) apparatus that could be fixed above the mouthpiece. It consisted of a small nickel tube, like a cartridge, that could be filled with disinfectant. From the tube a diminutive blind soaked in the disinfectant was drawn by means of a loop or hook over the mouthpiece and fastened to a button underneath it. When the user had finished speaking, the blind sprang back and disinfected itself. For a disinfectant Mr Young recommended a 40 per cent solution of formalin. 'The blind does not in the least interfere with the sound,' he claimed. 'I have used the apparatus between London and Portsmouth with perfect success.' Of greater public appeal was the Sterling sanitary mouthpiece, made of glass with a metal ring on the base so that it could be substituted for an existing mouthpiece. It could also be unscrewed and sterilized by boiling. 'Much better speaking is obtained... persons using the telephone can see the

One way to avoid 'catching some-thing' from the phone was to use a sanitary mouthpiece, which could be unscrewed and sterilized.

(BT Museum)

mouthpiece is clean and so get nearer to their telephone when speaking.'

The hazard seemed even greater after the publication of Francis J. Allen's article 'The public telephone call office as a factor in the spread of disease'. In this he reviewed the results of Klein's examination of six swabs taken from mouthpieces. One, taken from an instrument at a railway station, revealed the presence of tubercle bacilli, the cause of tuberculosis. Two guinea pigs were injected and, when killed 23 and 27 days later, had numerous tubercle bacilli in the spleen and were diseased elsewhere. The postmaster-general, questioned in the House, claimed that it was 'exceptional'. His successor, similarly questioned in 1912, cited the 'prolonged study' of the appropriately named Dr Spitta, a bacteriologist who had studied phones in a sanatorium, that 'the transmission of tuberculosis through the medium of the telephone mouthpiece is practically impossible'. Nevertheless the atmosphere was ripe for the 1911 founding of The Phonotas Company, offering a cleaning and sterilizing service.

Concern about direct damage to the ear seemed to die down. A 1904 study of the 450 switchboard operators on the Munich exchange noted that 'none had left on account of any ear lesion'. Over the border another problem of interest to doctors at large presented itself. In 1906 a Viennese had frequently phoned his doctor for professional advice but, on being sent a bill, had refused to pay. Finding in favour of the doctor, an Austrian judge stated that professional advice 'must be paid for, whether it was given in the consulting room, or by letter, or by telephone, or at the bedside. The special knowledge of the practitioner, acquired with difficulty after long years of study, could never be a subject of "sweating".'

At the same time the phone could also be an intrusive nuisance, interrupting a doctor during a consultation and taking undue precedence. The only satisfactory answer seemed to be the employment of a competent assistant to deal with calls. On the other hand, time could also be saved by transmitting patient data. In 1910 trials were held in London of an electric stethoscope with a phone device that amplified sound 20 times or more. This caused some consternation to the patients being examined but was perfectly audible by medical men in various parts of London. From such trials a whole new skill of telemetry in medicine was to develop. Meanwhile Christian Science healers were using lines for 'absent treatment'. There was much faith in sending live information, as the *St Louis Post Dispatch* reported in 1908:

> Mrs Pennord, a wealthy woman farmer, of Louisiana, has just had her tomb built. In the lid of the coffin are several air holes, and a telephone is placed near the headrest, and is connected with the house of the cemetery keeper. Thus the fear of being buried alive is reduced to a minimum. The tomb has become an object of interest to visitors.

In spite of the growing use during the Edwardian period, when the Post Office took over the private-enterprise National on 1 January 1912, the UK lagged behind the USA, Germany, Norway, Sweden, Denmark, Australia and New Zealand in phone density. Enmity between public and private enterprise had not helped. When assets of the National were to be transferred to the Post Office some local managers gave orders for their stores to be buried. In the USA there was enmity between the Bell companies and the independents, evident in rate wars and sometimes leading to fisticuffs and the cutting of competitive lines, but the contrast with the UK was most marked. It was not just in numbers but in attitude, an observation made by Arnold Bennett in *Harper's Monthly*:

> What strikes and frightens the backward European almost as much as anything in the United States is the efficiency and fearful universality of the telephone. Just as I think of the big cities as agglomerations pierced everywhere by elevator-shafts full of movement, so I think of them as being threaded under pavements and over roofs and between floors and ceilings and between walls, by millions upon millions of live filaments that unite all the privacies of the organism – and destroy them in order to make one immense publicity. I do not mean that Europe has failed to adopt the telephone, nor that in Europe there are no hotels with the dreadful curse of an active telephone in every room. But I do mean that the European telephone is a toy, and a somewhat clumsy one, compared to the seriousness of the American telephone. Many otherwise highly civilized Europeans are as timid in addressing a telephone as they would be in addressing a royal sovereign. The average European middle-class householder still speaks of his telephone, if he has one, in the same falsely casual tone as the corresponding American is liable to speak of his motor car... Is it possible that you have been in the United States a month without understanding that the United States is primarily nothing but a vast congeries of telephone cabins?

So much were these cabins used that their outward-swinging doors became a hazard to passers-by, especially commuters rushing for trains. An initial solution to the problem was a partition that slid inside the booth. This gave way to a hinged folding door, introduced in 1910.

On 2 November 1911 the first meeting of the Telephone Pioneers of America was held in Boston, attended by Pioneer No. 1, Alexander Graham Bell. To start catching up, the British Post Office followed another American pioneer, Almon B. Strowger, a Kansas City undertaker who in 1889 had patented an automatic exchange to put the choice of number in the hands of the subscribers, however distraught, and not at the discretion of the operator, who might make a connection to a business competitor. Strowger believed he was losing business through operators being bribed by rivals. In 1892 the first of his automatics was installed at La Porte, Indiana, which the *Chicago Herald* described as 'a telephone exchange without a single petticoat'. Produced by jewellers and instrument makers, it worked, and confounded the many sceptics. Based on a model Strowger had built in a circular collar box, using 100 pins and a lead pencil, the design seemed to open up a whole new world. 'Goodbye to the hello girl' became a familiar expression. The automatic telephone and later the dial were advertised as the 'girl-less, cuss-less, out-of-order-less, wait-less telephone'.

The original La Porte instruments had five push buttons in a row. To call 21, the user pushed the first button twice and the second once. That was fine for simple numbers but users tended to lose count on longer ones so Strowger introduced a large dial with numbered vanes, which later became finger holes. It was so large and cumbersome that people called it 'a pie-pan', but it was a great improvement over push buttons. During the Spanish–American War of 1898 a dial system was installed in the White House so that the President could communicate promptly with members of his cabinet. Automatic calls were set up more quickly than those via an operator: 'A twist of the wrist and you are connected to your party'.

The rotating dial was patented in 1896, put into service in Milwaukee and in Albion, New York, and developed by the Bell System from 1900. It was an independent company though that introduced a dial with a letter as part of the directory number, in Los Angeles in 1906. A Strowger automatic exchange was installed in Berlin in 1899, whereas the first in France was not until 1913, in Nice. In 1912, Regina, Saskatchewan, decided to rebuild with automatic after a tornado demolished the exchange, and the British Post Office made two experimental installations, one at Epsom and the other in its own headquarters. Australia and New Zealand were not far behind. Automatic operation had to be developed because as the number of subscribers went up the cost of serving them went up even more. As one American phone manager put it: 'All I have to do is to get enough subscribers and the company will go broke.' This development in the handling of information would much later be applied to materials. In a sense Strowger's system was the prototype of the automatic factory that would be Chaplin's fantasy of *Modern Times* (1936) and would be discussed as a serious possibility from the late 1950s.

By 1914 about one third of Britain's phones were in London. In 1901 the Chancellor of the Exchequer had stated that 'telephonic communication is not desired by the rural mind'. True, there was a suspicion of it. A woman in Kirby Muxloe, Leicestershire, was by no means alone in answering with the disbelieving question, 'Are you there?' A Somersetshire clergyman wrote to the manager of the Bristol exchange on behalf of a parishioner:

> Sir, Complaint is made by widow B— at Ellen's Cottages, that telephone wires are so close to her roof as to be a nuisance and – as she asserts – actual messages are audible. I should feel obliged if this could be rectified.

Overhead wires presented another nuisance. Around Norwich, to reduce fatalities from birds flying into them, cork game guards were fixed to wires by a man sitting in a bosun's chair. Masses of birds could be a nuisance. In South Africa crows often built their nests on poles with old bits of fence wire, which could be dislodged and cause interference, and in Australia cockatiels chewed the wires. It was open season for shooting parties, but their shot-gun pellets could damage the wires. Poles could decay, which increased interest in preservatives and was an incentive to laying cables underground. Such cables in the USA were vulnerable to gophers, which chewed the insulation.

The big problem in bringing the phone to rural areas was expense. Long lines were needed for few subscribers. According to the *Scientific American* of 31 March 1900, one solution was to use what existed:

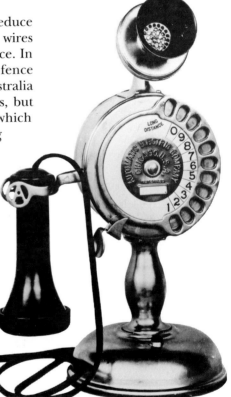

> We have been favoured... with particulars of the unique telephone line... which is now in use between the cities of Anderson, Pendleton and Ingalls, Indiana... The line is unique in that it employs as a conductor such a common, everyday commodity as the top wire of a barb-wire fence, the continuity of the line being assured by special devices at highway and railroad crossings.

Using this technique, graziers were able to exercise much closer daily control over large tracts of land. Not all the credit belongs to the legendary cowboys.

By far the most favoured method was the party line, introduced in 1891 in New York City to provide lower cost service to more people but sometimes called the farmers' line. In rural areas perhaps as many as 20 subscribers participated, each being called by his own number of rings,

You could hardly miss the dial on early automatic phones.
(AG Communication Systems Corporation)

Winter storm damage to overhead lines at Elora, Ontario, Canada, in 1908. (Bell Canada Telephone Historical Collection)

Social Uses of Rural Telephones.

Suppose you didn't have a telephone and wanted to get up an impromptu party, in the country, what would you do ?

You would have to hitch up your horse, early in the afternoon, and drive for miles around to your different friends. After this drive you would be so fatigued in the evening that you wouldn't want to see your friends.

How differently this party could be arranged if you had a telephone.

In less than half an hour, you could ring up your friends, living miles away, and invite them to come, without trouble or fatigue.

More than ninety per cent. of the rural telephones used in this country are manufactured by us.

A post card with your address will bring you further particulars about them, with cost of installing, etc.

You can build and operate your own telephone line.

The Northern Electric & M'f'g. Co., Ltd.

427 Seymour St.
VANCOUVER.

599 Henry Ave.
WINNIPEG.

Cor. Notre Dame & Guy Sts.
MONTREAL.

Use address nearest you.

No. 302

This 1908 Canadian advertisement appeared in The Farmer's Advocate. (Bell Canada Telephone Historical Collection)

perhaps a combination of long and short or in Morse code. Of course, more than one person might want to talk at once and there was always the possibility of being overheard, especially if it was known to be a call to the doctor, with comic or exasperating results. In defence against nosey neighbours some immigrants resorted to their native language, which gave them privacy and, as they heard the clicks of phones being put down, a better line without the need for shouting. Back in Germany and Austria privacy of conversations was assured by an automatic cut-off switch.

In sparsely populated areas the humble phone was the first modern convenience, annihilating the distance between isolated farmsteads and relieving rural solitude, 'the lones' as farm women called it. Out in the sticks there was not much business for the Baird Secret Service System of Chicago, which produced gadgets to foil eavesdroppers with the slogan 'Let Us Stop Your Rubbernecks'. Yet a pastime like a three- or four-way conversation or broadcast music was often at the inconvenience of would-be business users. Getting party lines going was generally a co-operative enterprise, making use of the available men and materials. In New Zealand, for example, settlers constructed lines on frail supports, using bottle heads as cups to carry the wires. Woe betide anybody who used them for target practice. More news came into small communities that way and was exchanged. Farmers were brought closer to the town and did not necessarily have to go in to transact business, which helped make their work more productive.

By 1907 so great had been the growth of rural telephony in the USA that the states with the densest concentration of telephones per population were not in the East, where development started, but in Iowa, Nebraska, Washington, California and Nevada. In 1910 there were about 50 farmers connected to the South African phone system, mainly in Cape Colony and merely linking the farmer to his nearest town. To encourage more connections, a special party-line tariff for up to ten subscribers was introduced in 1912, and an article in the *South African Agricultural Journal* set out the merits. Demand was greater than the funds available and there were delays in the supply of light iron carrying-poles from Britain because of strikes.

The absence of phones meant that old ways of life persisted and that a new form of cultural division existed in society. Mary Corbett Harris recalls life in North Wales:

> When my parents came to the vicarage, Llanfachreth, Merioneth in 1903 there were no telephones nearer than Dolgellau, four miles away, where there was one at the post office. Even the doctor did not have one for he said it would be a waste of money as no one else had one. As there was no public transport and few farmers were lucky enough to have a pony, it meant walking to Dolgellau along very rough roads and precipitous hills. So no one had the doctor unless they could possibly avoid it with the result that homemade cures were widely used. One old woman had a marvellous cure for shingles, another such an effective ointment for piles that people walked miles up a mountain to get a pot, large and filthy cobwebs were put on cuts that were bleeding badly. My mother found that castor oil and common sense dealt effectively with most of our ailments. Even the squire in his large Georgian mansion had no telephone.

When the aristocracy did have an installation it occupied a lowly place in the household. The Duke of Richmond and Gordon, on the Goodwood Estate in Sussex, had it on a wall in a passage, where it was regarded with the same element of suspicion and disdain that had a few years before been associated with the introduction of the horseless carriage. Baron De L'Isle and Dudley had a wall instrument outside the kitchen with a candlestick phone as an extension. It may have been used to summon the police and the fire brigade when suffragettes attempted arson in 1913. Little thought seems to have been given to making users, often parlour maids, comfortable. They usually had to stand up to speak, often in a dark corner of somewhere like the morning room, or in the hall amid the smell of goloshes and wet coats. In the circumstances it was considered *infra dig* to put one's phone number on a calling card.

Being American, Henry James was a writer receptive to modernity. He had a phone in his flat in Carlyle Mansions, Cheyne Walk, Chelsea, and, after moving to Rye in 1898, called a little room off the hall in Lamb House 'the telephone room'. Not far away in Sussex at Bateman's, where Rudyard Kipling and his wife moved in 1902, there was no phone. Although Kipling had been a journalist, he rarely used the instrument and disliked intrusive calls. Taking a romantic view of radio, the medium of the future, he looked upon the phone as something to be used in local emergencies, as in his story *An Habitation Enforced*, in which an American recuperating from overwork in English rural isolation with his wife is at first concerned about the proximity of the telegraph office for business, gets used to rural peace, and has a phone installed only when his wife is expecting a baby.

In a letter of 28 May 1909 to Mrs Rothenstein, A. E. Housman apologized:

> I hope that my conversation through the telephone yesterday did not sound brusque. I am very little accustomed to using that instrument. I was very sorry not to be able to come to the theatre with you, but I had an engagement out of town for the evening, and I was just leaving the college to catch my train when the beadle told me that someone had been enquiring for me.

Joseph Conrad, who did not speak a word of English until he was 19 and whose pronunciation sometimes puzzled his own family, managed without the instrument. He told friends to send him a wire or a letter, both of which could be relied upon to arrive quickly, and the secret agents in his stories never had to resort to other methods. For another European, Franz Kafka (in 1914), the new instrument could be terrifying:

> I find that even in or during telephone conversations I can say nothing, owing to my total lack of quick-wittedness, and my preoccupation with this disability

The Japanese appetite for Western technology is evident in this cartoon, c.1913. (NTT)

makes it almost impossible to understand anything (it is not very different when talking face to face).

Later, Joseph K. was summoned that way to his first interrogation in *The Trial*, and he did not phone during his arrest.

It was different in the USA. The young James Thurber, born in 1894, grew up when songs such as 'Kissing Papa Thro' the Telephone', 'Hello Ma Baby', 'Love by Telephone', 'My Own Little Telephone Belle', 'Hello Central Give Me Heaven', 'A Ring on the Finger is Worth Two on the Phone', 'The Kissaphone', 'I've Got Your Number' and 'Please, Miss Central, Find My Mama' were popular. Much later in life, he remembered that his mother took the receiver off the hook during thunderstorms, and he could also recall without effort the numbers of several high-school chums.

To the young it was a romantic device. *Telephony* carried this shock-horror story in 1903:

> 'It's appalling,' said an elderly aunt, who was spending a week in town, 'to see how they use the telephones nowadays. Only last night, when there was a dinner party on, Mary, who was dressing, answered the telephone which is in her room. And it was one of the men calling her up to say that he had been detained down town and was dressing then as quickly as possible, but didn't want dinner to be kept waiting for him. There the two of them stood talking to one another just as if they were entirely dressed and had stopped for a little chat on the street! I tell you this generation is a little too much for me.'

In the UK one lady was said to have suggested to the postmaster-general that, to increase his departmental revenue, marriage proposals by phone should be compulsory. Doubtless Swiss lovers welcomed the service introduced in 1912, whereby subscribers could be told who had called in their absence. It helped remove doubts and added zest to the day.

The young Vera Brittain recorded in her diary for 4 May 1914:

> Just as we were going to bed the telephone rang violently; we managed to get on after a few minutes' trouble & of course it was from Roland Leighton at Lowestoft. He rang up ostensibly to tell Edward he would meet him at Leicester on Wednesday but really to talk to me. I took the wire after he had addressed a few remarks to Edward, & when I offered to let him talk to E. again he said 'No don't, I would rather talk to you.' So we spent about ten minutes making absurd remarks through the telephone. I was cold and sleepy when I first got up to go to bed, but now I am warm and intensely conscious of life.

8189   PLEASE, MISS, GIVE ME HEAVEN. ROTARY PHOTO E.C.

" If you please, Miss, give me Heaven, for my Mamma's
    there ;
You will find her with the Angels on the golden stair ;
She'll be glad it's me who's speaking ; call her, won't you
    dear,
For I want to surely tell her we're so lonely here."

WORDS BY PERMISSION OF MESSRS. CHAS. SHEARD & Co

*Belief in heavenly communications was
not to be confined to children.*

(BT Museum)

The great romantic was Richard Le Gallienne, who enthused over the phone in *Modern Aids to Romance*:

> To take the telephone alone, surely the romance of Pyramus and Thisbe, with their primitive hole in the wall, was a tame affair compared with the possibilities of this magic toy, by means of which you can talk with your love not merely through a wall but through the Rocky Mountains. You can whisper sweet nothings to her across the sounding sea, and bid her 'sleep well' over leagues of primeval forest, and through the stoniest-hearted city her soft voice will find its way.

He went on in *The New Pyramus and Thisbe*:

> The wall is no longer a barrier, but a sensitive messenger. It has become, indeed, in the words of Demetrius in *A Midsummer Night's Dream*, the wittiest of partitions, and the modern Pyramus may apostrophise it in grateful earnest:
> 'Thou wall, O wall, O sweet and lovely wall... Thanks, courteous wall.
> Jove shield thee well for this!'

Jove was also the god honoured by generals triumphant in war.

CHAPTER 7

PUTTING THE LINES THROUGH

After a Serb fanatic murdered Archduke Ferdinand, heir to the Habsburg throne, and his wife in Sarajevo on 28 June 1914 the terms of the ultimatum to Serbia were discussed within Austria on the phone. With the 84-year-old Emperor Franz Joseph, who originally had a desk instrument for decoration only, at the end of what was probably a poor line to Bad Ischl, his Alpine summer retreat, it was the views of ministers in Vienna led by the aggressive Foreign Secretary Berchtold that prevailed. On 23 July a stiff-termed ultimatum was sent to Belgrade, demanding a reply within 48 hours. None was expected. When a conciliatory reply was received, it was rejected by Berchtold, bent on war. Thereafter communications between the great powers were concluded in a headlong rush before they actually broke down.

German expectations were for a short sharp war, like Bismarck's military campaigns. According to the Schlieffen Plan, in a down-swing through the plains of Belgium and northern France, Paris would be taken in six weeks. An element in such a rapid advance was good communications, as used in the Russo-Japanese War ten years earlier, and colourfully described by Herbert Casson in 1910:

> In the supreme emergency of war, the telephone is as indispensable, very nearly, as the cannon. This, at least, is the belief of the Japanese, who handled their armies by telephone when they drove back the Russians (1904–05). Each body of Japanese troops moved forward like a silkworm, leaving behind it a glittering strand of red copper wire. At the decisive battle of Mukden, the silkworm army, with a million legs, crept against the Russian hosts in a vast crescent, a hundred miles from end to end. By means of this glistening red wire, the various batteries and regiments were organized into fifteen divisions. Each group of three divisions was wired to a general, and the five generals were wired to the great Oyama himself, who sat ten miles back of the firing line and sent his orders. Whenever a regiment lunged forward, one of the

In the confusion of wires snaking across the mud of the battlefront it was a wonder that communications got through. Some were intercepted by the enemy. (Imperial War Museum)

soldiers carried a telephone set. If they held their position, two other soldiers ran forward with a spool of wire. In this way and under fire of the Russian cannon, one hundred and fifty miles of wire were strung across the battlefield. As the Japanese said, it was this 'flying telephone' that enabled Oyama to manipulate his forces as handily as though he were playing a game of chess.

In 1914 Belgium was quicker to fall than France, an under-equipped country lacking rapid communications. German headquarters were 200 miles away in Luxembourg; at a vital point in the advance on Paris one field commander acted without reference to headquarters, which lost control of the situation; and in the crucial battle of the Marne liaison was by motor car. The French knew their communications systems were poor. Probably since before the war, they had used the term *téléphone Arabe* to describe a superior method of communication, the 'bush telegraph' or 'grapevine' they had encountered in their North African possessions. Such an attitude was to persist until almost the end of the conflict. General Sir Hubert Gough summed up the military situation confronting the combatants: 'The problem is controlling events when you have gone beyond the plans which

Dogs unreeled cable for field telephone lines. (Imperial War Museum)

are cut and dried.' By the autumn the two sides had dug themselves into trenches for what turned out to be a long war of attrition, most unlike the electrical war predicted by Marinetti, the Italian Futurist.

Lines connected headquarters with successive levels of command right out to the battlefront, which formed the shifting base in a hierarchy of communication. For example, the development of artillery demanded a reliable liaison with forward infantry. High points behind the lines, such as towers, hills, telegraph poles, trees, even captive balloons, were useful as look-outs. Observers could phone in their reports on the effectiveness of shelling, and from that information new instructions could be given about direction, range and elevation. It was not the kind of duty for which pigeons, telegrams, or visual signals made by winking heliographs, fluttering flags and flashing lamps were suitable. In the Australian official history of the war, C. E. W. Bean describes the attack on Lone Pine in the Gallipoli campaign:

Reinforcements were called for. An attempt was first made to signal this request by 'Morse-periscope', an apparatus with which the attacking battalions had been provided, and which was not unlike a miniature window-blind at the end of a stick. The word 'reinforcements' was deciphered, but the dust and smoke of the enemy's shells smothered the rest. A quarter of an hour later the signaller himself dashed over No Man's Land with the message. In the meantime two others had run across the open with a telephone line, over which further messages began immediately to be received.

Phones also emphasized how vulnerable those in the front line were compared with those in the security of the rear. While casualties piled up, the generals sat at their desks. In their own defence they argued it was the only possible place for an overall view. General Charles Mangin pointed out that if he got up and 'went marching about the front line, I would be commanding no more than one or two companies'.

At first civilian instruments from French towns and villages were adapted for field use, mainly point-to-point. As demand increased so exchanges were employed, either from abandoned civil installations or devised in army signal workshops. By mid-1915 the phone had become essential on both sides, and expectations of its efficiency often exceeded actual performance. Civil equipment was not rugged enough for field conditions and, in the damp and mud of the trenches and other primitive shelters, faults soon developed. Maintenance became a severe problem until more robust and weatherproof boards and phones designed and manufactured back home were shipped out. Cable was paid out from reels on the backs of horses or, in the front line, scouts. Soon there was a tangle of wires, some in use and some cut, some disappearing into No Man's Land, with electrical interference between them, a knotty problem to be sorted out by signal corps. Often under fire, perhaps in the dark, men had to recover disused cables, which had sometimes been sucked into the stiff soft clay; proper working lines had to be labelled and maintained, and some sort of order brought to the chaos. Burying cable six feet down – the Germans believed in ten – away from shellfire was by no means easy and was not always possible.

Henri Barbusse observed in *Le Feu* (1916) that what was left over could be used:

> As for Marthereau's puttees, they are not both of the same hue, for he failed to find two fagends of greatcoat equally worn and equally dirty, to be cut up into strips. There are legs wrapped up in rags, too, and even in newspapers, which are kept in place with spirals of thread or – much more practical – telephone wire.

If it was not available, it could always be 'found'. One cavalry unit cut out some 100 yards of cable serving a divisional headquarters and used it as a picket line for horses. At other times it could get in the way, as it did for Barbusse's fatigue party:

> 'Look out for the wire!' The telephone wire undulates above the trench, and crosses it in places between two posts. When it is too slack, its curve sags into the trench and catches the rifles of passing men, and the ensnared ones struggle, and abuse the engineers who don't know how to fix up their lines. Then, as the drooping entanglement of precious wires increases, we shoulder our rifles with the butt in the air, carry the shovels under our arms, and go forward with lowered heads.

So advantageous was the phone that there was a danger of systems becoming overloaded. Conversations were often longer than expected. Many soldiers had never encountered the instrument and were getting used to it. The civilian equipment in early use was not designed to be heard amid artillery and rifle fire and messages had to be repeated. Inevitably there were misunderstandings, summed up in the joke of the message sent as 'Send reinforcements we're going to advance' being received as 'Send three and fourpence we're going to a dance'. Getting messages mixed up, taking them down wrongly, throwing them away and leaving the phone off the hook were only to be expected from a simple-minded dog fancier from Prague, the hero of *The Good Soldier Schweik*. Occasionally it was more serious. In Gaza in 1917 two generals, who through delays in receiving information had got a wrong impression of the way the battle was going, talked at cross-purposes on the phone, with the result that the strategic Ali Muntar heights were abandoned unnecessarily, giving the desperate German commander an unexpected advantage. Sometimes language was a problem. As late as 1918 some British switchboard operators had difficulty in getting connections through French exchanges and interpreters had to be employed.

Convenient though the phone was, it also presented a risk. Both sides soon became aware that conversations in the front line could be picked up and overheard. In the tangle of wires on which the insulation had been damaged it was not surprising that there was cross-talk. Strips of barren, shell-pocked land changed hands after a minor breakthrough and in the heat of the moment there was little concern for the security of communications. Codes were one answer, but easily ignored or forgotten, with consequent loss of life. More practical on the British side was the 'fullerphone' scrambler, introduced in 1916. So great were the advances in interception devices that, in March 1918 before mounting its great attack, the German High Command forbade the use of phones within seven miles of the front.

Interception in established civil networks was much easier and the atmosphere was ripe for the development of the practice against civilians. The Defence of the Realm Act (DORA), passed four days after the declaration of war, gave the British government powers *inter alia* 'to secure the safety of any means of communication'. Whipped up by propaganda, war fever ran high and anything that smacked of the enemy was suspect. 'Slackers', conscientious objectors, pacifists, internationalists, and anybody who was in the slightest bit 'foreign', perhaps through having a strange accent or listening to unpatriotic music or reading contaminated literature, was easily regarded as subversive or disloyal. Even the officially neutral USA had to keep watch on the Germans, who were sinking vessels in the Atlantic and sabotaging its own industry at home. After Congress declared war on 6 April 1917, the atmosphere became worse. On both sides the infringement of civil liberties – to prevent people obtaining or communicating information that could be useful to the enemy and the introduction of surveillance of all types – was an acceptable price to pay for ultimate victory but the situation would not change immediately peace came. Temporary measures resulting from spy mania became permanent attitudes.

In the Great War the phone was not just a communications device. It had a smaller role as an instrument of detection. After Bell had used his telephone probe on President Garfield in 1881, Sir James Mackenzie Davidson devised a similar instrument in 1884. Doubtless early casualties prompted *The Lancet* to announce in December 1914 that he had improved and simplified the previous model, more effective now that X-rays could locate a piece of shrapnel or a bullet. The probe emitted a sound on contact, making it more accurate than a simple physical probe, which could not distinguish between bone and bullet.

A feature of trench warfare was enemy tunnelling and mining. To detect it, on the Allies' side a seismophone was devised. Working on a principle similar to that of an earthquake recorder, it used a sensitive microphone to pick up the noises of enemy sappers. An operator sat on a box containing the equipment and recorded his observations. Direction was determined by triangulation, and built into the equipment were means for determining distance in different types of soil. Once the enemy was located, appropriate counter-measures could be taken. The seismophone was made in the UK and used on the Western, Italian and Russian fronts.

Seeing what had been accomplished on land, the Admiralty wanted something similar to detect enemy submarines menacing British merchant ships. The hydrophone, first ready for service in October 1917, consisted of a torpedo-shaped body containing listening devices towed at a given distance below the surface by a transmitting cable. On a British trawler or destroyer an enemy submarine was detected by amplifying the distinctive sound of its engines and plotting where it was loudest. At that point depth charges were dropped, the order being given over a phone. According to its class, a warship had from 50 to 70 action stations connected to its exchange. Not all stations had fixed phones, especially in exposed positions, where portable instruments, weatherproofed and often loud-speaking, were plugged in according to need. Up above, airships equipped with their own specially designed systems, including throat transmitters, patrolled in search of enemy submarines. Throat transmitters, sometimes called laryngaphones because the small transmitter was held by a band against the larynx, were also used by divers. Their receiver was carried on a headband.

They were a help to Royal Navy divers salvaging £5 million worth of gold from the liner *Laurentic*, which hit a mine off Malin Head, County Donegal, in January 1917 and sank in 120 feet of water. One afternoon Diver Blachford was trapped by a steel plate falling on his back. Within 15 seconds he was able to say to his commanding officer: 'Give me all the air you can, sir.' When the pressure was increased, he said coolly: 'That's right. Give me more yet and get another diver down here as quickly as possible.' He received so much air that the roar of it drowned the sound of his voice and pressure had to be reduced to hear what he was saying. Diver Clear, sent down to rescue him, having fixed slings under the plate, was able to give instructions to the surface: 'Take in the slack... Now very carefully.'

Removing the gold from the tangled wreckage took more than one season. In 1922 Diver Light, seeing a gold bar sticking in the sand, tied up his air- and life-lines and crawled in head first. As his legs were higher than his head, they became buoyant and he floated out backwards, halting helplessly 40 feet from the bottom. Water from other parts of his dress began to flow down into his helmet. Threatened with drowning, he phoned his predicament to the surface. Diver Blachford, decompressing at the 30-feet level, was sent down. When he cut the tie, Light shot to the surface carrying Blachford and his equipment, some 300 pounds, like a toy balloon. Light was put in the decompression chamber to prevent an attack of the 'bends' while Blachford returned to the 30-feet level.

America's entry into the war in April 1917 made a dramatic difference to the scale of phone use. The largest wartime system so far created was that for the American Expeditionary Force in France. When the first troops of the US Signal Corps landed in June 1917, they found themselves in a strange land with its own language and equipment. Not having adequate supplies of their own, they had to improvise. A phone culture was superimposed on one aspect of life in an under-equipped country. France

Any strange-looking apparatus in France
could be a phone.   (BT Museum)

had 1 ½ phones per 100 of the population to the USA's 14. Whereas the Americans were accustomed to the phone the French were not. One American remarked that any peculiar thing hanging on the wall in a French residence might be a phone. They were not provided by the government as part of an installation but bought from shops and varied in their efficiency. It was not until 1918, when communications headquarters were moved south from Paris to Tours, that construction of the network began in earnest. Nearly 23,000 miles of wire were strung permanently. The Paris directory issued in June 1919 contained five local exchanges and a list of 326 towns all operated and reached over the American-installed system.

At first the US Signal Corps tried to run a service with French soldiers who spoke both French and English, but it was unsatisfactory. French bilingual women operators were little better. General Pershing, commander-in-chief of the American Expeditionary Force, later said:

> One of the crying needs when we once began to use our own lines was for experienced operators. Instead of trying to train men of the Signal Corps, I requested that a number of experienced telephone girls who could speak French be sent over, and eventually we had about 200 girls on duty. Some doubt existed among members of staff as to the wisdom of this step, but it soon vanished as the increased efficiency of our telephone system became apparent.

A standardized switchboard was also brought in from the USA. Another technical advantage the Americans had was the advent of repeaters, which amplified speech at regular intervals on a route, enabling much clearer conversations to be carried farther on lighter-gauge wires. The British adopted the development, making a trial installation in 1918 to improve cross-Channel communications between the Royal Air Force headquarters at Nancy in the north-east and the Air Ministry in London. After the Armistice, to help speed return to a new normality, further repeaters were installed on trunk routes to improve long-distance communications, for example London–Paris, and from Tours to Antwerp and Rotterdam. During the Peace Conference an installation was made at Turin on the Rome–Paris line.

In the USA, where the communications industry came under federal control from 1917, phone development still proceeded apace. Indeed, the government instituted in 1918 something long wanted by the Bell System, a service connection charge payable by new subscribers. In many small communities far from metropolitan newspapers and in the absence of radio the phone became the main source for war news bulletins. These were typed up and posted on the exchange window, which became a daily gathering point for folk eager for news from the front. In much of the rest of the world, for civil purposes, development practically ceased.

In South Africa, for instance, work on farmers' lines was suspended for lack of money and materials, and the introduction of automatic exchanges was delayed until 1922, when the first was installed in Cape Town. Plans made in 1914 for the complete reconstruction of the Hong Kong system were shelved. It was impossible to get the equipment and the local phone company had some financial difficulties through the fluctuating rate of exchange between the local dollar and sterling. In Singapore, where the central exchange was seriously damaged by fire in 1916, a 200-line switchboard had to be borrowed from the Raffles Hotel. One of the few places where service continued to expand, along with the economy, was Japan. Newspaper cartoons showed people crushing into kiosks, and in exchanges girls had to stand behind operators to help with the volume of calls. In 1918 Manila, capital of the Philippines, became the first city in the Far East to have an automatic exchange installed.

Nowhere was the symbolic importance of the phone in warfare better shown than in Petrograd during the fall of the provisional government and the Bolshevik seizure of power. The exchange was a building that was fought over and where, in the middle of John Reed's *Ten Days that Shook the World*, the classes confronted one another:

> Tired, bloody, triumphant, the sailors and workers swarmed into the switchboard room, and finding so many pretty girls, fell back in an embarrassed way and fumbled with awkward feet. Not a girl was injured, not one insulted. Frightened, they huddled in the corners, and then, finding themselves safe, gave vent to their spite. 'Ugh! The dirty, ignorant people! The fools!'... The sailors and Red Guards were embarrassed. 'Brutes! Pigs!' shrilled the girls indignantly, putting on their coats and hats...
>
> The Commissar of the Military Revolutionary Committee, little Vishniak, tried to persuade the girls to remain. He was effusively polite. 'You have been badly treated,' he said. 'The telephone system is controlled by the Municipal Duma. You are paid sixty roubles a month, and have to work ten hours and more... From now on all that will be changed. The Government intends to put the telephones under control of the Ministry of Posts and Telegraphs. Your wages will be immediately raised to one hundred and fifty roubles, and your working hours reduced. As members of the working class you should be happy...'
>
> Members of the *working class* indeed! Did he mean to infer that there was anything in common between these – these animals – and *us*? Remain? Not if they offered a thousand roubles!... Haughty and spiteful, the girls left the place...

The employees of the building, the line-men and labourers – they stayed. But the switch-boards must be operated – the telephone was vital... Only half a dozen trained operators were available. Volunteers were called for; a hundred responded, sailors, soldiers, workers. The six girls scurried backwards and forwards, instructing, helping, scolding... So, crippled, halting, but *going*, the wires began to hum.

In exile Lenin had got used to using this instrument of organization and had one on his desk in Petrograd for guiding the revolution. In the ensuing civil war, from the Kremlin he maintained contact with Trotsky and the victorious Red Army at the front. Tolstoy imagined absolute power as Genghis Khan with a phone, but not even Lenin's authority and threats could conjure up a good line to the Kremlin when he was recuperating at Gorki from an attempted assassination.

In the UK the improved London to Birmingham cable was completed, linking the capital to the centre of the small-armaments industry. The only new work considered essential was for equipping coastguard stations, including those in Ireland; munitions and other plants on war work; and hotels and mansions adapted as government offices, like those for the US Navy headquarters. Almost 13,000 skilled men were released by the Post Office to the armed services, some of their work being done by women. They could not, however, climb poles and act as line inspectors. By 1915 remaining outside male staff had to wear armbands showing they were engaged in work of national importance, otherwise ignorant members of the jingoistic public could abuse them for dodging military service. In 1914 the Automobile Association decided not to retain patrolmen if they were eligible, and some of its roadside boxes were closed. When there were Zeppelin raids, public and private switchboard operators found themselves dealing with extra traffic. In Oxford, exchange operators received air-raid warnings by telegram from London, 55 miles away, and then phoned the information to neighbouring police and fire brigades. One advantage the Post Office did take of the war: in 1915 it overhauled its rate structure, raising its charges to discourage continuance of the flat-rate service.

Trunk calls, which were by no means an on-demand service, were still comparatively rare, usually being made only in an emergency or if the purpose justified the cost. A Sussex garage proprietor dealing in Ford cars, then made in Old Trafford, Manchester, found it a convenient way of arranging collection. Vehicles were not yet delivered by the manufacturer and the 180-mile drive down from Manchester took two days, which, added to the train journey up, meant a three-day job. The same proprietor found the instrument useful in arranging contract ploughing and reaping, with local farmers wanting to make use of his newly acquired tractor. A telegram

Lenin needed two phones in the Kremlin for consolidating the Russian Revolution.

(Central Lenin Museum)

was still the cheapest method of 'immediate' communication and, in the absence of a phone, was also used over short distances.

Even in business the phone could still be a novelty. Lloyds Bank in Uttoxeter, Staffordshire, was not on the phone, and one day the nervy manager received a letter from Birmingham asking him to supply some information as soon as possible by phone. He went to the box in the nearby post office and got in such a dither that at the end of the conversation he bolted with the receiver still in his hand and trailing a length of flex behind him. He never tried again by himself, always taking the cashier with him as interpreter. For people like him the *Evening News* had carried out 'a campaign of investigation and popular telephone instruction', as a result of which 500,000 copies of a helpful booklet, *Telephone Trouble*, were published in 1915. Its purpose was to 'prevent many common misunderstandings'.

To overcome enforced separation from the opposite sex, the young generation was getting accustomed to using the instrument. It could bring the best and worst of possibilities. Vera Brittain noted in her diary for Monday, 15 March 1915:

> I was getting ready for bed this evening when a telephone message – which with a kind of presentiment I had been half expecting all day – came for me from Roland in London. The beloved voice made me shiver with apprehension, thinking of the time when I should hear it no more. He tells me he is going to the front – not in ten days' time – but on Saturday. I said I supposed he wanted me to say I was glad about what had happened but I was not even going to pretend to. He only laughed. Telephoning is very unsatisfactory & there was such a noise going on I could scarcely hear anything. However, I went to Mother & Daddy & announced my intention of going to London to say goodbye. They demurred a little at first but gave in sooner than I expected.

On Monday 27 December her entry read:

> I had just finished dressing when a message came to say that there was a telephone message for me. I sprang up joyfully, thinking to hear in a moment the dear dreamed of tones of the beloved voice.

But the telephone message was not from Roland but from Clare (Roland's sister); it was not to say that Roland had arrived, but instead that a telegram had been received:

> 'T223. Regret to inform you that Lieut. R. A. Leighton 7th Worcesters died of wounds, December 23rd, Lord Kitchener sends his sympathy. Colonel of Territorial Force, Records, Warwick.'

The arrival of the telegram boy was a feared event.

In the exigency of war some couples married quickly to enjoy at least a brief time together. Miss E. Nelson had to resign as a Post Office telephonist to marry in the early days of the war, thereby losing a marriage gratuity of some £30. She was four days short of the necessary six complete years of service. She had worked two months longer than six years but, under the rules, neither her first month as an unpaid learner nor her second as a five-shilling (25p) a week trainee counted. Through her union she pleaded that 'The short notice is regretted, but is due to the unexpected arrival of my intended husband and short leave granted for our marriage'. Bureaucratic hearts were unmoved.

By 1916 the Post Office was modifying switchboards for operation by blind ex-servicemen. Phones were installed in country houses used as convalescent homes for casualties. This probably occurred at Longleat, the Wiltshire home of the Marquess of Bath. In the Merioneth village of Llanfachreth the squire's large Georgian mansion became a hospital for shell-shocked officers. Now the vicar had to walk only a mile to phone the doctor, who by this time had found the instrument useful.

Increased public use of the phone made coin boxes more attractive to thieves. In New Zealand they went to the trouble of designing a special tool that could open the coin box in a few seconds. To combat their ingenuity, burglar alarms were installed. After a spate of thefts in Norwich, two Post Office engineers wired up an alarm and a bolt to jam the door of a call office. The trap worked and a man was caught with the broken coin box. Admitting other break-ins, he was sent to prison. His captors shared a £3 reward but were warned not to do it again for fear of trapping an innocent party.

The circumstances of war brought more people in contact with the phone, some of whom had never contemplated using it. Their experience was not necessarily in the best of circumstances: in waterlogged trenches, out in No Man's Land, exposed on a ship under fire, in emergencies and moments of sorrow. It took the 1916 floods in the Netherlands to alert local inhabitants to the possibilities for signalling in emergencies. In Victoria, Vancouver Island, the news of the Armistice was so great that the load on the phone lines blew the switchboard out. As if the war were not enough, in 1918 there was a world-wide influenza epidemic. Unable to leave their homes or offices, more people made use of the phone, or had somebody use it for them. It threw an extra load on exchange staff, themselves subject to the epidemic, and revived interest in hygienic phones. One, sold by travelling salesmen in Denmark, where almost 10 per cent of the population died from 'flu, amounted to a small tear-off toilet roll stretched across the mouthpiece. Similiar devices were marketed in the Netherlands, one of them being called the Clinophone.

In unexpected ways use of the phone spread in society, both in a class and geographical sense. In the UK more people in the upper and lower classes encountered it and it reached into some rural areas. Yet the net effect of the war was to sharpen the differences in phone usage among nations and generations.

At the beginning of the war Gordon Selfridge had put on each order desk in his new provisions and tobacco departments a phone free to

This Dutch advertisement, from 1920, was probably inspired by the international influenza epidemic. A similar device was used in Denmark.
(Netherlands PTT)

customers so that they could check purchases with their households. He enlarged the store's information bureau, providing guidance on new items of interest such as service pay, allowances, and war pensions. Selfridge was an American example on Oxford Street to a nation that was not really phone conscious. He might have given an idea to Frank Richards for an incident in a special Christmas number of *The Magnet*, in which Billy Bunter uses Mr Quelch's phone at Greyfriars School to order a guinea pudding from Chunkley's Stores in Courtfield. The pudding, charged to Quelch's account, is to be delivered to Bunter. Richards amusingly spins the incident out by giving Chunkley's an efficient operator who promptly transfers Bunter from one department to another, from livestock to confectionery to Christmas bargains.

> They had ever so many departments at Chunkley's Stores in Courtfield. It was quite like a London stores. A customer might spend an hour on the telephone before he got what he wanted.

At the other extreme was Sir James Barrie, who had a phone installed at Adelphi Terrace House in 1918 but always kept it hidden in the second drawer of his desk because he hated to see it and the ring made him jump. He also deplored the over-use of the device in plays as a means of getting in 'the story so far'. To him it was something to be whimsical about. In his 1915 burlesque *Rosy Rapture, The Pride of the Beauty Chorus*, Barrie could well have provided the tongue-twisting title 'Which Switch is the Switch, Miss, for Ipswich', but the song was composed by three others.

In the USA there was a much more expansive approach. On 25 January 1915 Alexander Graham Bell in New York, using a model of his first phone, again spoke the words 'Mr Watson, come here, I want you!' to his former assistant 3,000 miles away in San Francisco. President Wilson in Washington also spoke to Watson and there was a call from Boston, where the phone had been born, to San Francisco. That year 'Hello, Frisco' was the hit tune of the Ziegfeld Follies. At the annual dinner of the National Geographic Society held in Washington on 7 March 1916, the fortieth anniversary of Bell's patent, all 800 guests had a phone. After the meal, they took voice voyages to Seattle, San Francisco, Ottawa, El Paso and Jacksonville, following on a large map the lit transcontinental routes: Chicago, Omaha, Denver, Salt Lake City, Pocatello, Boise, Walla Walla, Portland, and finally Seattle. They 'heard the Pacific's surf beat upon its rockbound coast, while they themselves were on the very threshhold of the Atlantic!' From sea to shining sea.

To Americans, art and technology mixed well. In 1916 Robert Frost discovered the instrument in a nature poem, 'The Telephone'. Carl

Sandburg celebrated a more humdrum method of communication in 'Under a Telephone Pole'. Una Schwirtz, the feminist heroine of Sinclair Lewis's *The Job*, used the liberating instrument to introduce herself to 'the object of her secret commercial affections', the man who was the key to her ambitions.

On 14 February 1916 the first Montreal to Vancouver call was made, routed through the USA, and on 11 May 'God Save the King' was played on a gramophone in San Francisco to the entrancement of many prominent persons in Montreal. When America's Unknown Soldier was buried at Arlington National Cemetery on 11 November 1921 the ceremony was heard on two coasts. The addresses of President Harding and others, the hymns, the artillery salute, and the drumbeats were carried by phone to New York and San Francisco and there projected by public- address apparatus to the assembled thousands. Neutral Switzerland also carried on developing its network and service during the war. On 26 July 1916 it introduced its first regular special service, relaying at 10.55 a.m. over the phone network the time signal from the Eiffel Tower transmitter. Other countries had a lot of catching up to do.

But a peace had not been won. It was betrayed before the war was over. On 10 November 1918, the evening before the Armistice was signed, the German Social Democrat leader Friedrich Ebert, who in the final weeks of the conflict had relieved the military of the burden of accepting defeat, received an unexpected call in Berlin on a secret line of which he had been unaware. The call was from General Groener of the High Command at Spa in Belgium. During it, the two apparent opponents agreed to fight against the popular revolution that had spread throughout Germany in just five days and that in theory Ebert was now leading. Had the revolution succeeded, it could have brought a genuine and lasting change to the political complexion of Germany. As it was, the myth of 'the stab in the back' was born, that the Social Democrats had betrayed the military. It would live to fight again.

CHAPTER 8

FOR EMERGENCY USE

Wartime experience of the phone, perhaps associated with the pain of trench feet, the irritation of lice, against a background of explosions, or with the breaking of bad news, hardly encouraged peacetime use. Captain Plugge, ex-Royal Flying Corps and later an aptly named commercial radio promoter, was most unusual with 43 phones in his London flat, five of them by the bath. Jeeves, and P. G. Wodehouse's other comic characters, living in a perpetual 1920s, often communicated by telegram even though the phone was available. It was about 1920 that the American slang term 'phoney' or 'phony' came into the UK. According to *Brewer's Dictionary of Phrase and Fable*, the word derived from 'fawney' an underground term for the imitation gold ring used by confidence tricksters. Marshall McLuhan, however, in *Understanding Media* quotes the New York *Evening Telegram* from 1904: 'Phony implies that a thing so qualified has no more substance than a telephone talk with a supposititious friend.'

Sir Edward Elgar, back from peaceful Malvern because of his wife's illness, wrote on 3 December 1919: 'If I have to live again at Hampstead composition is off – not the house or the place but London – telephones etc all day and night drive me mad!' In fact, he had one in his Worcestershire home from about 1905 and used it frequently. As so often, what was a convenience to him was a nuisance in the hands of others.

To the young Lydia Scalia marooned in the West of England it was a great attraction:

When I first came to London in 1920 I had never even seen a telephone. I had grown up in Eastcombe, Gloucestershire, a small Cotswold village where there were none. I was absolutely fascinated by it. I had no idea what it was. My father was a schoolmaster and I had written to the Post Office and got accepted without telling my parents. I was fed up at home, having run away in the war to make munitions.

telephonist's " Number, please?" and then, speaking with the lips **almost touching the mouthpiece,** he should state the number required.

FIRST the name of the Exchange and THEN the number.

The method of pronouncing numbers in Telephone Exchanges has been devised to guard as far as possible against inaccuracies and a description of the system may be of assistance to subscribers.

It is important to remember that the distinctive sounds of consonants become blurred in the transmission of speech by telephone and words containing the same vowels are apt to sound alike. Greater care is therefore necessary in speaking by telephone than is required in ordinary speech, if mistakes are to be avoided.

O	is pronounced as	"**OH,**" with long " O."
1	" "	"**WUN,**" emphasizing the consonant " N."
2	" "	"**TOO,**" emphasizing the consonant " T " and with long " OO."
3	" "	"**THR-R-EE,**" with slightly rolling " R " and long " E."
4	" "	"**FOER,**" one syllable with long " O."
5	" "	"**FIFE,**" emphasizing the consonants " F."
6	" "	"**SIX,**" with long " X."
7	" "	"**SEV-EN,**" two syllables.
8	" "	"**ATE,**" with long " A " and emphasizing the consonant " T."
9	" "	"**NINE,**" one syllable with long " I " and emphasizing the consonants " N."

ANSWERING A CALL.

The call should be answered promptly.

On taking off the receiver, the called subscriber should not say " Hullo !" or " Who's there?" but should immediately announce his name.

A householder would say : " Mr. Thomas Brown speaking."

" Mr. Brown's house."

I trained at a Post Office school in Paddington and stayed in a hostel for young ladies. I was frightened even to use a bus. Training was about six weeks. We sat in a row and someone at the back called and you were supposed to answer. All you did was to stare at this thing in front of you with a light on it – scared. The girl next to me kept saying: 'Somebody's talking in my ear.' With the headphones on you'd never heard anything like it before. You were wondering where the voice was coming from and why. You wanted to look back and the voice kept saying 'Don't look back. Look in front of you. Answer the telephone.' The light came up on the switchboard and you were supposed to answer it but you were terrified. The headphones were fairly heavy and there was the breastplate with a mouthpiece taped round your neck. You had to answer in set phrases and that's why people liked Post Office trained telephonists. It was an instilled discipline. If you answered back on the phone you got a P18 and you had to write out an explanation of why you'd done it. Voice-training was optional.

I worked in the Regent exchange, where there was one supervisor to the twelve girls. One girl was listening intently on her headphones. She was tapped on the shoulder and called out. Nothing was said for about an hour. It appeared that she was listening in to the Duke of Windsor. There was a system at Buckingham Palace whereby they could trace whether anybody was listening in. The call had come back from Buckingham Palace and they found the girl listening in on his conversation. Instant dismissal.

I was seven years with the Post Office and left to get married. I got a gratuity. It couldn't have been more than about £50 but I thought it was a fortune.

The phone was still very much a business instrument. In November 1924 the Exchange Telegraph Company service for stockbrokers handled over 12,000 calls in one day. By 1929 that figure had risen to over 18,000, with 1,500 'after hours' calls to be added. Selfridge's was then handling 40,000 calls a day and a newsroom had been established in the store for bona-fide journalists. One afternoon Selfridge saw out of his office window a storm brewing. He immediately phoned round the store to check stocks of raincoats. A large quantity was put on offer in the bargain basement at 12/6d (62 ½p) each and, sure enough, when the storm broke and people rushed in for shelter every raincoat was sold within half an hour. In Swansea, Thomas Garret Byrne, the manager of the Grand Theatre, used to confide in his telephonist the forthcoming attractions, with a friendly word not to pass the information on. He well knew that within minutes it would be around the town.

The instrument was useful to the growing number of motorists. In 1919 the Royal Automobile Club installed its first box, at Egham, Surrey, where users were trusted to leave in a tin their donations for the personal service provided. The Automobile Association started illuminating many of its boxes at night and in 1927 opened its first two boxes in Ireland. By 1930 it had a total of over 400. The services of Les Collins from his Brighton Road garage were even more in demand:

In the 1920s the quality of the tyres, which were small, was low and the roads had sharp flints, so tyres wore or had punctures fairly quickly. The price was high – £10 to £12 each. Tyre pressures were also high – 60 to 70lb. On Sundays there could be as many as 2,000 cars an hour passing our garage on the way to Brighton. Often we'd be called out down the road to repair or fit new tubes and tyres. One very hot Sunday I took a Renault two-seater down towards Brighton and collected nearly £200 – people often paid in sovereigns – in a suede bag with a ring.

The police, still mainly on push bikes, would call us out to an accident, sometimes to take the dark van for bodies – hearses were then horse drawn. In about 1928 we acquired a breakdown vehicle with a crane on the back. Before that we managed with timbers and jacks.

On the railways single phones were being installed for administrative use in offices and at stations. At Charing Cross Station in 1922 the pre-payment coin box with buttons A and B was introduced. When a caller asked for his number he was told how much money to insert. If the connection was made, he pressed Button A and was able to speak to his party; if it was not, then by pressing Button B he got his money back. This type of coin box was generally introduced from 1925. Needless to say, people tried not to pay or make the box pay out. One method was to speak through the receiver, and children were fond of blocking the returned coin chute with chewing gum. The designer prudently left a hole in the tray at the bottom of the chute for urine/fag-ash to fall through.

Professional people were still inclined to shy away from the instrument. Mr Frobisher, the elderly solicitor in A. E. W. Mason's *House of the Arrow* (1924), drew the line at brass plates, leaving them for Harley Street, but consented to having a phone installed – in the junior clerk's room. Another fictional elderly solicitor, Dorothy L. Sayers' Murbles, refused to 'have his chambers desecrated by a telephone' and had to use a neighbour's instrument to make a call. At this time the merchant bankers Baring Brothers had only one operator.

No such doubts assailed Northcliffe, who to his dying day wanted to be near a phone, the vital link to his newspapers, not always as well equipped as they might be. On his last return to London, the line at his town house, 1 Carlton Gardens, was declared out of order to prevent him from using it and exciting himself. The night editor of the *Daily Mail* told the staff on the Chief's private phone list that, if he managed to get to a working instrument and call in, they were to agree with him to keep him calm and later ignore any of his instructions. It was a long way from the day when one listed employee had raised his hat to the Chief as he answered his call.

Although the Great War was over, there were still military uses. Both sides used it in the French and Spanish war against the Riff rebels led by Abd-el-Krim in Morocco. After initial reverses, Spain established a link across the Straits of Gibraltar so that Madrid could talk directly to field headquarters at Tetuan. This played a decisive role in the ultimate victory in 1925. In the early post-war period primitive use was being made in air navigation. On the London–Paris journey one of the pilots used to phone in advance for the weather *en route*, including the visibility of the *Dog and Duck* pub 2½ miles from Tilbury police station.

In 1921 the Anglo-Irish negotiations to bring an end to the 'troubles' and agree the basis of a treaty were, according to Sean McBride, hampered by the difficulties of making a call between London and Dublin. There was only one instrument available in 10 Downing Street. More than once Irish delegates had to return to Dublin to consult de Valera, head of the

Max, Lord Beaverbrook.

1928

In the right hands a phone can confer remote power, captured by David Low in his 1928 cartoon of Lord Beaverbrook. Staff on Beaverbrook's newspapers hoaxed colleagues by imitating their master's voice.

(David Low Trustees)

republican 'government', before signing a final settlement. Perhaps the journeys were politically as well as practically preferable. Calls could have been tapped. Under pressure from Lloyd George during the final night of negotiations, Michael Collins and his colleagues signed – without any consultation over the phone. During the Hague Conference 1929, when the Labour government suspected that lines between England and the Netherlands were being tapped, it 'resorted to one of Lloyd George's expedients': using Welsh speakers with codes for key words and proper names.

Two authors whose international reputations were to grow gave the instrument a distinct personality. James Joyce's *Ulysses*, first published in 1922 but describing events in Dublin on 16 June 1904, has eight references. For instance, the roguish and flirtatious Blazes Boylan asks: 'May I say a word to your telephone, missy?' and the *angst*-ridden Leopold Bloom had in his list of sins: 'Unspeakable messages he telephoned mentally to Miss Dunn at an address in d'Olier Street while he presented himself indecently to the instrument in the callbox'. Marcel Proust, for whom at times the phone was the only link with the world outside his bedroom, in volume one of *The Guermantes Way* described operators as 'the ever infuriated servants of the Mystery, the umbrageous priestesses of the Invisible, the Young Ladies of the Telephone'. The theme was developed in his posthumously published *The Prisoner*, for example:

> I was now ready, but Françoise had not yet telephoned... Half an hour later the telephone bell began to tinkle and my heart throbbed tumultuously with hope and fear. There came, at the bidding of an operator, a flying squadron of sounds which with an instantaneous speed brought me the voice of the telephonist, not that of Francoise whom an ancestral timidity and melancholy, when she was brought face to face with any object unknown to her fathers, prevented from approaching a telephone receiver, although she would readily visit a person suffering from a contagious disease.

It continued to be a device useful to thriller writers. In Dorothy L. Sayers' first novel *Whose Body?* (1923), her detective Lord Peter Wimsey was introduced to the case by his mother over the phone. Taking the call he 'sat down to the telephone with an air of leisurely courtesy, as though it were an acquaintance dropped in for a chat'. Early in the novel a character who has never used the instrument resorts to it to tell him that her son has been arrested, and Wimsey's man Bunter always seems to be taking or giving phone messages. It is used in *Unnatural Death* to lure the solicitor Mr Trigg to his doom but he manages to escape. In *The Unpleasantness at the Bellona Club* (1928) it has a humorous role in the chase after the fictitious Oliver.

Bunter has to ring up two-and-a-half columns of Olivers in the directory but, weeks after the event, the Metropolitan Police trace 'Oliver's' call from Charing Cross Underground station. In a 1926 *Strand Magazine* story, 'The Bullet' by J. J. Bell, a poisons expert is detained by a 'wrong' number so that a deadly type can be stolen from his laboratory.

Five years later the murder of William Herbert Wallace's wife prompted discussion of whether the message left for her husband, an insurance agent, at a Liverpool café was part of his careful alibi or a trick by the real murderer. The call, made from a box near Wallace's home just before he arrived in the café, asked him to call at a non-existent address the following evening at a time when his wife was murdered. In a case that Dorothy L. Sayers described as one that 'could have only been put together by the perverted mind of a detective novelist', Wallace was found guilty, the verdict being overturned on appeal. Britain's first talking picture and Alfred Hitchcock's debut as a director, *Blackmail* (1929), featured a call office in a newsagent's as a dramatic location, and at Scotland Yard a convenient call saves the heroine from making an unnecessary confession of a killing in self-defence.

Edgar Wallace was never far from a phone. He used it especially for betting, typically staking about £100 per day, sometimes ringing a theatre staging one of his plays to check the takings so that his chauffeur could go down and collect as much as £2,000 before a race meeting. Doubtless his heavy bets provided work for 'the Blower', the bookmakers' own phone service, via which money was laid off. When Wallace moved with his family into the Carlton Hotel he had a private line to his flat so that he could quickly summon one of his secretaries. So prolific was his output that there were jokes about callers offering to hold on while he finished the episode of his current serial.

Another writer never very far from the instrument was Hilaire Belloc:

Tonight in million voiced London I
Was lonely as the million pointed sky
Until your voice, Ah! so the sun
Peoples all Heaven, although he be but one.

Once he got to an instrument he spent ages on it, although he did not like to have one in his fifteenth-century home, King's Land, at Shipley, West Sussex. When his son-in-law, Reginald Jebb, was being received into the Roman Catholic Church and was reciting the Creed in Latin, Belloc tapped the priest on the shoulder and enquired 'Excuse me, father, is there a telephone in the sacristy?' His fellow Roman Catholic author G. K. Chesterton was less keen on the instrument but had one in his Beaconsfield home, using it to discuss forthcoming issues of *G. K.'s Weekly*, produced from offices in Essex Street, off the Strand. When Belloc came into the office he usually made for the phone.

Shaw had a link between his house at Ayot St Lawrence and his writing hut at the bottom of the garden. In this period, like other dramatists (with the notable exception of Pirandello), he became more conscious of the instrument as a dramatic device, using a field phone in *Annajanska*, and in *Back to Methuselah* the videophone of AD 2170 was introduced. In reality, progress was swifter. In 1927, six years after the play was first produced, Bell scientists staged a videophone demonstration between two buildings in New York.

There were still plenty of people who had not caught up with present-day uses. D. H. Lawrence seems to have done without it. Arnold Bennett noted in his journal for 9 October 1924:

> Friendships made between young women on the telephone – solely. I have come across more than one instance of this. They like the tones of each other's voices and the things they say. And the friendship grows. Then comes an invitation to tea or another meal. 'Do come.' 'I should love to.' etc. I wonder what the results are. But I never hear. This method of companionship (sightless) is very queer.

Bright Young Things, especially women, took to it and gabbed away. Noel Coward captured the affinity in a 1923 monologue *Sorry You've Been Troubled*. Poppy Baker, a flapper lounging abed, hears from the police that her husband has jumped off Waterloo Bridge. His death is of small moment to her, a feeling that becomes plain in her chit-chat with friends. Unfortunately for her, it was a false report: the suicide was not her husband but the man upstairs.

In the freer post-war atmosphere the phone was the kind of boon to lovers that Le Gallienne had romanticized over. It was a more secular age, in which 'the book' meant the directory rather than the Bible. A young man could catch a girl unchaperoned, perhaps in her boudoir, or at least in a hall where her parents could hear only one side of a passionate conversation. Exercising his imagination on her surroundings, he could pour forth endearments from a call box for a few pence, feeding in more to demonstrate his attachment yet still paying a small price for being together, a price that he could afford several times a day. Frequency of calling as well as the words that were breathed, with all the appropriate intonations, brought home the ardour of a relationship.

The situation was described by the critic George Jean Nathan in *The Theatre, the Drama, the Girls* (1921):

Flappers and new-style phones were a natural fit. (Bell Canada Telephone Historical Collection)

A favourite hymn, for some American worshippers. (Stamps-Baxter Music & Printing Co., Inc.)

When the estimable Bell conceived the idea for the telephone, little did the good soul reckon that it would turn out, in time, to be an important and unwitting agent in the dealing of the deuce to the young female of the species. That, more than any other thing, the telephone has been instrumental in bringing the young woman of today to a point where her grandmother wouldn't recognize her, that it is in no little degree responsible for her increasingly loose manners and looser habits, any mother who takes the time to realize the situation will doubtless agree. It is not so easy... for a flapper to sit next to a man on a sofa and, without blushing, tell him to press his ruby lips to hers. The telephone gives the flapper courage – and more, it permits a girl to lie in her bed and to talk with a man lying in his bed; it permits her, half-clothed, to talk with him a moment after its ring has made him hop nude out of his bathtub. Its delicate suggestiveness is not lost in these instances. The most modest girl in America, the girl who blushes even at a man's allusions to his chilblains, once she gets her nose in a telephone mouthpiece acquires a sudden and surprising self assurance and aptitude at wheeze.

The 1928 Broadway musical *The Five O'Clock Girl* was based on a phone operator falling in love with a young man sight unseen.

When the ardour at one end of the line was not matched at the other, the difference in mood was not always caught or appreciated. What one party saw as an open door was being closed afar off, and failure to perceive or accept this led to calls becoming a nuisance, even a form of importuning from which young men had to be restrained by magistrates. The absence of ringing could be bliss, as for the couple who sang 'Tea for Two' in the 1925 musical comedy *No, No, Nanette*. They didn't want it known that they owned a telephone. For quite different reasons Queen Mary was believed never to have used the instrument.

'Some women can't see a telephone without taking the receiver off,' remarked a character in Somerset Maugham's play *The Constant Wife* (1926). There were husbands who held out against installing it because they feared that their wives would be gossiping away on it all day long or constantly interrupting them at the office. In an attempt to reassure him of her constancy, Edgar Wallace's wife 'Jim' called him at all hours of the day to account for her movements. For an unfaithful wife, such as Julia in F. Tennyson Jesse's *A Pin to See the Peepshow*, it was a means of making an appointment with a back-street abortionist. Later in the book, modelled on the 1923 Thompson–Bywaters case, a *cause célèbre* in which the wife and her lover were both executed for the murder of the husband, her use of the phone is part of the evidence against her:

But she hadn't known she was going to see Leo that night. They had quarrelled about it. Oh, why hadn't she written to him that last day, instead of just talking to him on the telephone? Then everyone would know she had made no arrangement to meet him.

A call was beginning to take the place of the calling card. Instead of leaving a card and expecting to be invited, people now called on the phone in advance of calling in person. One singer treated it like a card, giving his name and adding the description 'tenor'. Not surprisingly, he was addressed as 'Mr Tenor'. Emily Post averred in *Etiquette* (1922):

> Custom which has altered many ways and manners has taken away all opprobrium from the message by telephone, and with the exception of those of a very small minority of letter-loving hostesses, all informal invitations are sent and answered by telephone.

There was endless society discussion on the proprieties to be observed. To whom should one give one's number? At what point, especially for a woman, was it right to impart a number? Should the man or the woman make the first call? Etiquette writers gave various answers and those in doubt could easily find an authority to suit their fancy or flout.

Emily Post, while avoiding any pronouncement on the rights and wrongs of what to do, specified the form of reply, adding:

> In many houses, especially where there are several grown sons or daughters, a blank form is kept in the pantry:
>
> Will ....
> .... with M ....
> on .... the ....
> at .... o'clock.   Telephone number ....
>   Accept
>   Regret

These slips are taken to whichever member of the family has been invited, who crosses off 'regret' or 'accept' and hands the slip back for transmission by the butler, the parlor-maid or whoever is on duty in the pantry.

Lady Troubridge's *The Book of Etiquette* (1926) expanded upon that part of a servant's duties:

> Instructions should be given in answering the telephone. If asked who is speaking, a servant should reply, 'Mrs Dash's butler or maid' as the case may

be. He should speak clearly and courteously and, if it is necessary to take a message, say, 'If you will kindly hold the line I will inform Mrs Dash.' If the person inquired for is out, the message should be written down at once.

The employer should provide a telephone note-book and pencil, and a note-book and pencil for the hall table, and arrange that all written messages should be placed upon the table.

Household phones still featured in shop catalogues and some stores sold telephone tidies, often taking the form of crinolined ladies who provided temporary cover. They also helped prevent candlestick receivers from being dislodged during dusting, for which maids apologized to the exchange.

One thing helping to provide more interesting employment for women was the growth of rural telephony, which had been urged on the postmaster-general by the National Federation of Women's Institutes in 1927. Often this meant using party lines. In South Africa £300,000 was set aside for farm line development during 1924–6, with farmers themselves supplying the unskilled labour and road transport and undertaking ordinary maintenance of their shared lines. Response was so enthusiastic that more money was required to extend the service. Farmers were brought closer to markets, merchants and vets.

During the Irish 'troubles', equipment was destroyed and, when they were settled, the inadequate network had to be reconstructed and developed. Over half the subscribers were in the Dublin area and only the southern and eastern parts of the country were really served. By 1930 the only considerable places without service were the western parts of Mayo and Donegal. Nevertheless, in spite of modernization, the Irish pace of life remained leisurely. Such developments were not always seen as a blessing. Landowners in Andalusia saw the modernization of the Spanish network as a threat to a way of life, 'allowing revolutionaries to talk to each other from city to city'.

In January 1919 the borough surveyor of Dorchester wrote to the grand old man of English letters, Thomas Hardy OM, asking if he would like to share with the borough council in providing a joint phone service to his home at Max Gate and to the council's sewage works nearby. On 19 January Hardy replied, saying that he would be happy to go along with the plan if it proved feasible, depending on the cost and the meaning of the term 'joint service'. Under this or some other arrangement, Max Gate was connected (Dorchester 43) during 1919. On 8 January 1920 Hardy wrote to Edmund Gosse telling him that there was a phone in the house but that he himself was 'uncallable, not being able to hear what is said'. After his death, his widow Florence told a visitor that he disliked it and refused to use it. On the night he died, 11 January 1928, a call was put in just after 9 p.m. to his brother and sister, who lived about a mile and a half away, but as they did not answer the phone when they had gone to bed they did not get the news until a servant arrived from Max Gate early next morning.

In Norfolk, Marquess Townshend at Raynham Hall (Fakenham 47X) shared a line with a relative and it was well used by one or the other, except when the branches of trees interfered with the overhead wires, mainly in winter. The phone was by no means universally used among the aristocracy, either because of their rural remoteness or personal disinclination. In 1923 Lord Curzon at his country seat in Somerset, Montacute House, heard by letter that he had been passed over as Prime Minister. Montacute was not on the phone.

In Hampshire, Lord Montagu had it (Beaulieu 6) taken out of Palace House between 1919 and 1924 because he wanted to relax after working in London during the week. When coming home he would arrange by telegram for a car to meet him at Brockenhurst station. He thought in terms of the telegram, and guests at Palace House were provided with telegram pads in their rooms. A Post Office boy came up on his red bicycle to collect messages. If Lord Montagu wanted to use a phone on Fridays and Saturdays there was one in the estate office, which also had a private system for the estate. That system had its own poles, which the Post Office also used. When the phone was put in again at Palace House in 1924 there had been some growth in the local system, and his number was Beaulieu 51. Lord Montagu felt it was a *public* phone and you did not entrust anything secret to it. You wrote a letter. His estate manager never used on the phone the name of somebody involved in a business matter, and they were well served by the traditional services of the Post Office. A 9.30 p.m. letter from London would be on the breakfast table in Beaulieu next morning.

Lord Montagu's suspicions of the privacy of the phone service were not without foundation. Section 4 of the Official Secrets Act 1920 laid down that any Secretary of State could issue a warrant for the interception of telegrams and phone calls in and out of Britain. In the village post office people would come up to the counter and ask for a call, take it in the red box in the corner, which was not entirely soundproof, and then pay at the counter. Some felt that it invited the attention of gossips. In a North Norfolk village the postmaster regularly listened in to phone conversations, explaining to his two five shilling (25p) a week female assistants that it was his business to know what was going on. Some subscribers were aware of this. One particularly irate farmer used frequently to interrupt his conversations with the command 'Get off the line, ------!' The postmaster often used overheard information to his own advantage. As a sideline he was willing, when asked, to use his car as a taxi. The station was about a mile from the centre of the village and at the foot of a long and tedious hill. On hearing that people would be visiting friends or relatives in the village, arriving by a certain train, he would contrive to be at the station and offer them a lift. Some, of course, thought it was a kindly act, only to find that payment was always requested at the end of the journey.

On one occasion the village blacksmith was ordering urgently needed goods by phone from the nearest market town, nine miles away. The firm said it would be unable to deliver them for two days. As the blacksmith and the supplier were trying to think of a quicker way a helpful voice came over the phone: 'I say, ———, what about so-and-so who comes through here to the next village every night? He'd bring them for you!' He also scrutinized incoming mail, digesting the contents of all postcards and unsealed letters. Telegrams he delivered in person, as befitted the dignity of his office, giving the message verbally, often with much comment and conversation, before handing over the buff envelope. So notorious did his activities become that word reached his superiors. He was moved and put under closer supervision by the Post Office.

People who fancied themselves higher up the social scale readily took advantage of the phone, as Stanley Ball, who owned an off-licence near the Brighton Road garage that did so well out of breakdowns, found to his cost:

The nearby village of Ifield was well-known for awkward customers and bad debts. There were quite a few houses let on short leases or furnished. These would be taken by people on leave from abroad or suffering from the post-war economic collapse. They would run up accounts and skip. Some houses had very bad names.

Awkward customers were important people who dealt mainly in London, particularly with Harrods, who would and did deliver anything from a kipper to a bunch of flowers daily. They had a night phone service and any order received before 8 a.m. was delivered that day, however small. These good people, whom one certainly could not afford to offend, might forget to order a bottle of vermouth or something and, expecting friends in the evening, would phone me about 6.30 for one bottle to be sent. Same price as Harrods, gross profit 2d or 3d [about 1p], delivered by motor cycle and sidecar, with Harrods getting an order for twelve bottles next day. One good lady regularly phoned about 7 p.m. on Saturdays for a bottle of French vermouth, frequently sold at a loss to get the order for gin, adding, 'and tell your driver to bring me over the *Evening News*', which was what she really wanted, the old man not having returned from the golf club. If I phoned in the afternoon to ask if she wanted anything as our van was coming out she would snarl 'No. And don't bother me.' All this would be charged to account, and God help you if you ever dared ask for payment.

Most people still regarded the phone as an instrument for emergencies – not the best of times to get to know it. Dr F. J. Waldo, coroner of the City of London, warned in *The Lancet* of 9 August 1924:

> Not uncommonly… on the breaking out of a fire, persons on using the 'phone merely say – 'Fire!' and without waiting to give their address, replace the receiver and await the arrival of the fire brigade, which, of course, never comes.

'F. W. W.' sprang to the defence of the apparently incompetent public by quoting the instructions in the London Telephone Directory:

EMERGENCY SERVICES. (FIRE, AMBULANCE, POLICE)
If in the case of emergency the Fire, Ambulance, or Police service is required, all that is necessary to answer the telephonist's query 'Number, please?' with the word, 'Fire', 'Ambulance', or 'Police', as the case may be. *Do not give the number.* (See instructional headlines.)

F. W. W. commented:

> I suppose this means, 'Do not stop to give the number of any fire station, but give your own name and address and number,' but it could be read: 'Do not give any number at all.'

To clear up the ambiguity the Metropolitan Boroughs' Traffic Committee issued new instructions on how to report an emergency by phone:

> In case of accident the telephone exchange should be asked for 'ambulance'; no number is required and no charge is made for the call, whether it is made from a public call office or from a private telephone. As soon as the caller gets through to the headquarters of the Ambulance Service, *particulars as to the locality of the accident or illness should be made together with the name of the caller.*

Not to be outdone, Dr Waldo pointed out that the existing instructions included the statement '(See instructional headlines.)'. All that a reader had to do was to turn to 'page 346 [and] find under "Fire Brigade", as follows: In case of Fire call Fire Brigade; no number is required. When Fire Station replies, give address of Fire.' Such a procedure was suitable for the calm of a coroner's office but scarcely for a flustered phone novice in the presence of a fire.

The phone was still regarded as an emergency instrument. (BT Museum)

Perhaps only once in a lifetime fire may break out in your home — but a telephone call then would be worth more than money can measure — it may save life and possessions . . . A telephone in the home relieves you of that worst form of anxiety — inability to summon help in urgent need . . . And the premium for the safest of all life insurances · the telephone — is a modest payment of approximately 10/- a month rental and a penny for each local call. Fill in the Inquiry Form now.

Fire – Police – Doctor – Ambulance . . .

TELEPHONE

INQUIRY FORM
To the Secretary, General Post Office, London
Please send me without any obligation on my part, full particulars of telephone service · its advantages and its costs.
Name (Mr. Mrs. or Miss)
Address
Town

An advertisement of the Post Office Telephone Service

The public was in general reluctant to use police call pillars on the streets, believing them to be for official use only. The pillars, prominent in regulation blue, gave callers a direct free line to local headquarters. In the public eye they were lesser versions of the more substantial police phone box, also in the official colours and upon the roof of which a light flashed too when the station wanted to call the policeman on the beat.

Nowhere was emergency use of the phone more important than in safety of life at sea. In 1928, responding to a message that a Latvian steamer was in danger, the lifeboat with a crew of 17 was launched from Rye Harbour, Sussex. Soon after, it was learned on shore that the steamer was out of danger and signals were fired to recall the lifeboat. They went unheard and the lifeboat continued its fruitless search. On her return she capsized in a following sea near the harbour mouth, losing all her crew. One year later a radio-telephone system was fitted for the first time in a British lifeboat. Had it existed before, lives might have been saved.

CHAPTER 9

DIALLING TONE

On a wider scale, the phone was an essential element in the fabric of society. Only when it was missing was its importance appreciated. The total destruction of the Tokyo system of 83,000 phones in the great earthquake and fire of 1923 not only made rescue and rehabilitation more difficult. Lack of reliable information undermined moral order as well. In the shock and confusion wild rumours spread and rampaging crowds murdered many Koreans, an historical enemy. In restoring order, communications were a priority and within four weeks 14,000 phones were in operation again.

Attitudes to the phone among British doctors remained ambivalent. Paying for entries in classified directories along with other trades and professions was generally regarded as advertising and hence to be avoided. Their numbers were in the alphabetical directories as normal subscribers and, if they were away, they could ask the exchange to route calls to a locum. On the other hand the doctors of Coalville, Leicestershire, decided in 1923 to give up their phones 'on account of the unreasonable demands made by patients who were unwilling to write a message or send a messenger'.

Public fears of 'catching something' had not been quelled. On 21 March 1923 the Minister of Health, Neville Chamberlain, in a parliamentary answer, stated:

> As the result of bacteriological inquiries made in this country and abroad some few years ago, it was held that the transmission of pulmonary tuberculosis through the medium of the telephone mouthpieces is practically impossible. In any event, the disinfection of telephone mouthpieces after each individual user would obviously be impracticable.

Post Office policy was to clean public call offices and disinfect the phones every three days. In 1926 though it withdrew permission to fit glass mouthpieces. When fitting or removing them, users could damage the screw threads or the glass itself. Even if it became cracked or broken, there were those who risked cut lips or other injuries. For this reason the idea of a porcelain mouthpiece was rejected in 1923.

There was another menace, dealt with in a *Times* leader of 10 March 1927:

An Intrusion into Privacy

An annoying misuse of the telephone has lately been added to the minor worries of life. It is still rare, but it may become common unless it is sternly repressed. The makers, or the distributors, of some article or other, or the agents of some insurance concern, finding that the telephone directory is a useful guide to nearly all the householders in London, ring up private houses and flats with the aim of advertising their wares by telephone. This is an insolent encroachment upon the privacy of the home. The agent for sale who calls in person may be an annoyance, but at least such travellers bring their goods with them and are willing to submit them to examination. A circular, or a letter asking for an appointment, is easy to be considered, or lightly thrown away with its many fellows. A telephone call demands immediate attention. It must at least give unnecessary work and inconvenience. It may interrupt no one knows what serious study or business, or what engrossing recreation. It takes the called at a disadvantage that may be very grave, because there is no means by which the called can tell the state of things in the household at the moment. It violates the principle of the private telephone, which is a means of communication more personal than post or telegraph, and is intended only for the use of the household and its friends about their own concerns. Steady indeed must be the nerve and inexhaustible the patience of those who earn their living by making (always with brisk and cheerful voice) these calls for their employers. A hasty ring-off may well seem to them a blessing compared with the comments which they must often be compelled to hear in reply to their summons. But their nerve and their patience do not diminish the annoyance which they are paid to cause… But the commercial use of the private telephone, to which we have objected, is a use which commerce will surely find it wiser to discontinue.

There were persistent rumours that Bell himself disliked the instrument, the credibility of which was perhaps enhanced by his own oft-repeated quip: 'Why did I ever invent the telephone?' His widow Mabel set the record straight:

Of course, he never had one in his study. That was where he went when he wanted to be alone with his thoughts and his work. The telephone, of course, means intrusion by the outside world.

She was writing from their Nova Scotia home, not far from where he was buried:

> We never could have come here in the first place or continued here, but for the telephone which kept us in close touch with doctors and neighbors and the regular telegraph office.
>
> He saw to it that we should be able to reach that at any time, day or night. It was owing to this telephone system that we were able to come and stay up here last summer. Our physician lives sixty miles away in Sydney.
>
> I, myself called him up at half-past five a.m. that last day; he answered immediately, and all through that last day [1 August 1922] the telephone served Mr Bell faithfully and well, bringing to him first one then another whom he called for. Afterwards the telegrams from all over came pouring in day and night – telephoned over without delay or mistake… I shall always be so thankful that the telephone worked so well that last day – serving its father so loyally.

During his funeral service, just before sunset on 4 August 1922, all phones served by the Bell System in the USA and Canada were silent for one minute.

That must have annoyed some, so much was the phone part of the American way of life. It was essential for almost every type of business, large or small, legal or illegal. George F. Babbitt wanted it for 'selling houses for more than people could afford to pay'. Sam Spade needed it in his detective agency just as much as Al Capone running a boot-legging empire, which he even managed to do from the warden's phone when he conveniently got himself into prison in Philadelphia to escape vengeance for the St Valentine's Night massacre in Chicago. During prohibition operators got used to passing on orders for hogs. People were always ordering some red hog or white hog – in bulk. A consignment of prohibited beer or whisky could be arranged as easily as a contract killing, and federal agents tapped this source of information. In 1928, in a five-to-four decision, the Supreme Court ruled that evidence obtained through wire tapping was admissible in criminal prosecutions. Wire-tapping itself remained illegal.

With the addition of the classified section, the 2,500 directories were becoming a national buyers' guide, directing consumer to supplier and vice versa. During the great Florida land boom one buyer paid $1,500,000 for 425 acres around a Tampa golf club after making a five-minute call from Connecticut. He had never seen the property. The most intensive users were the Wall Street financial community, and the greatest density of phones per head of the population was in the farming state of Iowa. It was

The telephone company is made up of perfectly human people, doing their best to give the public good service in spite of unusual obstacles and insufficient revenue.

installed on almost 40 per cent of all farms, where it brought crop, weather and general news from the outside world. It helped to encourage co-operative growers' associations, the development of commodity markets and suburban homes for city employees. It enabled Jay Gatsby to lead a sumptuous life and indulge a romantic innocence on Long Island Sound far from the corruption in Chicago and Philadelphia upon which he depended for the money to entertain his fun-loving guests.

It was a source of information to the Red-scared authorities who tapped the phone of Felix Frankfurter, the liberal Harvard law professor seeking the release of Sacco and Vanzetti, the two Italian-born anarchists convicted in a rough and ready trial of armed robbery and murder. A similar thing had happened in Germany in early 1919, when the Social Democrat commander-in-chief in the civil war, Gustave Noske, personally ordered day and night monitoring of the phone of Karl Liebknecht, a leader of the Spartacists, a group of international revolutionaries. As a result, Liebknecht and his colleague Rosa Luxemburg were arrested in Berlin by right-wing soldiers, members of the *Freikorps*, and beaten about the head with rifle butts before being shot dead on the night of 15/16 January 1919. For absolute certainty, Rosa's body – the bullet in her temple was not necessarily fatal – was dumped in a canal.

Stalin realized the threat to the new Soviet state. In vetoing Trotsky's plans to develop a modern phone system he is reported as saying: 'It will unmake

This defensive advertisement, in a 1920 issue of the trade journal Telephony, *could have been made by most phone companies at almost any time in their history.* (*Telephony*)

our work. No greater instrument for counter-revolution and conspiracy can be imagined.' Perhaps he had remembered Lenin's dictum 'Electrification is the basis of democracy'. Henceforward tapping of phones was to become a systematic practice, not just in totalitarian states. In 1924 J. Edgar Hoover, a dedicated anti-communist, began his 48-year reign as head of the FBI. To him, intercepting calls was a modern investigative method of fighting the enemies of society, political or criminal, crossing state lines and operating on a national scale. Reds, racketeers, gangsters, kidnappers and, in the 1950s and 1960s, civil rights activists such as Martin Luther King were all legitimate subjects for surveillance. The more personal and privileged information he had on them the better. Its justification was the need to maintain a stable, secure society, a view shared by employers who gained information in labour disputes this way. Having benefited from the practice, the authorities in the USA and elsewhere were also interested in 'scrambling' so that, if intercepted, their own conversations would be unintelligible. There could be public secrets but not necessarily private ones.

On 20 May 1924 New York newspapers published pictures transmitted 522 miles from Cleveland over phone wires. It was not a first in facsimile but the method promised a greater future for photo-journalism. The New York *Sun* commented:

> New York not only talks with Cleveland; New York sees what Cleveland sees. Not the words a telegraph operator has taken down, but the light and shadow on human faces, the drift of ships on a river, the silhouette of a monument in a public square. These cities have never been linked so closely together before. Yet pictures by telephone simply round out an immediacy of contact that began long ago. First, dots and dashes; then the human voice; then trains and airplanes rushing back and forth with their cargoes of goods, books, newspapers. This has been the process by which a very large country has become in one sense very small.

Photographs and fingerprints could also be sent, the significance of which was not lost on Police Commissioner Enright of New York: 'This invention will give the police a tremendous advantage over the criminal.' Banking and legal transactions could also be speeded up.

In Ben Hecht's and Charles MacArthur's play *The Front Page*, a 1928 hit comedy-melodrama on Broadway, there were seven telephones on stage in the Press room of the Chicago Criminal Court Building, almost constituting characters and events that drove the plot along. In real life actors waited in silent rooms for the call that could change their lives. Not to be called was, as Irving Berlin summed it up in the title of his 1924 song, to be 'All Alone'. When the tenor Melville Gideon sang 'I've fallen in love with a voice', he meant a switchboard operator. She was a heroine in the American pantheon, performing a noteworthy daily public service. Occasionally she enjoyed brief fame, as did Miss Gladys I. Gibson, a private switchboard operator at a Mid-West hospital. In 1929, within two minutes of a blaze breaking out, gasping and choking she called the exchange: 'There's a fire here at the hospital – a terrible explosion – call the fire department, the police, ambulances – it's awful – and – ' There was no doubt that her instinctive reaction saved lives.

One US manufacturer advertised:

The Automatic Telephone Girl
Her nerves are steel.
She tells no secrets.
She speaks all languages.
Always on the Job – day and night – every minute.
Ever ready – ever eager – to serve *you*.

The accompanying illustration was part of an automatic exchange. In at least one place, the German-populated areas of Wisconsin, her language was not universal. There the inhabitants were dialling 'ein und zwanzig' or 'ein zwanzig', one and twenty instead of 21, and getting the wrong number. Another problem was that people had to be able to spell exchange names, e.g. in London Covent (not Convent) Garden. In Tokyo from 1926, looking up numbers for themselves, people had to get used to horizontal entries instead of the traditional vertical lines. In the bustling commercial city of Shanghai, which grew rapidly in the 1920s, most subscribers' dials bore Arabic numerals, with some having Chinese characters only.

Although the dial was being progressively introduced, on local calls automatically bypassing the operator, it was not the end of her calling. Her job might be that less personal – the Bell System was 20 per cent automatic by 1926, the fiftieth anniversary of the phone – but she worked in an expanding service. Manual switchboards would not disappear from the system overnight. Toll and long-distance calls had to be handled personally. As the system expanded so more operators were needed for directory enquiries, person-to-person and reverse-charge calls, and giving assistance to users in difficulties. From 1923 Bell Canada operators had to tell callers wanting to check the time: 'We are so busy that we have no time to spare.' Previously, from 6 a.m., these routine calls had turned switchboards into a blaze of lights. Some parents trained their children to ring the exchange if they were in trouble and there were always customers, like Cohen in the sketches by Joe Hayman, with a talent for getting in a muddle. Lydia Scalia saw it from her Post Office switchboard:

The Scandinavian subscriber as seen by the operator was a gruesome character. He understands that operators work eight hours and sleep eight hours, but nobody had ever told him that they did it at the same time.

(Telephone Museum, Copenhagen)

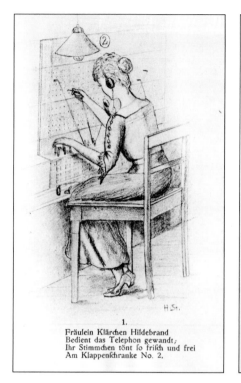

1.
Fräulein Klärchen Hildebrand
Bedient das Telephon gewandt,
Ihr Stimmchen tönt so frisch und frei
Am Klappenschranke No. 2.

2.
Versetzt zum Klappenschranke 2
Ward Praktikante Sorgenfrei, —
Ein Jüngling voller Uebermut,
Man hört am Amt jetzt nicht so gut!

3.
Am Klappenschranke No. 2
Der Dienst wird Klärchen einerlei,
Sie legt auf Klappen kein Gewicht,
Man hört am Amt oft lange nicht.

Young love is not allowed to get in the way of German efficiency at the switchboard in this 1928 series of cartoons by H. Starkloff.
(Bundespostmuseum, Frankfurt)

People were frightened of the dial when it first came. The users rather than the operators. The operators knew it would take a long time to take over from them.

Her employment prospects and those of her fellow operators were improving, even in Japan where there was an enormous recession and many people were cut off for non-payment. Young women were always coming and going anyway, partly because it was a demanding job, sometimes causing nervous complaints. For those leaving the public service there were opportunities in industry and commerce, where the job could be more personal, making connections for people whom she saw and knew. New York alone had some 35,000 private switchboards.

In London, subscribers dialled the first three letters of the exchange they wanted, e.g. FULham or HOLborn, followed by a four-digit number. Combinations of letters and figures were easier to remember than a string of digits but there were practical limits to the list of pronounceable or permissible exchange names. A brand name seized upon was VAT 69. The whisky had been blended by William Sanderson and Sons Ltd since the

4.
Am Klappenschranke No. 2
Die Klappen liegen Reih um Reih;
Man dreht sich müde — schreit hinein,
Was mag nur da der Fehler sein?

5.
Beim Klappenschranke No. 2
Schwört Sorgenfrei die ew'ge Treu,
Als der Direktor grad entdeckt,
Daß in dem Amt der Fehler steckt!

6.
Vom Klappenschranke No. 2
Verschwindet schnell Herr Sorgenfrei —
Fräul'n Klärchen ist voll Gift und Wut —
Am Amt hört man jetzt wieder gut!

1880s but it was given a new meaning when dubbed by the public 'the Pope's telephone number'. Alexander Pope, the poet who had a villa at Twickenham, was officially commemorated in the exchange POPesgrove; another poet BYRon at Harrow; the historian MACaulay at Battersea; and the sculptor FLAxman in Chelsea. The idea was popularized by a game, Number Please?, 'adaptable for all parties in home or social hall', in which players traced numbers via slips of paper.

While automatic dialling gradually spread for local calls, the repeater – first employed during the Great War – improved quality on long-distance lines. Visitors to the Wembley Exhibition 1924 could hear for themselves what a tremendous difference it made, even though it might be years before they benefited personally. Good quality was remarked on, as by Ernest Bramah's blind detective Max Carrados: '"Busy, Max?" chirruped the familiar voice of his friend the enquiry agent – incurably brisk and debonair even after its ten miles' journey along the wire.'

Improvements were adopted slowly. Far from catching up with North America, parts of the British Empire and Scandinavia in phone density and usage, Britain was a backward nation. To make matters worse, broadcasting

An inspector checks that a German operator's dress is at least 20 cm below the knee.

(Bundespostmuseum, Frankfurt)

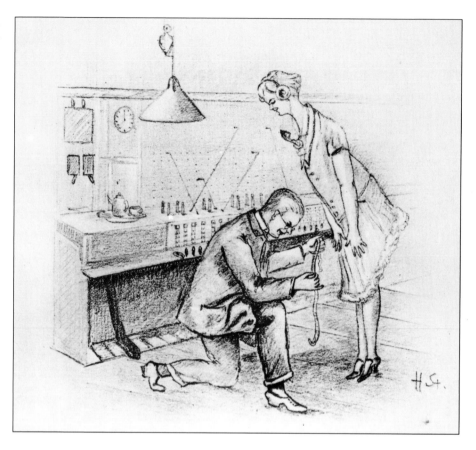

was a rival. Phone boxes were vandalized by thieves stealing parts to build wireless sets. A home phone could be a nuisance in calling away listeners-in. The success of wireless also dealt the death blow to the Electrophone Company. In 1926 the last Electrophone installation in London was removed and the mahogany-finished hexagonal tables at which typically four people had sat to listen through headphones were stripped of their equipment and sold as coffee tables for 7/6d (37½p) each, less than the cost of an annual wireless licence (10s = 50p). Having a wireless set was an international craze, and the theft of phone parts was widespread. In South Africa it was serious enough for comment from the postmaster-general in his 1924 report, and in Wellington, New Zealand, 27 call boxes were stripped in one night. This selfish vandalism, depriving legitimate users of the service, aroused public dissatisfaction.

Out of enlightened self-interest the British manufacturers formed in

DIALLING TONES.

GULliver.

WHEN *I dial G-U-L,*
Fancy weaves this potent spell :

Twenty years have slipped away
Swiftly as an idle day ;
Book in hand, I'm back again
In the schoolroom, *ætat* ten.
Homework lies neglected, but
I'm hull down for Lilliput ;
Sums and scales have failed to drag
Me away from Brobdingnag ;
Vainly call the dotted minims—
I'm far off among the Houyhnhnms,
Lost in that enchanted land,
I and *Lemuel,* hand in hand.

Fancy weaves this potent spell
When I dial G-U-L.

To subscribers, named exchanges had individual characters. Here, E. H. Shepard, best known as the illustrator of Winnie the Pooh, envisages the world of GULliver, a London exchange named after Jonathan Swift's early eighteenth-century traveller.

(Punch)

'An extra servant for less than a penny a day' was the theme of this 1920s leaflet produced by the New Zealand Post Office. It assured readers that 'people can live without Extension Telephones. They can also exist without vacuum cleaners, electric irons, typewriters, filing cabinets, and many other labour-saving devices. But, like these other things, Extension Telephones are very useful; without them we cannot live as comfortably or as efficiently as we should.'

(Telecom Corporation of
New Zealand)

1924 the Telephone Development Association, with the simple aim of promoting phone use. A typical advertisement ran:

THE TELEPHONE COSTS
NOTHING – to instal
NOTHING – for the calls you receive
A PENNY – for each local call you make
2/6 A WEEK – for Rental.
Still less outside London
Why aren't YOU 'on the 'Phone'?

Letters to the editor – Arnold Bennett lent his weight to protests about 'telephone inefficiency' in a letter to the *Daily Express* on 24 June 1929 – inspired articles, speeches, a cartoon film, pamphlets and posters all helped stir public opinion and emphasize the friendliness and necessity of the phone.

That was a job the Post Office itself ought to have been doing but it was under the thumb of a niggardly Treasury. It had secured in 1921 the abolition of the unremunerative annual flat-rate charge, but it lacked a creative approach. The fundamental problem was that the Post Office was 'a department of the Civil Service and as such is wholly staffed by Civil Servants. But the technique of the Civil Service is not necessarily well suited to the conduct of what is essentially a business undertaking.' The objective of the Telephone Development Association was to transfer phones from political control to an independent public authority.

In response to mounting public criticism the Post Office made some improvements. Cast iron kiosks were introduced in 1926, the first standard design of 1921 – an ugly model in concrete – having proved unpopular. The new kiosks were designed by one of the country's leading architects, Giles Gilbert Scott, knighted before the first installation. Classically elegant – their small windows on three sides were an array of Golden Rectangles – they were unobtrusive yet in vermilion easily visible. Ventilation was through perforated crowns in the dome. Unfortunately the Post Office was less imaginative in its buildings. Most of its designs for exchanges, dictated by the solid need to house machinery, were visually unexciting, whereas some London Underground stations could be architecture worth preserving.

In 1929, following the American lead in introducing 'French' phones, the 'candlestick' began to be replaced by a model with the transmitter and receiver together in one handset, a business convenience that *Punch* praised light-heartedly. At first there were problems in knowing which end to talk into. It also ended the prank of causing a 'howler' in the exchange.

Putting the earpiece against the transmitter on a 'candlestick' phone created a high-pitched whistle, infuriating operators. They recorded the incidents on a subscriber's card and sometimes retaliated by inserting a red peg in his number on the board, indicating a 'temporary difficulty on that line'. To get closer to the customer, the personal call service was introduced in 1929, and ADC, *a*dvising the *d*uration and *c*harge of a call, in 1930. Each improvement helped but they did not amount to a change of heart by the Post Office.

New horizons for the phone were opening up with advances in technology, such as repeaters. Yet European authorities had not grasped their significance or were doing little to exploit them. In 1922, the year of Bell's death, in Britain Frank Gill, in his inaugural address as president of the Institution of Electrical Engineers, asked two questions:

> Has telephony, during the 46 years it has been available, been of as much use to Europe as it might have been?
> Have the organizations, Government and otherwise, been permitted to do what they wished to do? The answer to both questions is most decidedly – No!

The contrast between US and European achievements was stark. And it could not be put down to the recent war. The Bell System was continental in reach whereas Europe consisted of various systems, their levels of service reflecting national attitudes. French operators were said to hate foreigners like poison and natives like medicine. It was not until 1925 that Denmark finally rejected linking broadcasting to the phone network. There was no practical basis for European nations to act in concert, however good their intentions. Peter Ustinov records that at the moment of his birth in Swiss Cottage at 11 a.m. on 16 April 1921, his father, the London representative of the German news agency Wolff Büro, 'was busy hollering the contents of a speech by Lloyd George down a defective line to Berlin'. Interpol, which needed good communications to trap international criminals, was founded in 1923 yet phone traffic between nations was 'meagre in quantity, slow and inefficient'. To emphasize his point, Gill superimposed American distances on a map of Europe:

> The direct distance between Brussels and Athens, or between Paris and Constantinople, is 1,300 miles – about the same distance as between New York and Omaha, or between Chicago and Salt Lake City, between which places calls can be made at any time. The direct distance over land between London and Baghdad is about the same as between New York and San Francisco, over which line conversations take place daily.

The French telephone system was nothing to write home about but postcards featuring it were worth the trip to Paris.

(Collection Historique, France Télécom)

Calling from one city to another was like two people talking to one another 70 or 80 feet apart in a reasonably quiet open field. Voices sounded like those on contemporary phonograph records. A speaker could hear his own voice in the receiver so loudly, however, that it temporarily reduced the sensitivity of his ear. That made it difficult to hear the speaker at the far end, especially when the latter had a weak voice or was not speaking close to the transmitter. Nevertheless, the link was there.

Britain was very much an offshore island, connected to the Continent by only 23 circuits, many of doubtful efficiency. When one of Gill's junior engineers, Norman Kipping, who had been working on the first long-distance cable in Sweden, made the first call from Stockholm to London, proposing to his fiancée Eileen, she was too dumbfounded to reply. Gill, seeing that such communications links had to be part of a concerted European scheme, declared that it was necessary 'to depute a body to do for all European nations that which no one nation can do for itself'. Two years later what amounted to a communications League of Nations was formed and started establishing common standards.

Concerted action was timely because the phone could now reach even farther, spanning oceans. On the night of 14/15 January 1923 the first experimental transatlantic radio-telephone call was made, a two-hour one-way transmission, from New York to North London. Further technical investigations were carried out and on 7 March 1926, the fiftieth anniversary of the Bell patent, the first two-way conversation was held across the Atlantic, when a group of newspapermen talked to each other from phone offices. The commercial service began on 7 January 1927 with an inaugural call by the two top phone officials. That first day 31 calls were made, costing £15 ($75) for three minutes.

Initially there was only one circuit serving the London and New York metropolitan areas. Over it, for $375 Arthur Murray taught the steps of the Black Bottom to a London dance instructor. The music-hall comic Harry Tate devised a sketch in which he ran a bookmaker's office. A New York client rang to place a bet and, when his horse won, Tate rang back to congratulate him on making a few shillings. Once again telephony was at the mercy of wireless amateurs. In early transmissions, especially on short wave, at least one side of a conversation could be overheard. One victim, a British stockbroker who called daily, had a personal interview with the postmaster-general over an interception. The interloper turned out to be a fellow freemason, who claimed he was trying to prevent the stockbroker being 'done'. Doubts about his claim – he was a bookmaker – made the American development of privacy equipment more pressing.

Young Lydia Scalia had now moved to the Ritz as a 30-shilling (£1.50) a week telephonist:

> The first transatlantic call I did was for a very famous singer and his bill ran into £75 – nearly a year's pay for me – and I was stunned. I was terrified. I thought it would be awful. I ran outside into the cashier's office and told them. They said it was all right... I used to get very excited when we had people like Douglas Fairbanks in. He was in the restaurant once and he had put a call in to Mary Pickford. When it came through he had to walk from the restaurant right the way up the corridor to where the exchange was, just inside the door. I was getting in such a state because I thought all these minutes were being wasted while he – he was quite short – walked slowly up to take the call. Everybody in the hall was agog – Douglas Fairbanks going to talk

to Mary Pickford on the phone. It was so expensive to me but to him it was nothing.

In 1928 the charge was reduced to £9 ($45) for three minutes.

Radio-telephony was on the move. In 1927 the Flying Doctor service, based on pedal radio, was started in Australia. The New York–London service was extended at both ends. On 18 July 1928, for example, Switzerland was connected via London to the USA, Canada, Cuba and Mexico. Within a few years other important but hitherto remote places were joined. In 1929 the link between the Netherlands and its East Indies was opened to the public. In the same year the second transatlantic link went into service, between Madrid and Buenos Aires, where only a few years before a Greek refugee from the Turkish massacres in Smyrna, Aristotle Socrates Onassis, had been a night phone operator. It was reckoned that by listening in to conversations he gathered enough commercial intelligence to start making his first fortune. From Buenos Aires a radio link was later made to New York.

In 1930 western and eastern Australia were connected and the continent was linked to the UK and New Zealand. On an Antarctic expedition the American explorer Admiral Byrd kept in touch with his headquarters at Dunedin, New Zealand, by radio. On his return in March a short-wave connection was made to New York and a two-way conversation held between Byrd in a Dunedin studio and the General Electric station at Schenectady. Global voice communications gave an immediate, personal impact to world events. In 1931 New Zealand began a regular radio-telephone service with the UK, and South Africa was added to the international network, which had grown in spite of the depression. At the beginning of 1927 no subscriber had been able to speak over more than 100 miles of water.

In 1929 Herbert Hoover recognized the pervasiveness of the instrument when he became the first US President to have one permanently on his desk. His predecessors had either had them temporarily – at one time Woodrow Wilson had three – or had entered a booth outside the executive office. In London Jimmy White, the ex-bricklayer turned financier, used to have a phone brought to his table at the Café de Paris in the evenings for dealing on the New York exchange during their afternoon. A rising market added to his appetite and enjoyment. When the crash came, at the end of October 1929, the phone helped to spread panic among the over-eager investors. On Wednesday 23 October, the day before Black Thursday, a sleet storm cut lines from New York to the Middle West, seriously damaging confidence. When the lines were restored, millions of disillusioned investors had much to talk about.

In the few years after 1927 radio-telephony spanned the world.
(BT Museum)

CHAPTER 10

SMALLER NUMBERS

The Wall Street crash was an event; the ensuing Depression a period. From late 1929 the economic situation worsened, reaching a low in 1932 and improving only gradually from 1934. The phone business was less affected than some others but nevertheless over three and a half million subscribers were lost in the USA between 1931 and 1933, about 15 per cent of the phones in service at the end of 1930. Behind that statistic were all the individual stories of lines cut off and people dropping out of society. The phone was a badge of class, one of the distinctions between 'haves' and 'have-nots'. To lose it was to become *déclassé*. There were always public booths, but these were for emergencies and pre-arranged calls, not for when the mood or need arose. Being without the phone was a loss of more than casual chit-chat.

Because of business failures, reduced incomes and unemployment, the Bell System dispensed with nearly 185,000 employees, mainly women switchboard operators. Among the independents, which in the roaring twenties had grown to some 8,500 companies, there were failures and mergers, reducing the total to about 6,000. Many served rural communities and, with the sharp drop in produce prices, the big problem was collecting payments. In lieu of cash, companies accepted items such as chickens, mules, wheat, maple syrup, even the labour of their customers. With this and equipment at low prices, some undertook dial conversion and construction programmes, getting ready for better times. Meanwhile, phone posts served more as handbill hoardings advertising auctions of farm stock, equipment and 'other articles too numerous to mention', often the last few pathetic family possessions, a doll, a couple of books...

Similar trends were reported from other primary producers around the world. At least until 1935 disconnections exceeded connections on South African farmers' lines, some of which stood idle. In Australia the postmaster-general increased provision for bad debts in 1930–1 but business picked up more quickly than elsewhere, partly because canvassers sought new business and persuaded people not to disconnect. In 1932–3 there was a net gain and by 1934–5 the previous highest total of phones, reached in 1930, was exceeded. An innovation the postmaster–general remarked on with satisfaction was 'the arrangement whereby new telephone subscribers in the metropolitan areas and large provincial centres are spoken to by telephone shortly after they are connected, for the purpose of welcoming them to the service and ensuring that they are familiar with the operation of the instrument. Female officers with pleasant personalities and voices were selected for this duty and experience has demonstrated that the innovation is welcomed by new subscribers.'

World recovery was not to come until the Second World War. Until then phone service had to be sold and stay sold. It was not just a demand service to be supplied at customer request. In rural areas sales faced competition from hard roads, automobiles, radios and other electrical appliances. 'Heigh-ho, the dairy-oh, the farmer takes a phone' was the motto of the Bell Canada sales force as it undertook extensive rural canvassing to recover Depression losses. Saskatchewan was unashamed about mixing sentiment and business on its billing envelope:

Four points to keep in mind during February:
1 February 14 is St Valentine's Day.
2 The year 1936 is Leap Year.
3 Any proposal can be made (ever so privately) by Telephone and no matter whether he is at hand or far away.
4 There are cheaper long-distance rates every Sunday all day and also after 7 p.m. each weekday.

During the Depression, to stimulate demand, advertisements appeared like this one from Peninsular Telephone Company in Florida.
(General Telephone Company of Florida)

As late as 1937, on the day of its president's funeral, the Peninsular Telephone Company in Florida, the third largest non-Bell company in the USA, was able to close all its phone offices except the long-distance switchboards, and there a minute's silence was observed.

While the US states with the highest density of phones were losing them, Britons were being made aware of their lack of progress. A 1930 survey showed that the greatest density was not in busy commercial cities but in residential towns. As to be expected, London came first with one phone per 9.2 inhabitants. It was in 1930 that the London phone book last appeared in one volume; the next year it went into two. Second to London was Guildford, a market and dormitory town in Surrey, followed by eight watering-places or seaside resorts: Harrogate, Bexhill, Eastbourne, Bournemouth, Southport, Tunbridge Wells, Worthing and Torquay. One explanation was that their populations fluctuated with the seasons, these places being under-equipped in summer, over-equipped in winter. Way down the list in 44th place was Aberdeen, with one phone per 22.7 inhabitants, and a Scottish reputation for not originating calls. In the granite city phones were said to be for incoming calls only.

From her switchboard Lydia Scalia had a very different view:

> The slump didn't seem to affect the use of the phone by the sort of people who came to the Ritz. The hotel guests were mainly Americans, who were great users. They were never off the telephone when they were in their rooms.

Her switchboard, in the hall until about 1932, when it was moved upstairs away from everybody, was a social spot:

> People used to come in and talk to you. When you got through on their call they were quite excited. If they tipped, it was rare.

Perhaps the switchboard was moved out of reach of high-spirited young gentlemen:

> The college boys were scamps. They'd come in and cut off the telephones, put plugs into different places so that people at the other end were talking to someone else. I used to have to fight sometimes to get them off the phone.

Otherwise, life was ordered:

> The Season would start and go right the way through the summer. You knew exactly who was coming and when: Ascot, Cowes Week and the other social events in the calendar. There was very little to do before 10 o'clock in the morning. At first we only worked one at a time. Then there were two of us on the board. We never bothered about a night operator. One of the porters could deal with what there was, like people going to nightclubs. The winter was quieter.

One person who found the Ritz a refuge was the Duke of Windsor. To evade people on Piccadilly he used to nip in through the swing doors and hide in the booth just inside.

Public facilities were not convenient, as *Standard News*, the employee magazine of Standard Telephones and Cables, observed in July 1930:

> The total number of call offices (including kiosks) at March 31st was 31,091, of which 6,016 were in the London telephone area. This is a figure that we would like to see very greatly increased. Who has not experienced the well-

nigh hopeless task of looking for a public telephone in certain parts of London and, above all, in provincial towns? The new red kiosks are certainly a great improvement on the old type of booth, but there are too few of them and generally it is necessary to search for a small enamel sign, often lost amidst a number of other signs, which denotes that somewhere in the building there is a public telephone. As likely as not the building is shut when you want to use the telephone. The instrument itself may often be found in some public place, where everyone can hear your conversation. Sometimes the telephone is in a small shop. As you enter, the proprietor comes forward from the back room expecting a customer, and when he finds that you merely want to use the telephone, he does not exactly welcome you. Having finished your call, moral cowardice probably forces you to buy something which you do not want, as a sop to the shopkeeper. Undoubtedly there is ample room for improvement in our public telephone facilities.

Of course some people had difficulty in using the phone. A Hampshire butcher always got a number the digits of which were one less than those he dialled – like 756 instead of 867 – because his fingers were so fat. Impatient subscribers helped the dial on its way to save time. Getting 255 could be a problem if you could not find the second 5 on the dial. Then there was the retired colonel who was dashed if he would be dictated to by a lifeless and soulless directory and who jolly well wouldn't remove his receiver before dialling if he didn't want to. Some people wanted to be given meaningful numbers, like the year of their birth, their car registration number, or the date their mortgage would finish. Even better for a London business was to have a seven-letter name that could be spelt out on the dial, but the coincidence of business and exchange names was rare. Novices still gave numbers without exchanges.

Dialling anonymously was a boon to the obscene caller. Prosecution though was not for obscenity, as in the following sample case, reported by *The Times* on 19 June 1930, makes clear:

Improper telephone calls
After a week's remand in custody, Jack Ellis, 39, a printer's clerk, of Felix Street, Lambeth, was sentenced by Mr Fry, at Bow Street Police Court on Tuesday, to one month's imprisonment with hard labour, for fraudulently causing to be consumed the amount of electricity involved in a telephone call and obstructing a girl telephone exchange operator in the course of her duty. It was stated that, in consequence of someone ringing up girls at the Temple Bar telephone exchange and making improper remarks, a special watch was kept. The next time this happened the girl engaged the caller in conversation long enough for an officer to get to the call-box. Mr Fraser, prosecuting, said

that this sort of conduct was very much on the increase, and the Postmaster–General was determined to protect his servants from the nuisance.

Often, while the victim kept the caller talking and engineers in the exchange monitored the line, a policeman had to pedal like fury to catch the offender. The Post Office Act 1908 was amended in 1935 to incorporate the offence of 'molestation'.

For some, the abusive caller, grossly invading privacy, was yet another reason to berate the Post Office. Agitation against its inadequacies continued. In December 1930 the *Daily Express* reported that the Baird Television Company's French subsidiary was co-operating in an experiment to marry phone sound to a television picture on long-distance calls; that the new phone link with Australia cost £6 for three very crackly minutes; and ferociously attacked the Post Office for the 'plodding pace' at which it dealt with demands for new lines. Via the Telephone Development Association, the equipment makers stressed the effects an expanding service would have on employment in many trades, including metal, timber, paint and building. They wrote to the Conservative Prime Minister, Stanley Baldwin, but it was a Labour postmaster-general, Clement Attlee, who in 1930 approved of the first advertising of the phone by the Post Office.

Pressure mounted to such an extent that the government was forced in 1932 to set up a select committee under Lord Bridgeman to examine the Post Office organization. As a result, administrative changes were made but it was the new energetic postmaster-general, Sir Kingsley Wood, who brought a new spirit. Publicity was taken over from the Telephone Development Association (TDA) and he revelled in it, like most of his predecessors seeing his office as a stepping-stone to higher things. Outside Post Office headquarters he was glad to be photographed despatching motor cyclists on a promotional tour. On their sidecars were mounted giant phones. The new 'micro-telephones' or 'hand combination sets' were also available in silver, bronze, ivory, jade green and walnut. Demand trunk working, introduced in 1932, meant it was no longer necessary to book every long-distance call and wait for up to an hour. Most calls could be connected immediately. A 1920 US advance also reduced 'side tone' so that the caller did not hear his own voice too loudly. An advertising campaign was run on a theme originally developed by the TDA: 'You are wanted on the phone'. The slogan was used to frank letters and produced the inevitable story of the old lady who struggled into the village post office from her remote cottage and asked who wanted to speak to her.

Under Sir Stephen Tallents, who transferred to the Post Office from the Empire Marketing Board on its disbandment in 1933, bringing the film unit with him, documentaries were a new medium that was exploited. Titles

Outsize phones were used by the British Post Office in a promotional road show. (BT Museum)

such as *Telephone Workers, The New Operator, Under the City* and *The Coming of the Dial* were not exactly crowd-pullers but talking pictures were still novel enough to get a group together at a women's institute or village hall for free entertainment. In 1935 the Post Office started road shows and by 1937 had six projection units running at large exhibitions and trade fairs. Most productions were educational and suitable for schools. Sometimes the effects were subtle, as in *Song of Ceylon,* where phone conversations are only one of the background voices of business and commerce. Humphrey Jenning's *Speaking from America* was openly didactic about the transatlantic radio-telephone service. Cavalcanti was able to make the installation of a phone line up a Swiss mountain visually and aurally interesting in *Line to Tschierva Hut,* and in a different version with J. B. Priestley, *We Live in Two Worlds.*

The Fairy of the Phone was a humorous musical film, in which only the fairy was a professional actress and the rest of the cast were Post Office employees, telling people who could not be bothered to read the directory preface how to use the instrument. Harry Watt's *North Sea,* based on a real incident among deep-sea fishermen, dramatized the ship-to-shore radio

The judges for the most popular of Britain's phone services, the speaking clock. (BT Museum)

service and was shown in commercial cinemas. Through the GPO Film Unit the talents of directors and producers such as John Grierson and Basil Wright were developed, and, with others, became a national asset. Early in the Second World War the unit was taken over by the government, became the Crown Film Unit, and produced instructional and propaganda films to aid the war effort. Meanwhile Sir Stephen Tallents became the first public relations controller at the BBC, which in 1938 established an enquiry bureau to answer listeners' queries.

For the first time the Post Office was actively selling its phone service. It engaged a firm of consultants to prepare a course in phone salesmanship. Opening with a 96-page handbook looking at selling from the subscriber's point of view, the course ran to six volumes. As in all good selling, the emphasis was on meeting needs and providing benefits, such as not having to go out on a wet day. At first salesmen found it hard, and they came back excited at the prospect of one new subscriber. Soon there were new services to promote, such as the transfer-charge call and the cheap night rate of one shilling (5p) maximum for three minutes anywhere inland between 7 p.m. and 5 a.m., both introduced in 1934 to help boost trunk calls. More long-distance circuits were added. In 1936 three more improvements were made: TIM, the speaking clock, was introduced in London; 'pips' were sounded every three minutes on timed calls; and a new kiosk, the 'Jubilee' model, made its appearance.

Undoubtedly the innovation with most public appeal was the speaking clock. It was not the first in Europe, having been introduced in Paris in 1933, The Hague in 1934, and Switzerland in 1935. New Jersey had had it since 1927. In the first year from 24 July 1936 it registered nearly 13 million calls, fully justifying Post Office efforts to find the Girl with the Golden Voice. All fifteen thousand established women telephonists in England were eligible. Among them was a 24-year old Blackburn telephonist, Kathleen Ferrier, who left school at 14 to work for the Post Office and enjoyed singing in Lancashire concerts. She won several competitions but not this one staged by her employers. Judges for the nine unseen finalists were John Masefield, the poet laureate, Dame Sybil Thorndike, the actress, Lord Iliffe, Stuart Hibberd, chief announcer of the BBC, and Mrs E.D. Atkinson of Burley-in-Wharfedale, representing the perfect phone subscriber. They demanded from competitors a voice that was beautiful in quality, having fullness of tone, with nothing niggardly about it, and nothing rasping in the breathing or in the note. It had to be impersonal, as detached as the voice of a bird, without trace of over-emphasis or personal advertisement, with nothing of the theatrical, and free from accent.

Each finalist had the same test passages: poetry from Milton's *L'Allegro*, prose from *Treasure Island*, and sentences such as were to be used for the talking clock. The winner was Miss Ethel M. Cain from Croydon, a blue-eyed slim blonde in her mid-20s who in her spare time was an amateur actress. She received a prize of ten guineas (£10.50) from the postmaster-general, Major Tryon. Her voice was recorded photoelectrically on a glass disc and played by scanning the disc with a beam of light, like the sound-track of a moving picture. Why so many people wanted the exact time, especially as it was available on the radio, was not clear. Certainly the first of the recorded information services was a striking success.

Better-off people were getting the phone habit and buying items such as directory covers and phone pads in well-known stores. Although it was good etiquette to call before dropping in unannounced, such calls could themselves be an intrusion on privacy. In *Private Lives* (1930) Noel Coward produced the perfect put-down to a caller in the midst of a crisis: 'Madame est partie pour Madagascar.' Somerset Maugham remarked: 'In heaven when the blessed use the telephone they will say what they have to say and not a word besides.' The novelist Norman Douglas sighed for an age when there was a different kind of peace: 'We can hardly realise now the blissful quietude of the pre-telephone epoch.' It was a scientific development that H.G. Wells wanted modified into a 'one-way telephone, so that when we wanted news we could ask for it, and when we were not in a state to receive and digest news, we should not have it forced upon us'. That other prophet of the scientific future, Aldous Huxley, was fortunate in having his wife as an amanuensis to answer calls and take messages.

Not that the habit of using the phone was universal. Evelyn Waugh deplored it, or affected to. Leonard Woolf managed to spend less time talking on it than almost anyone else. His side of a conversation was usually confined to about six monosyllables, after which he rang off. An heroic act spoken of among neighbours but never attempted was to call him and say: 'I just thought I'd ring you up for a chat.' Lady Ottoline Morrell had to emphasize its use, as in a letter of 10 June 1932 asking Ruth Mantz to tea: 'Please *Telephone if you can come.*' In another letter giving a choice of Monday or Friday for tea she asked: 'Could you please telephone which you prefer.' The reply of course would have left no letter for posterity and there were those who bemoaned the decline in the art of letter-writing and the fall in popularity of the postcard. Had the Bloomsbury group, who often dashed off notes to one another several times a day and made great use of the fast penny post, been keener on the phone we should know less about the minutiae of their lives. The blessing is mixed.

A boon to rural areas was the introduction in 1929 of a small automatic exchange, which brought the phone to communities too small even for a postmaster-cum-operator type of exchange. Because night-time calls in manually served rural areas were relatively few, full-time operation was not generally justified. At night, some subscribers could be connected through to a full-time switchboard, though this cost extra. Sometimes the operator had to be woken by a buzzer and, as it was usually for an emergency, subscribers often felt they were waiting an age for an answer. To minimize delay, a postmaster who removed his wooden leg for the night used to slide down the bannisters. For this feat he was paid, like other standby operators, one penny per call.

Automatic exchanges ensured a better night's sleep for operators and, in some ways, improved service. More kiosks were also provided. In 1935, as part of the silver jubilee celebrations of King George V, every village with a post office was to have a kiosk and, to mark the Post Office tercentenary, villages without post offices were also to have a kiosk, under certain conditions. A feature of the new Jubilee kiosk was a small mirror in which users could admire themselves instead of whiling away the time scribbling on the wall and directory. Between 1935 and 1940 the number of kiosks almost doubled, from 19,000 to 35,000.

Bringing phone service to remote areas was hard work for the engineers, still regarded as a rough crew not necessarily deserving motorized transport. Eric Clayton worked in the Norwich area:

Everything had to be manhandled. Men would push the pole-carts laden with stores for miles, erect the route and then walk home again. Fitters would travel for miles festooned with their stores and tools in all weathers and still be expected to be clean in subscribers' houses.

Expansion also meant a greater demand for operators. The parents of Z in Shaw's comediettina *Village Wooing* (1933), based on Mrs Jisbella Lyth, the postmistress of his village Ayot St Lawrence,

> had great ambitions for me. She wanted me to be a parlourmaid in a great house. He wanted me to be a telephone operator. He said there is no future for the great houses and a great future for telephones.

Service was mainly still personal. The community telephonist, often known by name, was a prime source of information and could be a co-ordinator in an emergency. On 7 October 1930 subscribers in Cholderton on Salisbury Plain received a breathless call from their operator telling them that the airship R101 had crashed in France. In the Gloucestershire parish of Down Ampney with Poulton, subscribers often gave or sang to the operator, a good churchwoman, the first line of an *Ancient and Modern* hymn and she would put them through to the right number. Personal service was not always the best. A war-wounded postmaster could be off-colour and his wife was partly deaf:

> Postmistress: Number please.
> Subscriber: I want Salisbury 291.
> Postmistress: What did you say?
> Subscriber: Salisbury 291.
> Postmistress: George, I can't hear what they say.
> Postmaster: Oh well, never mind. Tell 'em the number's engaged.

Cecily Hammond, who, after matriculation, wanted to become a librarian, at 18 was forced by her mother ('It's a good job with a pension, my dear') to become an operator at Tenterden, Kent, later working in the larger town of Ashford:

> When I started it was a part-time job, mornings only. The sort of people who were on the phone were tradespeople, professional services, farmers, the station, bus office, cinema, and those with money. Some calls, like the fishmonger to Grimsby, were so regular you could put them through without asking. Ordinary folk used call boxes... It's a fallacy that telephonists have time to knit. Life was fairly busy. There were a lot of calls in the mornings

concerned with deliveries. Grocers and butchers delivered to people's homes. It wasn't quite so busy in the afternoons and then it picked up again with cheap-rate calls in the evening.

Some people could be exceedingly irritating, never saying please or thank you. There was a social difference between the fairly well-to-do subscriber and the telephonist, although to work in the Post Office was quite a distinction and the subscriber depended upon the telephonist to get the call. Working for the Post Office was like working for a bank. The Post Office didn't take anybody. They were a bit fussy. You felt you had a certain something. Having been to a grammar school I had a reasonable voice and I spoke the King's English. You had to use certain expressions. You couldn't say what you wanted. For instance, you had to say that the line not the number was engaged. You weren't supposed to deviate from the standard phrases. People often didn't ask for numbers but people by name. Forty years later I can still remember the numbers from 1 to about 200 from the manual board. Local people often didn't bother with directories. We knew one another if only by voice. You couldn't be rude to anybody – they'd know who you were. When you went past an address you'd associate it with a telephone number. You knew which people would say something to you and which wouldn't when you were waiting to get a number or whatever. As the exchange got bigger you lost touch with people. You just couldn't remember them all, just those you were asked for most often.

You would go to the ends of the earth to help, say, directory enquiries with local information. For instance, a farm and a farmer's name were often different. There was a great satisfaction in helping people to find a number, especially using your local knowledge. You never gave a preference. If somebody asked for a taxi you gave more than one number and let the caller choose. You could give information like near or far but the Post Office did not want to be seen to be promoting one of its users against another.

At the time of the Munich crisis, when people were digging air raid shelters, everything went mad. I suppose they were making arrangements with their relatives on what they were going to do. I remember somebody being cut off their call in the morning and I didn't get them reconnected until the afternoon. The exchange was bunged up with calls, incoming and outgoing.

Some country folk, like the primitive Starkadders of *Cold Comfort Farm* (1932), carried on undisturbed by such modern conveniences. Bernard Thomas looks back on his life as a lad on the family farm in North Wales in the mid-1930s:

If you needed a vet, it meant a return walk of 14 miles and you took a chance of finding him at home. Curiously, there always appeared to be work for the horses to do at such a time, so that a horse could not be used as transport for calling out a vet.

The same applied if you needed a doctor except that it was only twelve miles return and not fourteen. In cases of childbirth I often felt the baby would be walking before the doctor arrived. In consequence no doctor was ever called; we just managed on our own with the help of herbs and common sense. My mother was one of nine children and I was one of seven.

When it came time for sheep-dipping I would walk four miles to post a postcard to tell the police, who had to be present. A constable would arrive on a bicycle in the afternoon.

At threshing time, usually towards the end of January, as we were at the end of the valley, the engine of the outfit blew its whistle to indicate 'steam up', but owing to the folds in the hills, about four farms were out of reach of the sound. As a result someone had to visit these particular farms (usually me) and tell them we needed help.

Attendances at churches, chapels and funerals were much greater. Such meetings enabled one to exchange news, convey messages and discuss the low (always) market prices, condemn the ruling government policies and grumble about the terrible weather we always seemed to have.

In rural areas the phone was not as much used for law and order as it ought to have been. Police houses were often without it, the force network was patchy, and use was not a habit. In Hitchcock's 1935 film of John Buchan's *The Thirty-Nine Steps*, the sheriff remarks to the police during the arrest of Richard Hannay for murder: 'It'll save you the cost of a trunk call.' Scotland Yard find the phone book useful though to check on the authenticity of his associate Pamela.

The detective stories of Dorothy L. Sayers reflect current usage. In *Busman's Honeymoon* (1937), when Noakes' body is found, PC Sellon has to be fetched by messenger and he in turn summons the superintendent by phoning from the post office. Most calls in *Five Red Herrings* (1931) are made by the police. None of the artists in the Galloway colony is on the phone apparently, and the situation in rural Devon, as depicted in *Have His Carcase* (1932), is even worse. Harriet Vane has to walk for three hours to find one to report the murder of Alexis. Earlier, it takes her six minutes to get an urgent trunk call to a London newspaper, and in *Gaudy Night* (1935) more than once she has to wait as long as 20 minutes for a call from London to Oxford or vice versa, still longer for a call to Rome.

In cities response had to be rapid to catch criminals making a quick getaway by car, especially after 'smash-and-grab' raids. Kiosks themselves were a favourite target, thefts increasing nearly a hundredfold in the bad years of the Depression from late 1931. The 'G-Men of the GPO' had

Skiers at the Swiss resort of St Moritz had the use of an emergency phone while in the UK the introduction of 999 as the emergency number was a gift to cartoonists (OPPOSITE).
(Musee des PTT Suisses, Berne /BT Museum)

alarms fitted in profitable boxes, many in railway and underground stations, so that they could pounce on somebody using keys illegally. Alarms were of limited value, sometimes leading to wrongful arrests. Greater success was achieved by installing more complex locks and leaving simpler combinations as bait. One criminal, Percy Wallis, unlocked coin boxes and waited outside in a 'high-power' car while an accomplice removed the

"PERHAPS, AFTER ALL, THE BROWNS' TELEPHONE NUMBER IS NOT NINE-NINE-NINE, DEAR."

money. If a policeman approached, Wallis slipped the keys into an envelope and posted them back to himself. Convicted for stealing and receiving, he was sentenced to four years' penal servitude.

In 1933 the chief constable of Brighton was experimenting with pocket radio sets, and in London the Flying Squad was keeping in touch with the Scotland Yard information room by wireless. The introduction of '999' calls in the London area in 1937 increased at a bound the percentage of immediate arrests. Broadly speaking, out of every ten emergency calls, six were for the police, three for the ambulance, and only one for the fire brigade.

The '999' idea arose from a Wimpole Street fire in November 1935, when five women lost their lives. A neighbour complained that she had dialled '0' to summon the fire brigade, which arrived before the exchange answered. In fact somebody else had already called the brigade and the exchange staff were busy handling consequent calls. The incident highlighted the fact that an operator could not identify when a call was a matter of life or death. To make assurance double sure, a '999' call caused a large red lamp to glow as well as a special switchboard lamp, and a loud buzzer sounded. One newspaper described it as 'a special buzzer which would do justice to the *Queen Mary* or any other liner in distress'. Such was the noise of this klaxon that some girls had to be carried out. Someone discovered that a tennis ball muffled the mouth of the buzzer adequately and the Post Office ordered local engineers to go out and buy them. They sufficed until adjustable covers were fitted.

People wondered why '999' and not '111', which was quicker to call because the dial had a shorter distance to travel. When fault pulses occurred on a Strowger automatic exchange they could come up as a '1', a succession of them triggering a spate of emergency calls. Numbers beginning between '2' and '5' were allocated to subscribers. Those from '6' to '8' were in general kept for inter-exchange dialling, leaving '9' for essential and emergency services, e.g. '9' and 'T' were the same on the dial so it began TIM for the speaking clock. As '999' originated with fire, great pains had been taken to ensure that it could be dialled in darkness, in smoke, or under trying conditions. Kiosk users also had to be able to dial it without inserting money. This meant modifying dials, on which '0' for operator was already a free call. The simplest and cheapest method was to make the same facility available on the adjacent number, '9', although the two numbers could be manipulated to obtain free calls. On trials in the Guildford area, '999' proved a success. Easily remembered, the general purpose emergency number was extended nationwide, but only Glasgow was added before war broke out.

CHAPTER 11

NEW CONNECTIONS

To business, recovering from the Depression, the instrument was becoming almost essential. Tommy Trinder joked about a theatrical agent who ran his business from a phone box. You could tell how busy he was by feeling the warmth of the box. Out of the office, Beaverbrook ran his papers by phone and scribbled notes; his political opposite Walter Layton by pregnant silences on the phone. A sign of economic recovery was the installation of thirteen more boxes at the Stock Exchange. For the man with a crowded desk, the Post Office introduced the Walligraph, a phone on a flexible metal trellis. Secretarial sets enabled a boss to have his calls filtered, adding to the superiority of both self and secretary, who could become guardian angel or dragon against callers.

Perhaps the business most helped was retail distribution. In Edgbaston, a well-to-do area of Birmingham, maids would phone a shoe shop for pairs of slippers to be sent to madam 'on appro' and the delivery boy would take six to eight boxes of assorted colours in his bicycle basket. The instrument helped corner-shops to compete with a personal service against the growing number of chain stores, which found it handy in day-to-day operations such as reordering items in fashion. An exception was Burton's the multiple tailor, which did not have phones in its branches. The founder, Montague Burton, was an immigrant who started as an outfitter with one shop. By 1929 Burton's was a public company with 400 shops. Burton believed in attracting custom by giving the maximum possible value for money and reducing all unnecessary costs. At a fixed cost, instructions posted from head office could be in a branch the next day. In his personal management of the company though he used the instrument a lot. For many years he conducted the business from his library at home. At the office he had phone points installed on the roof so that he and his secretaries could work in the open air, for which he had a passion.

The cost of calls, especially trunk calls, was a major concern to users. To reduce them, in 1933 Pilkington Brothers had teleprinters installed in its headquarters at St Helens, and in Doncaster, London and Birmingham.

Trunk calls could only be made on urgent business with the permission of the general or departmental manager. Even a company such as Standard Telephones and Cables, largely dependent on the Post Office for its business, did not encourage the use of the phone. Joan Smith, a junior in the patent department, reports:

> There was only one telephone between about 12 people. That was on the supervisor's desk. None of the girls used the phone for normal business.

Selfridge, exploiting the extended possibilities, in 1932 made the first commercial broadcast from London to New York via the transatlantic radio-telephone. Another man who did not think twice about cost was Edgar Wallace. When working on the script of *King Kong* in Hollywood, he frequently called his wife in London or on holiday in Switzerland, finding speech more comforting than letters. A three-minute London call cost $45 (£9) with $14 (£2.80) for each extra minute. When Gerald du Maurier had altered the first two acts of his last play, *The Green Pack*, Wallace dictated a changed third act from Hollywood, the only time he was known to have used the phone for dictation.

At times the phone made the seemingly impossible possible. On 5 November 1930 Sinclair Lewis received a call from a Swedish newspaper correspondent telling him he was the first American to win the Nobel Prize for Literature. Thinking it was a joke, he began imitating the man's accent. The first transatlantic wedding by phone took place between two Swedes on 2 December 1933, an international ceremony reported by among others the *Detroit Free Press*:

> That Cupid works as effectively with modern ohms and kilocycles as with legendary bow and arrow was demonstrated Saturday.
>
> In an office of the Michigan Bell Telephone Co. in Detroit sat Bertil Hjalmar Clason, nervously consulting his watch like any bridegroom on his wedding day. Nearby was Judge John D. Watts, ready to perform the marriage ceremony.
>
> Also present were the witnesses, Bertil's brother and sister-in-law, Ragnar and Moussja Clason, and their daughter, Margarite. The hands on the watch which Bertil stared at ticked towards 9 o'clock, the hour set for the wedding.
>
> In a similar setting in Stockholm, Sweden, sat Sigrid Sofia Margareta Carlson, the blushing bride, also consulting a watch which was ticking toward 3 o'clock.
>
> As the watches reached 9 and 3 o'clock respectively, telephone head-sets were adjusted, operators in Detroit, New York, Stockholm and London closed telephone circuits, radio technicians in Scotland and Maine twiddled gadgets

Guests at the inauguration of the radio-telephone service between Bermuda and the USA on 21 December 1931 heard the first call on individual receivers. One guest remarked: 'Tell Wall Street to get to their offices earlier for there are thousands of orders from Bermuda awaiting them.' An exaggeration in the recovery from the crash of 1929, but the new service did quicken the pace of business and strengthen the Bermudian role as an offshore financial centre. Since 1890 it had relied on undersea telegraph cables for international communications.

(Bermuda Telephone Company)

and ohms and kilocycles whipped the 'I do's' and 'I will's' in Swedish and English across the earth's surface. 'I pronounce you man and wife,' boomed Judge Watts into his transmitter, and Bertil and Sigrid were one.

Bertil met Sigrid last year, while he was visiting Sweden. It was love at first sight. They planned to marry immediately, but before their plans matured, Bertil was recalled to Flint, Mich. to resume his duties as draftsman for the A.C. Spark Plug Co.

Then they planned to be married in Flint as soon as he could bring her to the United States but these plans conflicted with the United States immigration laws. Checkmated in that plan, Bertil consulted Carl Berglund, Swedish consul to Detroit, about the legal aspects of another plan – marriage by trans-Atlantic telephone. Mr Berglund could find no legal obstacles and Saturday's unusual wedding was the result. Intentions were filed in Stockholm according to Swedish law. The marriage licence was issued by the clerk of Genessee County. The ceremony and the attendant conversation took about seven minutes only, four minutes of which was charged to the groom.

The wedding cost him $47.50, considerably less than many conventional weddings. Before long now his bride, coming to the United States in the non-preference quota as his wife, will join him at his home at 1825 Lawndale Ave. Flint.

The groom is 31 years old and the bride 28.

In the bride's parents' home an extra receiver was connected so that the notary public could overhear the ceremony, but in the USA Federal immigration officers regarded the inter-nation hook-up as an evasion of the immigration laws and, later, the Labour Department ruled the long-distance wedding invalid. The ceremony had to be performed again when

AT&T, the world's largest phone company, stressed how accessible the rest of the world was by 1933.

(AT&T Archives)

WEAVING THE WORLD OF SPEECH

DAILY, as upon a magic loom, the world is bound together by telephone. There, in a tapestry of words, is woven the story of many lives and the pattern of countless activities.

In and out of the switchboard move the cords that intertwine the voices of communities and continents. Swiftly, skilfully, the operator picks up the thread of speech and guides it across the miles.

She moves a hand and your voice is carried over high mountains and desert sands, to moving ships, or to lands across the seas. London, Paris, Berlin— Madrid, Rome, Bucharest—Capetown, Manila, Sydney—Lima, Rio Janeiro and Buenos Aires—these and many other cities overseas are brought close to you by telephone.

Every day go messages vital to the interests of nations, the course of international business, and the affairs of individuals.

Great progress has been made in the past few years in extending the scope of this service, in speeding connections and in giving clear transmission. Today, more than 90% of the world's telephones are within reach of your Bell telephone.

AMERICAN TELEPHONE AND TELEGRAPH COMPANY

Sigrid arrived from Sweden in March 1934. At the end of the decade Herbert Farjeon produced a witty revue sketch *Long-Distance Divorce*, in which Hollywood star Sunbud Snowflake is interviewed in bed at 3 a.m. by Fleet Street reporters two months after her marriage.

The first round-the-world phone conversation was held on 25 April 1934 between Walter S. Gifford, president of the American Telephone and Telegraph Company, and T.G. Miller in a nearby office. The call was routed via San Francisco, Java, Amsterdam and London back to New York. Later in the decade one Abe Pickens of Cleveland, Ohio, put in calls to national leaders such as Chamberlain, Franco, Hirohito, Hitler (who, not understanding English, transferred him to an aide) and Mussolini. His efforts made no marked contribution to world peace and cost him dearly, some $10,000.

Nevertheless, the word was getting around. Ibn Saud, founder and first king of Saudi Arabia, persuaded the older sheikhs and guardians of Islamic law that it was not an evil instrument and could carry the word of God. More practically, like radio, it was a means of uniting his new large kingdom, won by conquest. Christian missionaries in places such as Africa found a party line handy for keeping in touch with other residents and with the local Post Office. In 1930 Professor Tsung-tse of Peking noted that Chinese use of English loan-words had grown since the 1911 revolution. The professor presented only a meagre list but H. L. Mencken found equivalents for four Americanisms: poker, vaseline, charleston and telephone (te-lu-feng). In the decadent Berlin of Christopher Isherwood's stories, realized in the film *Cabaret*, phones between nightclub tables were used for soliciting. For exchange operators though conditions were strict. They had to be of German nationality, aged between 18 and 30, single, or widowed without children, debt-free, and at least 156cm tall. Their detailed instructions on handling callers included what to say if men asked them out to dinner.

Differences in the pace of development were marked. Half the world's 38 million phones in 1937 were in the USA. New York City had more than all France, with its population of 42 million. In Times Square booths, some of the directories wore out every four days. Two of the city's office buildings had as many phones as the whole city in the early 1890s. Chicago had more than all South America, and Los Angeles more than Africa. Endless such statistics were evidence of American superiority. Yet it was not one big system. There were hundreds of 'mom and pop' companies serving local communities, and in San Francisco the Chinese colony had its own pagoda-like exchange, its interior in red, black and gilt. Directory characters were brush-written and photographed for printing. Locals insisted on calling by name not number so operators had to relate the names and numbers of some two thousand five hundred subscribers. The net cultural effect of the phone though was to help spread English as the international language. Not that people rushed to make international calls in the wake of the Depression.

Even at sea one was in touch. Radio communications were used commercially between ship and ship and ship-to-shore in 1925 when Antarctic whalers were equipped with radio-telephones. So successful were they that whale catches had to be restricted. Experiments were made in the mid-1920s on cross-Channel steamers but the Atlantic offered more to all parties. The first conversation between the normal phone service on land and a ship at sea was from the *Berengaria* to Trappes, France, in 1929.

The first commercial radio-telephone service began on 14 February 1930 between the White Star liner *Majestic* and the UK. The *Evening Standard* commented: 'Shoe-lane, E.C., spoke to the ship in mid-Atlantic as easily as a call goes through from the City to the suburbs.' And the captain told the paper: 'What passengers regard as one of the greatest advantages is that they do not need to put any "tuppences" in the box, and that if they are not connected with the person on shore to whom they desire to speak, no charge is made.'

The service soon extended to other liners and Western European nations. 'Hello folks!' ran one advertisement. 'I'm speaking from the Atlantic. Why not a wonder talk – through space – with your friends?' At the Ritz, Lydia Scalia found: 'It was very exciting talking to the ships in the Atlantic. Again Americans. The British were afraid of the cost for one thing.' They could always wait until docking at Southampton, when links to shore were soon established and calls cheaper.

A new era in undersea salvage was started by the lure of over £1 million in gold and silver aboard the P&O liner *Egypt*, since her 1922 collision with a French cargo ship, lying in 360 feet of water. To operate at this depth, where the pressure would have crushed a diver in a flexible suit, an Italian company used a rigid chamber equipped with a phone. From this, on 30 August 1930, a diver confirmed the identity of the wreck, located by sweeping the sea-bed with a cable for 15 months after five years of failure by others.

The precious metal was salvaged solely by diver's orders. He instructed the crew above when to lower explosives or drop grabs: 'A little to the right – to the left – six inches farther out.' It was a slow process and it depended entirely on what the diver could see below and the careful, quick response above. The final haul was landed in July 1935. Never before had gold been recovered from such a depth. In 1934 a deep-sea diving record of 3,028 feet was established in a steel bathysphere, and strange fishes were described to expedition members on the surface.

A 1931 cover of a French popular science journal depicts the replacement of the operator by an automatic switch.

(Collection Historique, France Télécom)

To the populace at large, phones were still remote and sophisticated devices more likely to be read about, admired or laughed at on stage, screen and wireless than experienced firsthand in the home. In the USA in 1930 Coca-Cola used a picture of a girl making a call ('Meet me at the soda fountain') on its tin-plated serving trays, but to the British public the phone was the kind of convenience the King and Queen had on their special train during their visit to Canada in 1939. Italians used the term 'telefoni bianchi' to describe the elegant light-coloured interiors of the period characterized by white phones, first seen in the 1931 film *La Segretaria Privata*. Avoiding serious issues, these escapist films were acceptable to the Fascist censor. They went with the silken boudoirs and ritzy furnishings of the Hollywood dream world. That it was a shallow world was not immediately apparent. In Canada the affluent could get coloured sets in ivory, grey, statuary bronze, and oxidized silver. The paint, only sprayed on to the metal, chipped easily. A lot of maintenance was required to keep them looking impressive.

Phones, far from being inanimate instruments, were almost characters in themselves, and the talkies exploited their many moods. They could carry the disappointing message that 'Miss Otis Regrets'. From 1936 it was one of 'These Foolish Things'. Britain's ambassador of song, Al Bowlly, loved to look 'In My Little Red Book'. About the same time the French were singing 'Tous va très bien, Madame la Marquise', in which the butler assures her when she calls that everything is fine, except that her grey mare has died, and… until finally he admits that the chateau has burned down.

In 1930 Dorothy Parker wrote a short story *A Telephone Call*, a woman's anguished prayer for her lover to call, and Jean Cocteau's one-act monologue *La Voix Humaine* was staged by the Comédie Française. A jilted girl holds an interrupted conversation with her lover and, as he slips from her, the instrument becomes her lifeline and then a means of symbolic suicide. She wraps the cord around her neck. In the 1932 film *If I Had A Million*, a millionaire picked eight beneficiaries at random from the phone book, and in *Grand Hotel* Greta Garbo played a love scene to the instrument. In Hollywood, studio extras never left their phones unguarded, even having long extension cords to the john, in case central casting called. New York's most exclusive exchange, BUtterfield 8, gave John O'Hara the title for his second novel, about a young call girl, Gloria Wandrous. She can be picked up on the phone or her calls to clients deliberately not answered. Assignations are made, a message not passed on. In the background, the instrument is part of the web of city life, used by young and old, by rich and poor.

A novel use developed during the decade was in judging contestants on a national radio show, Major Bowes' *Amateur Hour*. In selected cities banks of operators recorded votes and sent them to the New York studio, boosting

Where else could you buy 'Three Minutes of Heaven'? (BT Museum)

"Meet me at the soda fountain"

Drink Coca-Cola
Delicious and Refreshing

The Coca-Cola Company, Atlanta, Ga.

MUCH depends upon a good start. That's why women meet so often at a cool and cheerful soda fountain to begin shopping and marketing—to pause to join friends and be refreshed with an ice-cold Coca-Cola. This pause that refreshes puts all on good terms with themselves and with the world. ▼ ▼ ▼ There's a cheery top-of-the-morning feeling in a glass of ice-cold Coca-Cola. A tingling, delicious taste. A cool after-sense of refreshment. A perfect blend of many flavors, it has a flavor all its own.

THE BEST SERVED DRINK IN THE WORLD Served in its own thin, crystal-like glass. This glass insures the right proportions of Coca-Cola syrup and ice-cold carbonated water. The final touches are to add a little finely chipped ice and stir with a spoon until the sparkling bubbles bead at the brim.

IT HAD TO BE GOOD OVER 8 MILLION A DAY TO GET WHERE IT IS

By the 1930s phones were established in American popular culture. This advertisement appeared in The Saturday Evening Post *on 1 June 1929.* (Archives of the Coca-Cola Company)

audience participation and heightening the tension of the event. How accurate this method was in measuring popularity was another matter. In 1936 the *Literary Digest* predicted from its phone poll that the Republican candidate Alf Landon would beat President Roosevelt by a landslide. The

Jean Cocteau's 1930 monologue La Voix Humaine *has attracted many actresses, among them Hildegard Knef.* (Siemens Museum)

result was the reverse. Two-thirds of US households did not have phones and the prediction was unrepresentative. Theoretically in touch with the world at large, phone owners were not necessarily aware of what was going on out there. Extra operators had to be called in rapidly in many places on Sunday, 30 October 1938, when Orson Welles broadcast his radio fantasy *War of the Worlds*, supposedly reporting a Martian invasion and causing frightened listeners to flood switchboards with frenzied enquiries.

In *The Summing Up* (1938), Somerset Maugham noted:

> The drama pictures the manners and customs of the day, and in its turn affects them, and as these change minor changes follow both in the trappings and in the themes. The invention of the telephone, for instance, has made many scenes redundant, has quickened the pace of plays and has made it possible to avoid certain improbabilities.

Other people, places, events and moods could be electrically transported, instantly, on the spot, without clumsy stratagem. The technique was well used by Noel Coward, himself a great phone user, in the 1936 *Hands Across the Sea*, a one-act lampoon on those much-travelled socialites the Mountbattens. A comic-strip character first appearing in *Action Comics* in

1938 had only to enter a phone booth to transform himself into Superman, emerging to defy gravity and other physical and social limitations in his unceasing fight against evil. In 1939 Hollywood celebrated the original invention of the phone with *The Story of Alexander Graham Bell*, with Don Ameche playing the title role. Disowning a native inventor, the UK screened it as *The Modern Miracle*.

Seth, the Emperor of Azania in Evelyn Waugh's *Black Mischief* (1932), when deciding on the design of his Victory Medal to be struck by Mappin and Webb of London, wanted on the reverse the figure of Progress holding in one hand 'some small object symbolic of improved education... a telephone might do.'

Previously communications in his empire had been hampered by tribesmen pulling down lengths of copper telegraph wire to adorn their women. Jeanne de Casalis, a revue artiste, in 1934 appeared at the Alhambra in a sketch entitled *Mrs Feather*, an appropriate name that became known to millions through the wireless, where her phone was easily imagined. In the 1934 story *Death at Broadcasting House*, in which an actor is strangled while on the air, a six-minute call from Brighton gave the murderer an alibi.

On 22 January 1934 Sir Edward Elgar supervised a recording of his work from his sick-bed in Worcester by phone to the No. 1 Studio at Abbey Road, where the London Symphony Orchestra was assembled. After Gramophone Company staff had set up their equipment, tested it and moved it into his sick-room at 3.45 the plan was:

> 4.0 p.m. The orchestra will play through to Sir Edward Elgar the complete *Triumphal March* lasting 9 minutes, after which we will hear Sir Edward's comments and corrections. We will then record each side once in duplicate. After the recording of each side, Sir Edward will be asked if he is satisfied with the performance.
>
> Should time permit, a repeat recording will be made of the *Dream Children* and *Woodland Interlude* made earlier in the afternoon, in each case obtaining Sir Edward's comments.

No connection was made until 4.15, by which time he was impatient, but the novelty perked up the drugged and dying composer, who made comments improving on the performances. Later, in his clear moments, he recalled the hour with great pleasure.

A. E. Housman, who detested modern conveniences, lived without a phone in Whewell's Court, Trinity College, Cambridge, but when he moved on 18 November 1935 into new rooms, B2 in Great Court, he had one installed for summoning help in an emergency. By then he had less than six months to live. Another Cambridge man concerned about the proximity of the system was Sir Montague Butler, Master of Pembroke – a conveniently situated pole helped undergraduates climb into college after hours. The local phone manager explained that moving the pole was impossible, so barbed wire was liberally applied. At Oxford a rule in Lady Margaret Hall was that 'undergraduates may not telephone women students except between 2 and 3 p.m.'

Exposure to germs again became a public issue after the subject was artificially and briefly stimulated in late 1930, when a few petty crooks posed as Post Office or Ministry of Health officials – they sometimes gave themselves away by being too well-dressed – and tried to fit outlawed glass mouthpieces to subscribers' phones to make a few shillings in hard times. A new distinction was drawn by Dr J. T. Smeall of Edinburgh Royal Infirmary, who discovered from swabs taken from 75 phones in the city in 1937 that there is 'a great difference between the bacterial content of the mouth-piece of the hand telephone and that of the instrument with the ear and mouth-pieces separate'. His explanation for the difference was that the transmitter of the hand phone was in a 'dependent position' so that 'aided by gravity the droplets from the speaker find a suitable nidus'. As the other type of phone was used in a horizontal position, it was less likely to retain any projected bacteria. Smeall's conclusion was that, even though 'pathogenic organisms' were present, the risk of infection was 'somewhat remote' because there was no actual contact with the mouthpiece. Nevertheless, he had a good word for the 'careful people [who] partially cover the mouthpiece with their hand and speak through the gap between thumb and forefinger'. Although it was not within Smeall's brief, there was another advantage of the separate earpiece: its use to the hard of hearing. They could put it against their hearing aid, a fairly bulky device often worn on the chest and concealed by a cardigan. In 1938 an amplifier was promoted for deaf subscribers.

European telephone administrations exchanged health information with American Bell, which faced a similar problem, made worse by advertisements designed to arouse public fears and promote the sale of disinfectants and sterilizing services. The verdict of the largest phone operating company in the world was unequivocal: 'This combined attention, both inside and outside the telephone business, and the experience with millions of telephones used each day for tens of millions of conversations, have not produced one authenticated case of disease transmission by the use of the telephone.'

Doctors pointed out that phones were a relatively insignificant source of contamination; that germs could be picked up publicly from money, door knobs, straps, handrails, library books and other inanimate objects; that most germs were short-lived; that the danger of disease transmission from inanimate objects was far less than from the living human carrier of infection; that, even if routine disinfection were justified, ideally a mouthpiece would have to be wiped after every conversation. A perfectly adequate measure was to wipe the mouthpiece with a damp cloth, taking care not to get water in the instrument. Responsible statements like this did not lessen the appeal of sterilizing companies. At least they left behind a nice smell and people not paying the bill could feel that it was a good thing.

Not even the Post Office was above playing on people's nerves. 'Fears and doubts thrive well in the home where the telephone is not', it said, depicting in the advertisement a husband distraught because his wife has not returned from a visit to friends. Another advertisement put forward the suggestion that anxious parents could use it to check with school on whether their children had left or were being kept in. This lapse in taste was sharply criticized in Parliament in 1936.

Children making a call, especially if they were from working-class backgrounds, often found the phone scary. A lad clutching his tuppence to make his first call, an emergency one to a doctor for a neighbour, was to remember vividly his frantic reading of the instructions in the call box. Phyllis Willmott, a grammar school girl who had learned with a boyfriend's help to make calls from a kiosk, as a junior assistant at the Times Book Club was 'by no means at ease in handling incoming calls on a private telephone... During the first few days I was stricken with panic every time the phone rang; the blood rushed to my face and my hands grew clammy with fear.'

The instrument was in many ways as unreal as the wristwatch phone, complete with TV screen, used by the comic-strip hero Dick Tracy. It was posh people, people with cars, who had phones. They were the sort of things presented to the Duke of York for his children, Elizabeth and Margaret. The *Daily Express* ran an advertisement in mid-1938 for changing the colour of your black phone, but the down-market 'cheese dish' celluloid covering for the base and the strip to wind round the handle were not very popular.

When Mass-Observation surveyed the way ordinary Britons went about their daily lives it never included the phone as a subject. Between 1930 and 1940 the number of phone subscribers grew from almost 1.2 million to just over 2 million. By 1940 total residential connections outnumbered business subscribers for the first time. Wireless though had a much greater appeal. Licences issued during the decade grew from just over 3 million to nearly 9 million. They did not obliterate the Electrophone service immediately. As late as 1937 two Bournemouth subscribers, Mrs Cooper and Mrs

Hatchcock, were still connected to local church services. On 18 October 1938 a Post Office memo briefly recorded the demise: 'It is understood that no subscribers are now connected to the Electrophone service anywhere in the country. No new subscribers will be accepted.'

There were occasions when the phone was apparently crucial. Twenty years after its significance had been seen in the October Revolution in St Petersburg, it was shown to be of similar importance for the communists wanting to wrest power from the anarchists in Barcelona during the Spanish Civil War. Controlling the exchanges, the anarchists were able to listen in to calls and cut people off. When visited by the communist chief of police during the siesta on 3 May 1937, they opened fire down the stairs. The situation escalated, opposing groups took sides, and by nightfall Barcelona was a city at war, even though a truce had been agreed at the exchange. Shooting in what was regarded as the centre of the city sparked off a trial of strength that lasted on and off for five days. It was a turning point. Thereafter the struggle was clearly one between two states, the republican and the nationalist. One way the communists recognized the situation in practice was by forbidding intercity calls.

Salvador Dali, the Spanish Surrealist, from 1936 to 1938 went through a phone period, which seemed to emphasize both the importance and the unattainability of communications. His *Lobster Telephone* (1936) consists of an ordinary phone that for its handset has a larger plaster lobster. A plain instrument in a precise dream landscape occurs in four 1938 paintings: *Imperial Violets, The Sublime Moment, Mountain Lake* and *Debris of an Automobile Giving Birth to a Blind Horse Biting a Telephone*. In retrospect, the most significant painting was *The Enigma of Hitler* (1937), which with some disregard for historical accuracy Dali later claimed in his autobiography *The Secret Life* 'constituted a condensed reportage of a series of dreams obviously occasioned by the events of Munich' (September 1938). Perhaps he was referring to the ineffective calls of the British Prime Minister, Neville Chamberlain, to Hitler over the changing political map of Central Europe.

In March 1938, on a German ultimatum, the Austrian Chancellor Kurt von Schuschnigg was replaced by the local Nazi Arthur Seyss-Inquart, who invited the German Army to occupy his country and proclaimed union with Germany. Three days earlier, warning of the event reached the British Foreign Office from Cairo, where a German general's phone was intercepted. Fully aware of his own role in the Anschluss, Seyss-Inquart commented: 'I am only an historical telephone operator.' His self-revelation was a euphemism for a messenger-

An ordinary 1930s phone, made on an Antwerp production line, was transformed by Salvador Dali into a work of art bought by the Tate Gallery in 1981 for £20,900. It was originally owned by an eccentric patron of the arts, Edward James.

(Lobster Telephone by Salvador Dali, 1936, ©DEMART PRO ARTE BV/DACS 1991. Tate Gallery)

boy, and his action drove people anxiously to the phone. In the Netherlands inland calls were restricted to three minutes and calls abroad to six minutes. After that, they were simply cut off. Jewish refugees who had fled from Hitler called relatives still in Germany and, safe in places such as London, often heard the reverberations in an empty room that were more eloquent than the non-committal replies to their questions: their families had been stripped of their possessions, which had perhaps contemptuously been thrown into the street. Equally contemptuous were the transcripts of calls from Czechoslovakia that Hitler made available to the British Foreign Office during the Munich negotiations. Communications to London and Paris from Czechoslovakia, his next target for occupation, went via Berlin, and interception was easy.

Meanwhile, British government departments had been preparing for wartime communications. Tapping of phones, hitherto requiring the authority of the postmaster-general, from 1937 had to be authorized by a Secretary of State. To combat the enemy within, there was an increase in the interception of mail, and in tapping: 17 taps were authorized by the Home Secretary in 1937, 20 in 1938, and 29 in 1939. Surveillance of Communist Party headquarters, begun in the 1920s, continued. Party members and 'fellow travellers' could have been plotting subversion in the armed services and industry. In 1938 sound insulation in House of Commons call boxes was improved, and some changes were made in the Rome and Berlin embassies, where security had been notably lax.

A War Office committee set up to examine army communications needs in wartime concluded that the number of phones would have to be severely limited. After the first few months of the Second World War, it soon became evident that demand had been underestimated and the number of circuits had to be increased. Fortunately, a more enlightened approach had been taken to the Defence Telecommunications Network (DTN), a hush-hush project dubbed, by those who knew, 'Don't Tell Nobody'. In early 1937 it was estimated that the Post Office could meet the demands of all three fighting services. By the end of the year it was clear that the demand from the Royal Air Force alone, partly because of its use of radar to warn of approaching enemy aircraft, had grown beyond capacity. So work began on a new network with alternative routeings connecting Fighter and Anti-Aircraft Commands with observation posts, airfields, gun and searchlight centres. Originally due for completion within three years, much of it was ready for the Battle of Britain in 1940.

CHAPTER 12

ON ACTIVE SERVICE

The Second World War, a more mechanized, active and complex conflict than the First World War, was to be fought on a global scale. In making use of intelligence and in the mobilizing of forces, on the home and battle fronts, communications played a much greater role. At first it did not seem so. Following the flurry of activity on the outbreak of war on 3 September 1939, which coincided with the busy Labour Day weekend in North America, the 1939–40 winter was a time of 'phoney war'. In the opinion of one British phone operator: 'It didn't make such an impact on us as the Munich Crisis.' Was it really necessary to suspend the transatlantic service? After the initial shocks of the declaration of war, the mobilizing of the services, and the evacuation of children, the British people waited for something to happen.

It did, with lightning suddenness, in spring 1940. Hitler's *blitzkrieg* secured Denmark and Norway in April, in May the Netherlands and Belgium, and in June France. Poor communications vitiated the efforts of Allied forces against the German onslaught. When the British Expeditionary Force (BEF) went to the Continent it intended to establish its own communications network. In the event it had to rely mainly on the public system. Ordinary subscribers' phones were requisitioned, not the easiest or most satisfactory way of getting urgent messages through. Military users competed for lines with a nervous and panicked populace. Language was a problem: many Belgian and French operators did not speak English. To ease this frustration, British operators were moved into civilian exchanges; to ensure priority, sections of some main exchanges were commandeered for military use.

Nevertheless, they were all makeshift arrangements on what were not the most reliable of networks, especially when the BEF was in rapid retreat. Calls between units on the move became practically impossible. Field cables laid during the advance were not necessarily in the best position for organizing retreat. Sometimes public call boxes had to be relied upon.

Movement on roads was slowed by the masses of refugees, horse-drawn traffic, vehicle wrecks and machine-gunning from the air. Trying to wend their way through all this were messengers, officers in cars, leather-jerkined despatch riders on motor cycles. Confusion was worse than among the German forces during the crucial 1914 battle for Paris. Messages were delayed, did not get through, or were garbled.

On the morning of 29 May, the day after King Leopold of the Belgians capitulated, Lord Gort, BEF commander-in-chief, moved his headquarters to the seaside resort of La Panne, just inside the Belgian border. Across the border was Dunkirk. La Panne, with its royal holiday villa, had a modern exchange on the route between London and Brussels, so that the King could keep in touch with the London Stock Exchange via the Channel cable. On this, Gort, cut off from the military high command in Paris and naval headquarters in Dunkirk, made his own arrangements with the War Office in London for an evacuation through Dunkirk. Gort drove there and told the French commander, who had no phone links to anywhere, what was to be done. By 4 June nearly 340,000 men, 225,000 of them British, were evacuated under land and air bombardment. A military disaster was turned into a morale booster. The 'Dunkirk spirit', which had originated in a flurry of cross-Channel phone calls, was a shining example of British improvisation that was often to be invoked.

That summer, communications again played a largely unnoticed role in a pivotal event, the Battle of Britain. Having subdued France but unable to secure peace with Britain, Hitler planned to invade. Before he could carry out Operation Sea Lion, he had to establish air superiority over the Channel. Fighter Command was outnumbered when the Battle of Britain began but pilot skills and technical advantages were to beat Goering's Luftwaffe. For one thing British radar could 'see' German planes coming before they reached the coast. The information was relayed to RAF operations rooms and airfields, and kept up to date by the Royal Observer Corps, which reported enemy movements past the chain of coastal radar stations.

The Post Office and its contractors had to extend and maintain the communications network, the nerve system of an embattled society now imbued with the Dunkirk spirit. Links had to be provided to new airfields and many overhead lines put underground to remove 'a flying hazard'. One such was that from the cliff top to Beachy Head lighthouse. More than once it was brought down by a German plane trying to fly below the radar, but putting it under the sea would have been expensive and difficult. Trailing cables or drifting barrage balloons often damaged overhead lines, isolating exchanges. In the Norwich area up to the end of 1940 more damage was caused in this way than by enemy action. No time could be lost in effecting repairs. Getting the right information to the right place in time enabled the best use to be made of the precious resources of planes and pilots when Britain was menaced as she had not been since Napoleon. The concerted effort worked. The final tally was 1,733 aircraft lost by the Luftwaffe, with 3,089 aircrew, and RAF casualties of 915 and 503 aircrew. By mid-September Hitler abandoned Operation Sea Lion.

To the British people, invasion was still a threat. Spies could be in their midst gathering intelligence about troop movements, bomber bases and convoy sailings. To combat the fifth column, the Ministry of Information used the campaign theme 'Careless talk costs lives'. One Fougasse poster showed a man in a call box saying 'But for Heaven's sake don't say *I* told you!' Around the box several Hitler heads were listening. The Canadian government also used the 'careless talk' theme in a picture-strip poster. It started with a soldier telling his sweetheart on the phone about a troop train and continued with a spy calling a saboteur. Although Canada was remote from the battlefront, the loyalty of some immigrants was uncertain.

'Tittle-tattle lost the battle' was another British government slogan of 1940, but it was the 'careless talk' that made the most impression. Mrs R. B. Hallaway recalls her patriotic use of the phrase:

> While manning a telephone I somehow dialled into a private conversation. The mention of an RAF base riveted my attention and within a few seconds it was obvious that two women were discussing the whereabouts of their serving menfolk. Assuming a sepulchral voice, I interposed 'careless talk'. The women gasped and whispered to each other: 'Did you hear that?' I repeated the warning. One woman instantly rang off; the other stammered out profuse apologies: 'I am so sorry. I did not mean to do it.' I repeated the warning 'Careless talk costs lives' and replaced the receiver.

For its part the government, along with the services, was using 'scrambling' devices for classified calls. Users at each end of the line pressed a button so that they worked in both directions. The Post Office and its suppliers had been developing them for the Defence Communications Network (DTN). Part of DTN was the installation deep beneath Whitehall of lines to government departments and to the bomb-proof bunker into which Churchill could descend from 10 Downing Street. From a cubicle that looked like a lavatory, he held pre-arranged telephone conferences with President Roosevelt in Washington (although Churchill far preferred the written to the spoken word). So huge was the advanced scrambler, imported from American Bell in 1943, that it had to be housed in Selfridges' annexe basement. It was not brought into use until May 1944, up to which time the Germans were freely intercepting inadequately

Having the longest undefended frontier in the world, the 49th Parallel, Canada was particularly concerned about the infiltration of spies. To warn people of the menace, in 1940 the government issued posters in the country's two languages, English and French.

(Canadian War Museum)

scrambled calls, sometimes making inaccurate translations, as in reading a reference to a meeting at Casablanca to mean The White House. The new scrambler, totally secure, was switched on exactly one month before the D-Day invasion of Europe. In the command centre red and green (scrambled) phones bore the warning 'No Speech On Telephone Is Secret'. It was the sort of warning that could have been heeded by de Gaulle, who in 1941 openly gave the dates of an African trip on a transatlantic call.

For nearly three months in 1940 Roosevelt was recording Press conferences and some private conversations in the Oval Office, using a microphone hidden in his desk lamp and in the basement a motion picture type of recorder. Probably his purpose was an accurate record for self-defence rather than some Machiavellian scheme. His secret wire-tapping directive of May 1940 encouraged the FBI under J. Edgar Hoover to step up internal surveillance, not just of Germans suspected of being Nazi sympathizers or Japanese on the West coast. Abroad, especially in Latin America where the Axis powers enjoyed local support, the State Department had phone and cable traffic monitored. In Britain, authorized tappings jumped from 29 in 1939 to 125 in 1940 and a peak of 180 in 1941. Between 1941 and 1944 the Ministry of Food was granted warrants – internally a Home Office warrant was called a 'how' – for the interception of 31 phones, presumably to check on black-market operations. Tappings were not to fall below 100 until the war ended in 1945.

The Security Service MI5 found setting up cumbersome equipment in holes and corners to record dial movements and conversations irksome. It was much easier to tap phones of those suspected of disloyalty, people such as Rajani Palme Dutt, the Communist intellectual, and Ismay Ramsay. She and her husband, the Conservative MP Captain Archibald Ramsay, were leaders of the Right Club, which had lists of people to be hanged from lamp-posts when the Germans invaded. Some members of the club were also passing secrets. Associated with them was Tyler Kent, a cypher clerk at the American Embassy in London who was leaking to the Germans details of secret cables between Churchill and Roosevelt. Anti-Semitic, anti-communist, Kent wanted the information released in the USA, where Roosevelt was reassuring the electorate that he was not going to embroil them in another European war. Arrested on 20 May 1940, Kent was held incommunicado until his trial *in camera* at the Old Bailey. He was sentenced two days after Roosevelt's re-election and deported in 1945.

In general, less was discovered about subversive organizations from phone taps than from infiltrating their groups. Robert Pollard, a Quaker conscientious objector and solicitor who represented other objectors such as the composer Michael Tippett at appellate tribunals, commented:

My office telephone was probably tapped. I have no proof of it but you could sometimes hear a click. All they would have got were girls' conversations with their boyfriends.

Not only separated lovers wanted to keep in touch. Since 1936 government policy had been to disperse vital industries into 'shadow' factories away from vulnerable centres. Large firms kept in constant contact with subcontractors, supervising daughter firms turning out war materials to specification. Deliveries were urgent to win the war. Working all hours, chasing progress, people who pre-war were restricted in using the phone now got into the habit of long-distance calls, regardless of cost. Government contracts were cost-plus anyway. Why not use the phone?

It was an essential part of emergency plans, as Margaret Powell remembered:

> We had all received warnings that in the event of a German parachutist invading our home we were to give him no help if he was wounded nor make him a cup of tea. We were to telephone the police. Leaving aside the fact that hardly any of us were on the phone – and what would the parachutist be doing while we rushed out to look for one – we were all determined that if the German threatened to shoot our children, we'd make him all the tea he could drink.

Further up the social scale the phone had its daily value. In Angela Thirkell's 1943 novel *Growing Up*, Sir Harry Waring's dinner is interrupted by half a dozen phone calls from friends and acquaintances:

> And so the county news came filtering in, from one marooned homestead to another. Such was the press of news after seven o'clock that Palmyra (called after Mrs Palmer) Phipps at the telephone exchange was often able to give a subscriber who couldn't get through to a friend the exact information she needed.

Lydia Scalia had returned to the Ritz:

> There was always an operator on duty at night. We had to warn people if there was a raid. When we heard the siren we let everybody know so that they could go downstairs. We were on the seventh floor and stuck. Run as fast as you could and you could never get more than two floors. The guests were mainly service people and there weren't that many of them... The only people who were concerned about the telephonist on duty were American servicemen. They used to come rushing up to see if you were all

What better place to leave a message than on the phone! Staff of the Prudential, Britain's biggest insurance company, did when they moved from the City of London to hotels at Torquay in the West of England.
(Prudential Corporation)

right. We used to duck down behind the switchboard. They'd ask us to go downstairs.

Large air raid shelters were equipped with phones.

Brenda Skinner started as a telephonist in Crawley, Sussex, in 1939, when the Post Office took on extra staff:

> There were about seven of us at the beginning of the war. Then the staff grew to four men on nights and ten to twelve day telephonists. By the end of the war the staff had more than doubled. More boards were brought into use with the extra work created by the services. Gatwick Airport was taken over by the RAF, which had its own switchboard for station calls. Detachments of Canadian troops were not far away. There was also more work in emergencies, dealing with police, fire, ambulance, ARP [Air Raid Precautions] wardens, doctors and so on. We tended to carry on during air raids and also did our turns at fire-watching. When a doodlebug cut out we sheltered behind the switchboard away from the windows. One of the problems in emergencies was dealing with people who weren't used to using the phone. They tended to shout, especially the very old or very young. Some forgot to press Button A. The telephonist could hear the caller but not *vice versa*.

Gulley Jimson, the impoverished painter of Joyce Cary's *The Horse's Mouth* (1944), took advantage of such ignorance: 'I never pass an empty telephone box without going in to press button B. Button B has often been kind to me.' More ingenious was a specially made wooden peg inserted into the 'O' to prevent the dial returning completely, the one-eighth of an inch overlap allowing a free call. A Navy call box at Lee-on-the-Solent was reckoned to hold the record for the highest calling rate and the lowest cash receipts.

After the wireless, the phone had arrived as a necessary means of communication. To provide the service that pre-war they could not afford, farmers erected their own poles and wires. Conversion to automatic working, in places delayed by the Depression, continued. In Liverpool, for instance, new exchanges replaced the manual ones bombed in May 1941. Such was the demand for phones that in 1942 the Post Office introduced shared service on automatic exchanges, and the telephonist's job became a reserved occupation. An indirect contribution to the war effort was waste paper. When scouts delivered new directories they collected the old ones for salvage.

Expanded and busier though the service was, personal contact was not lost and local knowledge still important. A Palmyra Phipps often came to the rescue. When Lady Waring was trying to get through to the nearby hush-hush camp, she could not remember the number, and the new girl on the exchange refused to tell her what it was or connect her. Palmyra came on the line:

'Is that you Lady Waring?... Was it the Dower House that you wanted?'... 'I'll put you through at once, my lady. Who was it you wanted?'

Lady Waring said Colonel Winter.

'My sister, the one that's got triplets, used to be second housemaid at Mr Carter's house at Southbridge School,' said Palmyra, 'and she says Mr Winter as he was then was ever so nice, but a very quick temper. He was engaged to Miss Rose, but they broke it off. Just one moment, my lady.'

New girls like Brenda Skinner took a while to get used to the working conditions:

We wore heavy bakelite headsets, which caused perspiration. At first I used to get a build-up of wax in the ears, which dried out. I had to have my ears syringed every three to six months for two to three years. We sometimes wore overcoats, either because there was a shortage of fuel or there was an emergency.

There was also a special gas mask for operators, with a built-in receiver so that they could work in a gas attack.

In 1942 the New England Telephone Company employed married women for the first time. Service personnel throughout the USA, many away from home for the first time, were using long-distance lines. To help them, phone companies set up lounges where they could wait in comfort, reading the magazines provided. Operators collected money when calls were completed. In military hospitals portable phones enabled patients to call from their beds or wheelchairs. Manufacture of phones for civilian use was prohibited by the War Production Board, so old stand-up phones were taken out of storage, reconditioned and put back in use. They were not enough to end the shortage, and waiting lists grew. Those with phones were asked to make only emergency calls or calls to do with the war effort. 'Keep all telephone calls brief... shorter calls may avoid further restrictions on war-strained services...long conversations are like double parking... they block telephone traffic and slow down or stop important military and war production operations.' Operators reminded customers 'to please limit your call to five minutes – others are waiting'.

In the UK, too, female engineers, officially called 'female assistants', appeared, doing jobs such as driving lorries, repairing and maintaining equipment, and testing phones. Swift repairs were often necessary to make

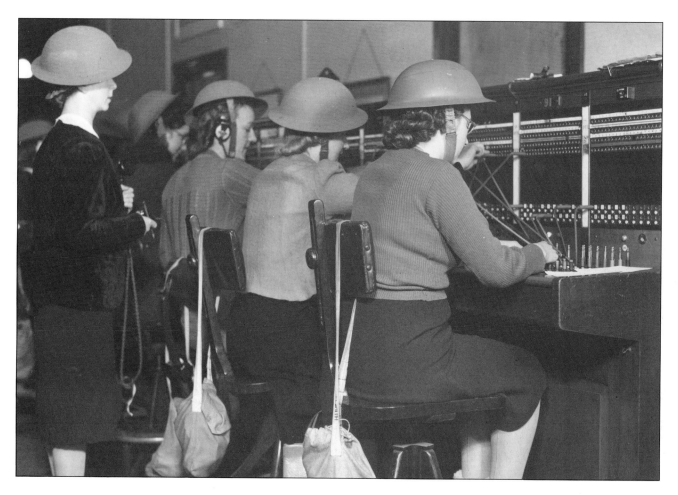

Operators in 'tin-hats' answering calls during an air raid, with gas masks handy. (BT Museum)

good enemy bomb damage and provide perhaps a temporary service. Nevertheless, with the demands on the service, delays were inevitable. John Lehmann in *Penguin New Writing 8* listed among his editorial problems:

> And when all the proofs are at last returned to the printer, our watchful solicitor may decide that one author has shown too great a levity towards a distinguished public figure or worthy organ of government; cuts have to be made, but when the printer is hurriedly rung up the Exchange suavely replies: ten hours' delay.

Pressure upon exchanges built up quickly during and after an air raid, as it had on a grand scale in the USA after the unexpected Japanese bombing of the American fleet in Pearl Harbor. That event was expected by the military but warning could not be phoned because that would have revealed Japanese codes had been cracked. A bicycle messenger delivered the telegram too late.

Through the Press, appeals were made to people not to call up their friends to ask: 'Are you all right?' Such calls overloaded an exchange just when it was needed by the emergency services. Lydia Scalia commented:

> People could be so stupid in a raid. Instead of leaving the phone alone they'd all block the lines trying to find out what had happened. When the bomb dropped on the bottom of St James's Street they didn't wait. They were so unreasonable. They only wanted to know what had happened to their own people. We were expected to be there to answer them.

Military calls could be given priority. An order would go through: 'Clear the lines.' An RAF officer in East Anglia who commanded 'Put me through to Jesus' was told by the operator 'Don't be so impertinent'. What he wanted was Jesus College, Cambridge, then the headquarters of No. 2 Initial Training Wing. The college was used to such japes, having frequently been rung on 25 December with the greeting 'Happy birthday'. For those who had to wait, delays could be agonizing. In 1944 Flight Lieutenant E. L. Jennings of the RAF was seconded to 401 Bombardment Group USAAF near Oundle in Northamptonshire. His wife and daughter had moved from Littlehampton on the coast, which had been bombed and machine-gunned, to the safety of Twyford near Winchester. Even there they were conscious of the bombing of Southampton. To see how they were, he put in a call. It took the GI on the base over an hour to get through, partly because he had to go via London in a blitz. Jennings waited patiently but anxiously. When he was eventually connected the GI asked: 'Say, sir, are you through?' Jennings replied 'Yes', the GI said 'Thank you', and immediately cut him off.

An indication of the importance of communications was the fact that they were becoming an item of not-so-subtle propaganda, something resented by George Orwell, literary editor of *Tribune*, in the 25 February 1944 issue:

> A short story in the *Home Companion and Family Journal*, entitled 'Hullo, Sweetheart', recounts the adventures of a young girl named Lucy Fallows who worked on the switchboard of a long-distance telephone exchange. She had 'sacrificed her yearning to be in uniform' in order to take this job, but found it dull and uneventful. 'So many silly people seemed to use long-distance just to blather to each other... She felt fed up; she felt that she was a servant to selfish

people'; and there was 'a cloud in her hazel eyes'. However, as you will readily guess, Lucy's job soon livened up, and before long she found herself in the middle of thrilling adventures which included the sinking of a U-boat, the capture of a German sabotage crew, and a long motor-ride with a handsome naval officer who had 'a crisp voice'. Such is life in the Telephone Exchange.

At the end of the story there is a little note: 'Any of our young readers themselves interested in the work of the Long Distance Telephone Exchange (such work as Lucy Fallows was doing) should apply to the Staff Controller, LTR, London, who will inform them as to the opportunities open.'

I do not know whether this is an advertisement likely to have much success. I should doubt whether even girls of the age aimed at would believe that capturing U-boats enters very largely into the lives of telephone operators... Hitherto there had not been any very direct connection between fiction and propaganda. That half-inch ad in the *Home Companion* seems to mark another small stage in the process of 'co-ordination' that is gradually happening to all the arts.

Life became more difficult where the phone was unavailable for co-ordination. On 31 October 1938 the Japanese cut the 120-mile cable between Canton and Hong Kong. Even when the Japanese occupied the colony in December 1941 they did not restore the link. Communication, in demand at home, was undesirable between subject peoples. Probably the cable in China was plundered for its copper, extracted for war purposes. In Hong Kong the Japanese did as little as possible either in exchanges or on subscribers' premises. If a line went out of order it was usually left connected but unrepaired. Through the occupation working lines fell from over 16,000 to about 5,000. In Singapore about half the main exchange was dismantled, metal poles replaced by wood, nearly half the phones removed, and most of the subscribers' switchboards smashed, thus sparing troops who would have supervised them.

In India, the first place where the phone was known to have been used in warfare, the network was barely adequate for existing civil needs let alone the extra burdens of wartime. The New Delhi exchange, for example, was designed for some 5,600 subscribers, and when a further 2,400 were added it was grossly overloaded. Staff in the main general headquarters building were served by three or four different switchboards, which led to all sorts of problems and delays. There were innumerable demands for small party-line and point-to-point field systems so that section heads could keep in touch with their staff. Improvisation was the order of the day.

Not until some six months after the Japanese attack on Pearl Harbor was there a comprehensive plan for building up the civil network. The Indian government was reluctant to commit itself to any large-scale expenditure

Bombing, as here in Vienna in October 1944, played havoc with communications. (Austrian PTT)

and there were difficulties and delays in obtaining equipment because of more pressing demands elsewhere. Construction and installation were a joint military/civil effort, with the main routes under the operational control of the military. One difficulty was a local shortage of skilled technicians. In spite of all the problems, many improvements were ready for the Burma offensive 1944–5. India was the base for all South-East Asia operations.

Security was a problem everywhere. Radio-telephones were convenient for mobile use but no secure scrambler existed and codes could easily be broken. They were therefore used mainly in the heat of battle. Behind the line, staff controlling troop movements and supplies found it easier to converse than send telegraph messages to and fro. Indeed, many admin staff booked calls for a fixed time, having their notes and queries ready. Relationships could become too cosy though and conversations too open. At larger headquarters the intelligence security branch installed monitors equipped with recorders. Conversations could be played back to indiscreet offenders.

The armed services were also dealing with rapidly changing situations. For example, Allied headquarters in Algiers expanded quickly and satellite exchanges were installed, not all connected to the main exchange. Sometimes a call had to go through three or even more switchboards within Algiers. Not until the end of the war were significant improvements made to military switchboards. Not all problems in keeping lines open were caused by the enemy. In rocky or sandy areas such as the Western Desert, where poles could not be erected, underground cables were sometimes damaged by vehicles crossing. They were also vulnerable to the tools of badly directed road repair gangs. Schoolboyish officers found insulators convenient targets in pistol practice. Using poles as route markers, drivers were apt to knock into them in poor light. Overhead lines suspended too low could be dragged down by high lorries or even put out of action by a badly sighted gun. Materials were stolen for sale in local black markets, and copper wire turned into jewellery was not the funny occurrence it had been in Evelyn Waugh's novel *Black Mischief.*

In Europe unfamiliarity with the phone was also not funny. When Rotterdam was being attacked by German parachutists in 1940 the young defenders did not think of using it to summon help or make their own actions more effective. When their country was overrun the resistance movement made up for the inactivity. Secret networks were established, using lines in existing cables such as those in the electricity and railway networks. The hub of the system, the Central Information Service, was in Amsterdam, connected to the north of the country and also to The Hague, which had 30 local exchanges concealed behind false walls and in ceilings.

In Rotterdam the most important exchange was in the Heineken brewery, reaching 40 other points in the city that others could not reach. To keep operating secretly, the Amsterdam installation had to be moved at least 13 times. In The Hague the exchange was known as 'The Cloister', and the ten operators were not allowed out, being kept fit by vitamin injections. It was connected to a separate secret network in the city run by the National Committee of Resistance.

In the north at Leeuwarden, telephone administration (PTT) technicians installed tiny microphones in the most important phones used by the German security commandant. These were connected to a bookshop storeroom, where six resistance workers kept a constant vigil in pairs. A nerve-wracking aspect of their work was overhearing arrested comrades tortured. They also overheard the names of collaborators and traitors and those whom they had denounced to save their own skins. Frequently those in danger were warned in time to avoid arrest. Information was also passed on to agents to give to London. Agents sometimes used the S-phone, which

The Danes did not lose their sense of humour under the German occupation. (Telephone Museum, Copenhagen)

permitted contact between a ground operator and an aircraft or boat.

Within the French PTT there was a similar pattern of activity. Early in the occupation it was local and dispersed. During 1942 it became more organized and from then on grew in strength and effectiveness ready for the Liberation. Resistance, active and passive, took many forms: going slow; hiding equipment and supplies (often to be used by the Maquis); operators listening in and passing on information; their postal colleagues intercepting mail to the German authorities, especially anything that looked like a denunciation of loyal Frenchmen.

One of the most spectacular successes was achieved by Source K, a group named after a PTT engineer Robert Keller who, when Paris was declared an open city in 1940, sabotaged principal long-distance cables radiating from the city. A plan was also devised for blocking them when the Allied invasion came. Meanwhile, in 1942 Keller and a few colleagues managed to eavesdrop on 70 circuits on the Paris–Metz route to Berlin for five months. Between April and September more than 60 conversations a day were being monitored and taken down in shorthand. Among them were conversations conducted by Hitler, Goering, Keitl, Jodl, von Runstedt, Doenitz and Goebbels.

From these conversations, important information was gathered about the strength and disposition of Wehrmacht, Kriegsmarine and Luftwaffe units, the names of their commanders and their plans of action. Intercepted conversations from Kiel, for example, yielded information about U-boat activities in the Channel and the Atlantic at a time when they were a serious threat to Allied convoys bringing food and war materials from North America. Such information was transmitted to London, along with reports about the politics of Vichy France, invaded by the Germans on 11 November 1942, and German reaction to the Allied landing at Dieppe on 19 August 1942. Of vital interest to London was what the Germans proposed to do in the event of similar landings. This information was needed in planning Operation Overlord, the code-name for the massive enterprise of the Second Front to liberate Europe.

The Paris–Metz tapping centre was dismantled in November 1942 because the Germans were requisitioning buildings in that part of Paris. Its place was taken by another centre, on the Paris–Strasbourg route, in December, but before Christmas Keller was denounced by a collaborator. Choosing not to flee and leave his wife and four children and his PTT colleagues to face the Gestapo, Keller was interrogated and deported with two colleagues to German concentration camps. Keller died of typhus in Belsen in March 1945, two months before VE Day. A long-distance cable centre and the Parisian street where he did his audacious work are named after him and a commemorative stamp was issued.

In Algeria in 1941–2 it was reckoned that microphones inserted in German phones by PTT technicians neutralized nearly 400 agents, unmasked traitors and gained intelligence on Italian naval communications. The technicians were an effective fifth column in the North African campaigns. In France, Lyons became the capital of the resistance. Besides being an established communications centre, it was not far from the Swiss border and the nearby mountains gave cover to the Maquis. Nevertheless, there were many arrests and tortures, especially by Klaus Barbie, the 'Butcher of Lyons'.

So concerned were the Germans about secure communications in the area that they imported a mobile exchange. Like a deluxe coach, the 15-metre unit was the only one in France. The other four were on the Eastern Front, where they replaced exchanges destroyed by the Russians under their 'scorched earth' policy. When the mobile exchange arrived in Lyons in June 1943 it was parked in the courtyard of the regional telecommunications centre and heavily guarded. Its presence was a challenge to a PTT employee Charles Spitz. He devised a plan whereby he admitted a saboteur who, in a lightning strike with two bombs, destroyed the exchange and its five operators. The saboteur escaped but Spitz was arrested, tortured and deported, spending time in Buchenwald. In 1946 he received the Croix de Guerre from General de Gaulle, President of the French provisional government.

All this work, useful in itself, came into its own during the Liberation, for which an increased effort was made. On 5 June 1944 BBC code messages alerted the Resistance to be ready for sabotage. At Saint-Lo in Normandy, for example, long-distance cables were cut to isolate coastal defences from the interior, and overhead lines to German garrisons were put out of service. These actions helped the American troops from 82nd Airborne Division who parachuted into Sainte Mère Eglise on the Cherbourg peninsula. In retaliation the Germans shot eleven members of the Resistance in the PTT at Saint-Lo.

What had been conceived as a communications network for the defence of Britain increasingly became one for mounting the offensive against Hitler in Northern Europe. The DTN attained its peak capacity in 1944, and railway communications had to be improved. The Great Western, for example, pre-war primarily a passenger network, had to be adapted for troop trains and armaments. Operating managers of the railway companies and service transport chiefs held daily phone conferences on traffic movements. Communications traffic was concentrated on the South Coast. Three large bombproof underground signals centres were built ready for the invasion of Europe: at Dover, Portsmouth and Plymouth. Portsmouth was used as the centre for D-Day, the landing in Normandy on 6 June 1944;

Plymouth for the Cherbourg offensive; and Dover when the Allies had advanced into Belgium. Within four days of the invasion a cross-Channel cable was providing communications between the bridgehead and General Eisenhower's headquarters to the west of London. Within a few months a further six cables were in operation. Among other things they were used for broadcasts by BBC and American war correspondents.

From the firm bridgehead the advance was so rapid that long-distance lines could not easily be established on an expanding front in the wake of the enemy. Sometimes he could be called up in the next village. Elsewhere, lines had been damaged by bombing, battle and German sabotage. Forward units diverted circuits for their own tactical use. It took some time for an overall strategic system to be implemented, ensuring regular contact between bases and the front line. These firm links were much appreciated by freed prisoners of war, who were able to get messages home to their loved ones. It was a time when a few words meant so much to so many.

During summer 1944 in the Netherlands many secret links were established, often under the noses of the Germans and in broad daylight. The Allied advance was helped by close knowledge of what was going on behind German lines, even to the moving of a machine-gun post. For example, the railway phone network from Utrecht was used for a month to get information about movements of German troop and supply trains to Allied intelligence in Nijmegen. Railway communications to Nijmegen were also used in Operation Pegasus I, organizing the escape of British airborne troops who had been landed at Arnhem in September 1944 to secure a bridgehead over the Rhine for an advance into the heart of Germany. Realizing how useful the leak had been, the Germans cut the cable, an act that contributed to the failure of Operation Pegasus II.

On the Allied side there were suspicions about underground networks. Eisenhower's Special Forces HQ did not completely trust them, fearing they might be used by the Germans for passing on disinformation. At one point an order was issued forbidding any more contact, but it had to be withdrawn temporarily after protests from within the German-occupied areas. During the 'hunger' winter of 1944–5, when many people ate bulbs to survive, communications were restricted to the occupied areas. Later, activity on lines increased. Where there had once been 50 calls a day, in the closing stages of the war there were as many as 300. In April 1945 a secret link was established between Resistance headquarters in Amsterdam and the commander of the Netherlands forces, Prince Bernhard, in the newly liberated centre of the country. Thus, underground communications continued right up to the last week of the occupation.

In the UK, Lydia Scalia put through the first post-war transatlantic call from the Ritz:

The Americans were dying to get in touch and had to book calls in advance. Two who weren't staying in the hotel had booked calls to their relatives through me. They had to come into my office to speak. When we got through it was all crying and we couldn't speak. We got his wife on the telephone and the poor man was so overcome – he hadn't spoken to her for two years – he couldn't speak. I cried too trying to keep the line open. It was so emotional to see a man... I couldn't speak either.

When the war in the Far East ended record numbers of long-distance calls were recorded in the USA. In the UK over 114,000 prisoner-of-war messages came in free of charge by Cable and Wireless from Hong Kong, Singapore and Rangoon to Colombo, for relay to London. Charles Graves described the occasion in his wartime history of the company, *The Thin Red Lines*:

The scene at the telephone room in the Cable and Wireless office in London was dramatic to a degree. Almost every department throughout Electra House, from Traffic to Messengers, was busy day and night. Consultations with the Post Office and the War Office and daily meetings of departmental heads in the Committee Room followed each other rapidly. One whole section of the telephone room was set aside to deal with the messages from the Far East. Some girls were detailed to find the telephone numbers of people to whom the cables were addressed in order to shorten their anxiety. Others were telephoning the messages before the re-addressed cables would have time to reach them. In hundreds of homes, men and women laughing and crying with relief after years of separation and silence, years of anxiety and doubt as to the whereabouts, even the existence of their sons and daughters, husbands and wives – heard the blessed works 'Safe... coming home soon.'

CHAPTER 13

ENGAGED

I n Japan after the war easily remembered phone numbers were auctioned. Without a proper directory service, they were a valuable business asset. In most places war had encouraged people to use and appreciate phones, and the habit was not going to be lost in peace. There were limitations, noted by Ernest Bevin at the Labour Party conference in Blackpool on 19 May 1945, just over two months before he unexpectedly became Foreign Secretary:

During the American occupation of Japan women from the US Army acted as exchange supervisors. (NTT)

You cannot settle the problems of Europe by long-distance telephone calls and telegrams. Round the table we must get, but do not present us with *faits accomplis* when we get there.

At the Foreign Office, Bevin believed he could solve the Palestine problem by creating a bi-national state for Arabs and Jews. Among his implacable opponents was the Zionist group Irgun Zvai Leumi (Hebrew for National Military Organization), to which a future Israeli Prime Minister, Menachem Begin, belonged. Its objective was to drive out the British and create an independent state, Israel. Furthering that cause, the most spectacular crime committed, or war aim achieved, depending on your point of view, was the blowing up on 22 July 1946 of the King David Hotel in Jerusalem.

Explosives packed into milk churns were smuggled into a kitchen. Above it was a restaurant and pillars supporting the upper floors where the British authorities worked. At least three phone warnings were then given: one to the hotel, one to the French Consulate-General, and the other to the *Palestine Post*. Adina, the young Irgun caller, asked each recipient to pass on her message. The hotel ignored it as a hoax; the French opened their windows to avoid flying glass; and the newspaper switchboard got through too late. Ninety-one lives were lost.

The world over, switching from war to peace was urgent. In the UK, as elsewhere, industrialists changing to peacetime production badly needed machines and materials in short supply. To speed things up, they made much more use of the phone than they had pre-war, and paid the rentals and calls of key employees who needed it at home. It proved its worth during the 1946–7 winter, the worst of the century so far, when road and rail transport were frozen in. At least messages could get through when people and supplies could not. That experience was an incentive to improve railway administration, for example by installing a system enabling conferences to be held without people leaving their desks. Growth in the system as a whole was evident in the number of directories issued to London subscribers: from 1948 it was four.

Some shadow factories remained remote, keeping in contact with their parent organizations and becoming the basis for growing industrial estates. With the ending of rationing and controls, markets opened up and the pace of business quickened. Sir Montagu Burton, who had kept phones out of his shops to reduce overheads, relented and allowed them into larger branches.

The social as well as the economic map changed. Young families moved to suburban estates and new towns away from cities such as London, Edinburgh, Glasgow, Liverpool and Newcastle. Separated from their extended families, they found the phone a way of keeping in touch. To a

A Portuguese display emphasizes the phone as a continuous link in society, helping post-war recovery.

(Telephone Company of Portugal)

working wife or mother with young children it was also more convenient than writing a letter. It helped to lessen feelings of isolation and led to new social contacts. Sociologists talked of 'dispersed social networks' and 'enlarging an individual's psychological neighbourhood'. Psychiatrists noted that paranoid delusions were shifting from being poisoned by the gas or menaced by electricity to being persecuted by the phone.

A telephonist observed:

> People were talking to each other in a social way. You didn't have to have a certain income to have a phone. We could see the exchange was getting bigger and different people coming up on the boards.

People who had never contemplated owning or using a phone were taking to it. When the 10th Duke of Argyll died, one was at last installed in Inverary Castle. That was in 1949, the year the post-war waiting list reached its peak. From 1950 the average annual rate of residential connections was over twice that for business. There were places that still managed without, such as Calke Abbey, the home of the Harpur-Crewe family. *Hoi polloi* without relied on the public service. Notices appeared in shops: 'No change given for phones'. Public kiosks were still growing in number and in 1947 the Royal Fine Art Commission re-endorsed Post Office red, used

In the rapid post-war expansion of the phone service, installing cast-iron kiosks was a hefty job. (BT Museum)

on nearly all cast iron kiosks since the 1920s, with the proviso that in areas of outstanding natural beauty and places of architectural importance light battleship grey with red window-bars was permitted.

A teenage girl in Pinner, Middlesex, phoned her mother in a remote Welsh village by calling the only public box at a time when she knew children would be playing there, as she had done. A child would go and fetch her mother, who lived nearby. Calls could be pre-arranged. A man who waited for 40 minutes by a box was told by the smiling woman who emerged: 'I always have a good gossip once a fortnight to a friend who lives in a village the other side of Cirencester and she rings me here the other week. So we keep in touch and thoroughly enjoy our natter.' Calls in a 15-mile radius were still untimed and in 1949 rural kiosks could be installed in areas on local authority recommendation, whether they were likely to pay their way or not.

With demand exceeding supply, in 1948 party lines were obligatory for all new residential applicants and those moving house. How satisfactory it was depended upon the other party. A great talker could be frustrating. A particular problem arose with doctors, who could have a party line at home if they did not practise there. To parliamentary questions about priority and privacy, the answer was: 'When doctors are asked to share telephone lines we try to find them a suitable person with whom to share – such as a lock-up shop – so that during the hours at which he is presumably not at the hospital the doctor has virtually an exclusive service.' One way round the problem was working as a group practice. Patients could get attention, and doctors uninterrupted half-holidays and weekends.

Party lines had their advantages. Sharing with a friend, you could enjoy conversations for nothing. If three was not a crowd, a party line could be an extension. In southern Illinois an Avon saleslady used a multi-party line. Having got the operator to ring one line after another, she made her sales pitch to about 90 per cent of her customers and took orders. When as many as 24 parties were reduced to four, she complained to the phone company president about the 'improved' service. A couple who retired from Glasgow to a West Lothian village found it provided a service close to a Scotsman's heart. As a private installation was difficult to get, they agreed to share a line with the local Co-op next door and pay for their calls. Time went by, no bills came and the Co-op manager moved. The phantom extension was used for five years, when on her husband's death the widow had a twinge of conscience and told the new manager. This early example of a 'freefone' service soon ended.

Shared service meant more work for operators. They had to ask which of the two numbers the caller was, at a time when exchanges were getting busy anyway. Cecily Hammond was well aware of the new pace in her small Kent exchange:

> If four people called at once and you were the fifth you had to wait to get an answer. It gradually got worse. Timing was not started until the parties were connected. That could be a burden when you were busy. Calls were popping up all over the place and you couldn't answer them. I was made assistant supervisor and I had to stand there and watch to see if they were all busy and if two calls came up to see which had priority.

Mrs Kettle worked in a larger exchange at Redhill, Surrey:

> It was a large horseshoe. Positions that weren't in use when I first started in 1948 were gradually opened. The exchange was also extended. We had an enquiry desk for new subscribers unfamiliar with the telephone. Originally two positions, it became four. They dealt with directory enquiries, how do I get through to Bristol, complaints etc. We used to get very busy if we had a 'flu epidemic in the exchange. You needed eight or nine arms… One very busy line was Victoria Coach Station, difficult to get… When I started there were the young and the older operators but during the 1950s there were more working mothers.

Expanding though the service was, it could still be personal, something appreciated by subscribers and suitably rewarded:

> At Christmas in Tenterden we used to get given boxes of chocs, chickens from the farmer, eggs. The doctor used to send a box of chocolates for the day staff and another one for the old man and his wife who worked the board at night. We used to get bottles of sherry and if you worked on Christmas Day it was beautiful. You used to have a hell of a time. There was competition to work on Christmas Day because you used to have such a lovely time. People were ever so happy and they'd ring up to see how you were getting on.
>
> Once a vet with six kids – we knew him well because he made a lot of calls – wanted a call put through to Father Christmas. He asked us if we could work something out. We told him to tell the kids to ask for Alaska 5000. We got a postman down in the sorting office to act the part of Father Christmas. We used various tones and one operator said Iceland, then Greenland, North Pole. The postman rattled his keys for the reindeer with their sleigh bells. We were all sitting listening in. We said we were the fairies connecting the calls. We only managed it once or twice because the kids grew up.

There were other red-letter days in the calendar. At Redhill

> On April the first we always had an instruction to beware of numbers like Chessington Zoo. People would ask for Mr C. Lyon, Miss G. R. Raff. Our standing instruction was 'Do you realize this number is Chessington Zoo?' There was a sudden silence and they would realize what they'd been put up to... Derby day was always busy with bookmakers.

Across the Atlantic lines were busy on a commercial festival such as Mother's Day in May and national occasions such as Labour Day in September and Thanksgiving in November. Between 1946 and 1956 phones almost doubled in number. Waiting lists had grown during the war; rural expansion and improvement programmes had been deferred; some rural party lines had over ten subscribers, and there was a concerted effort to reduce the number. Much had to be done, resulting in secure jobs for many. Growth of phone usage was mirrored by the post-war decline in the telegram service, evident in both the UK and USA. In the UK the greetings service was varied to stem the decline. Acceptance from August 1958 of greetings telegrams for delivery to a telephonic address made little difference.

When wage costs were rising, a labour-intensive service was giving way to a capital-intensive one, becoming increasingly automatic and do-it-yourself. More users were able to dial their own calls, even if over limited distances.

It helped keep down costs. To some, of course, the phone seemed expensive and out of reach. After a trunk call, Mrs Cotton, the housekeeper in J. B. Priestley's 1947 play *The Linden Tree*, puts down the receiver as if in dislike: 'She's goin' to ring yer same time tomorrow night. Money no object.' Automatic service on long-distance was still over ten years away.

To speed the introduction of automatic service, some New Zealand farmers were prepared to pitch in. A report in the *Southland Times* of 14 May 1952 described the project at Hedgehope, where farmers installed the poles, as 'an object lesson to other parts of the Dominion'. Their co-operation showed the old pioneer spirit of getting out and helping instead of sitting back and expecting things to be done for them. Of the 80 farmers who helped, most spent two or three weeks on the job, clipping six months off the project. Others followed. In Singapore, an unprecedented trade boom in rubber and tin, partly caused by the Korean War, led to the installation of new automatic equipment.

Going automatic usually meant having longer numbers, again creating competition to get easily remembered ones. Geoffrey Gardner, a Sussex estate agent, recalls:

> When the business expanded post-war we needed another number. Having done a lot of way-leave work for landowners, we knew the GPO people well. We got Crawley 1, which had been a call box. Our numbers were worth a lot to us because people could not easily forget them. Sometimes people thought that Crawley 1 could not exist. When we went automatic we wanted 12345 but we had to have 23456.

Growing interest in the instrument was reflected in plays, films, songs and books. The German comedian Karl Valentin wrote a sketch entitled *Buchbinder Wanninger*, about a bookbinder trying in vain to arrange delivery of repaired books to a large company and being shunted from department to department. In 1947 a one-act opera by Menotti, *The Telephone*, about a young man competing with its incessant ringing for his beloved's attention, was first performed in New York. More popular a few years later was 'Busy Line' sung by Rose Murphy. 'Call Me' featured in the 1945 film *Why Girls Leave Home* and 'Call Me Tonight' in the 1952 *Just for You*. In his piece about the 1953 floods, *Fen and Flood*, Patrick Hadley, professor of music at Cambridge, included a ringing phone. *Murder in the Telephone Exchange* (1949) was a first novel by June Wright, and a New Yorker short story, *Will You Wait?* by Robert M. Coates, was based on the idea of callers hanging on, jamming the lines and making communication impossible. Getting through to people in more senses than one was a problem for the bedridden, neurotic woman in Lucille Fletcher's radio play and film *Sorry Wrong*

Rose Murphy sang about her 'baby's number', Busy Line.

(BMG Enterprises)

Number. Discovering she is to be murdered, the invalid tries to summon help, becoming desperate when the phone seems to herald her doom. Also in 1948, Cocteau's exercise in hysteria was revived by Roberto Rossellini, who filmed *La Voix Humaine* as *Una Voce Umana*, an episode in *L'Amore.*

Making easy contacts was one of the aspirations of Holden Caulfield in J. D. Salinger's *Catcher in the Rye* (1951): 'What really knocks me out is a book that, when you've done reading it, you wish the author that wrote it was a terrific friend of yours and you could call him up on the phone whenever you felt like it.' Waiting for a vital message provided the suspense in the 1951 film *Chicago Calling*, in which a drunk who cannot pay his phone bill is anxious for news of his daughter's involvement in a car crash. Less successful was the 1952 *Phone Call from a Stranger*, four linked stories based upon the survivor of an air crash visiting the families of his travelling companions. *Time* commented: 'A cinematic party line on which several conversations are going at once, none of them coming across very distinctly.' Yet in Paddy Chayefsky's TV play *Marty*, later filmed, Rod Steiger's conversation conveyed the whole attitude of the girl at the other end of the line. The party line in *Pillow Talk* (1959) brought a triple-split screen.

The line being cut off was an almost predictable element in Agatha Christie's *The Mousetrap* (1952), destined to be the longest-running play ever. Isolation of a small group of people in a country house, however artificial, seemed never to lose its appeal. *Dial M for Murder*, also set in one room, did not immediately appeal to London theatre producers, even after it had been on TV. Suddenly, when the film rights were sold, it appeared on London and Broadway stages, was translated into 25 languages and produced in over 30 countries, becoming the best-known phone title. The record number of call cues, more than 50 of them, was achieved in *Plaintiff in a Pretty Hat* (1956).

Kingsley Amis's hero in *Lucky Jim* (1954) found it handy in his relationship with his landlords, the arty Welch family. To extricate himself from one of their boring cultural weekends, he arranged for a message to be left and, to hoax their son, disguised his voice as a reporter on the local paper interested in doing a story on his paintings. The instrument had a fatal fascination for him:

Barbara Stanwyck portrayed the terror of the bedridden victim in Sorry Wrong Number.

(Paramount Pictures)

Dixon looked at the telephone where it stood on a black plush cloth in the middle of a bamboo table situated in Miss Cutler's drawing-room. He felt like an alcoholic surveying a bottle of gin; only by using it could he obtain the relief he wanted, but its side-effects, as recent experience had proved, were likely to be deleterious.

Although he tried to imitate phone operators, disturbances on the line and somebody else, his ruse was rumbled by Mrs Welch. Roger Longrigg admitted that the titles of his first three novels – *A High Pitched Buzz* (1956), *Switchboard* (1957) and *Wrong Number* (1959) – were 'a gimmick to cause the books to be better remembered'. Muriel Spark's *Memento Mori* (1959) was based on an anonymous call, 'Remember you must die', and Ed McBain's *The Heckler* (1960) on a phone pest frightening people out of their business premises next to banks and jewellery stores. The prolific Belgian crime writer Georges Simenon used directories from many parts of the world as sources for the names of his characters.

Teilhard de Chardin, a priest out of favour with the Vatican for trying to reconcile science and the faith, saw radio and phone lines as the nerve links in society, but his philosophy was mainly published posthumously. By then the Pope had pronounced. Along with the telegraph, TV and radio, the phone achieved charisma on 12 January 1951. In an apostolic letter Pope Pius XII, who had long leads on Vatican phones so that people could kneel when speaking to him, recognized that:

> technical instruments of this kind... may even serve to impart religious instruction, to carry the voice of the Supreme Pastor of souls from St Peter's to the farthest corners of the earth, and to unite in wondrous manner the hearts and minds and voices of the faithful everywhere in public prayer to the Divine Majesty... an appreciable number of professional men, distinguished in the field of tele-communications, having petitioned Us, for themselves and their associates, to designate Saint Gabriel Archangel – who brought to the human race, when it was wrapped in darkness and almost in despair of its salvation, the long-awaited announcement of man's Redemption – as their heavenly Patron before the throne of God.

Accordingly, no less than an archangel was made the patron saint of telecommunications. St Gabriel's feast day, 24 March, did not coincide with World Telecommunications Day, 17 May, the date on which the International Telegraph Union was founded in 1865.

Phones were virtuous in other ways. They linked the outside world to enclosed orders of monks and nuns, each of which had its own rules for handling calls. Exchanges in Catholic countries were fittingly blessed by priests, some of whom sprinkled holy water too enthusiastically, causing short circuits. Convent-educated Irish girls were advised to take a directory to a party in case they had to sit on a boy's lap coming home. Like the advice about not wearing patent leather shoes, which reflected knickers, that may be a piece of local folklore. As few people had a phone, especially in the sparsely populated countryside, Irish directories were thin. More seriously, the installation of radio-telephones between Irish lighthouses and the mainland, mooted in 1938 but deferred by the war, went ahead.

On land, phones were being more used in emergencies. In Britain the street fire alarm was disappearing. Installation of the 999 service resumed and by 1948 all larger towns with automatic exchanges had it. Some fire and ambulance authorities adjusted their boundaries for the convenience of emergency calls. In 1950, when 116 men were entombed at Knockshinnock Castle Colliery, Ayrshire, for three days, they were reassured on a line to the surface. No such good fortune befell Alys Pearsall Smith, divorced from Bertrand Russell since 1921, who to her dying day hoped he would make an honest Countess of her. Having slipped on the stairs and broken some bones, she still doggedly tried to answer the phone herself to within a few hours of her death in 1950: 'It might be Bertie.' Two years before, one of his mistresses recorded that he started up in bed, as if a tiger was in the next room, crying 'The telephone'. It was not, but they got up and dressed, and a quarter of an hour later his wife phoned.

Desperate people were helped by a new lifeline established in 1953 in the City of London, at St Stephen Walbrook church by the Reverend Chad Varah. He publicized the number, MANsion House 9000, which could be rung at any time by anyone 'tempted to suicide and despair'. Callers, remaining anonymous if they wished, could tell their troubles to a sympathetic stranger, a Samaritan but not necessarily a Christian. An attempt at suicide is often a cry for help and it was reckoned that over 80 per cent of would-be suicides indicated their intention to do so. Much better they should be befriended, if only long enough to get them over a crisis, that they should not feel alone in the world but able to trust somebody. Eventually they might summon up confidence to meet somebody face to face.

It all began after the Reverend Chad Varah had an article in *Picture Post* about sex. Altogether 235 troubled people wrote to him Telling All. Among them were 14 he thought suicidal. Then he read that there were three suicides a day in Greater London.

What were they supposed to do if they didn't want a doctor or social worker from our splendid Welfare State? What sort of a someone might they want? Well, some had chosen me because of my liberal views. If it was so easy to save lives, why didn't I do it all the time? Ho, I answered myself, and live on what? And how would they get in touch at the moment of crisis? H'm. In an emergency the citizen turns to the telephone and dials 999. I looked at mine: FIRE, it said. But if you were on a ledge about to jump and needed a ladder, there'd be very few phones on a ledge with you. POLICE, it said. But at that time, suicide was a felony. (It was Samaritan psychiatrists among others who pressed for the law to be changed.) AMBULANCE, it said. Premature, surely? There ought to be an emergency number for suicidal people, I thought.

What I was the first at was setting up and advertising publicly an emergency telephone service for the suicidal and other despairing persons. Within three months, I had discovered that what such persons need in most cases is not the counselling I myself was offering but the befriending provided by the volunteers whom I gathered round me. Thus I was the pioneer of a sort of 999 for suicides on 2 November 1953 and a pioneer of a third method of therapy, namely the listening and accepting therapy which we call befriending, on or about the 2 February 1954.

There may well have been people who let it be known in their local area that they were willing to give pastoral help by telephone, and the best known of these was one who wrote a book about it called *God Gave Me a Telephone*. This was a one-man show and did not lead to an organization and was not concerned with suicide. It was an evangelistic mission – evangelism is of course forbidden to the Samaritans, who are non-religious and non-political.

The idea spread rapidly in the UK and Europe. In Bournemouth, for example, attempted suicides halved after the new service was established locally. In Berlin, where every year some 30 to 60 people tried to commit suicide on New Year's night, numbers fell to about four during the first three years of Samaritan activity. They were not the pioneers of phone lifelines. Alcoholics Anonymous, founded in the USA in 1935 and in the UK in 1947, made sure its number was in directories, libraries, with the probation services, churches and other bodies. In making a phone call, people with a drink problem were taking the first step to recovery, making personal contact with an ex-alcoholic who understood exactly what they were going through. Marie at London regional centre explains the importance of self-introduction:

It could even do a great deal of harm for us to approach a person with a drinking problem who has not asked for our help. We do not go through third parties. We want to talk to the person with the problem. Even if your wife rang asking us to give you help the answer would have to be a very positive no. It wouldn't work. I wouldn't send literature to you on the request of your wife but I would send it to her to show you when she felt the moment was convenient. We have doctors ringing in who in spite of their medical knowledge cannot help themselves. They will be treated exactly the same as anybody else. Alcohol is no respecter of people…

When I speak to an AA office I am on my way to recovery. Through our fellowship we identify with each other's feelings, fears, loneliness… The telephone is the lifeline for all of us, whether we are drinking or not.

She discusses phone counselling:

I personally don't see too much therapy in too long calls. To me it's very much better if I can reassure them and tell them that help is available and arrange as soon as I can for someone to talk to them face to face. To talk to alcohol is like talking to a stone wall. It's not always registering. What will reassure more than words are feelings. You can reassure a caller that you know where he is at, that you have been there.

Our phones are answered only by alcoholics, paid for and run by members for members. We don't tell them to pull themselves together, that they can do better. We know what they are suffering. By saying I am an alcoholic, I am married and I know how bad it can be the other person can identify with the feelings of loneliness and fear. Give as much practical help as possible at that time, suggesting what practical things they can do to keep their minds off their physical pain. Use of first names is a great help. You are talking to an individual.

There's also the sponsorship system. It's our lifeline. It's something I wouldn't want to be without now. We keep in touch with each other not just when we call in here and ask for help but we use it constantly to each other. If I get uptight – say I have a row with my husband, who is a recovering alcoholic with much longer sobriety than I – then I can call another woman and talk it out. If an alcoholic is sick and is still drinking I have to be very aware when I pick up the telephone that it is his or her first time to have actually said 'I need help'. This for an alcoholic who in the main has tried to do it on their own is a big stumbling block removed. It's the one I waited so many years to make, to know that I was completely beaten by alcohol. A person admitting he needs help is at rock bottom. You can be that way sleeping rough on the Embankment or in a penthouse on Park Lane. I had to be able to lose a terrific amount of arrogance to have been able to make that first call. That's the beginning of our recovery, when we get a glimmering of humility. When a person has made that first call it's my responsibility not to make it any harder for them.

The situation was well portrayed in the 1952 film *Come Back, Little Sheba*.

During the 1950s, a decade when so many good causes were discovered, the phone became a social service instrument. A suicide prevention centre was opened in Los Angeles. Churches on both sides of the Atlantic offered Dial-a-Prayer, meeting an unexpected demand. When the Hitchcock Memorial Presbyterian Church in Scarsdale, New York, publicized the service, the local phone system was temporarily jammed. In London, similar calls were mistakenly routed for a few days to the Locomotive and Allied Manufacturers' Association, whose switchboard had never been so busy. The power of the instrument was starkly demonstrated in 1949 in Camden, New Jersey, when a psychotic killer of 13 people paused in a desperate gun battle with the police to answer the phone in his barricaded room.

From 1954, when a system was inaugurated at Acton Hospital in London, patients were able to make calls from their beds. A coin-box instrument on a trolley was wheeled round the wards twice a day and plugged in. Initially it was used mainly for long-distance calls to people too far away to visit. Patients seemed better off than those outside needing treatment, who argued strongly for doctors to be accessible by phone. Why should they be so hard to reach when ambulances could be summoned by a control centre? Although phones were becoming more widely available, people were not necessarily more accessible.

CHAPTER 14

TAPPING SPACE

What had been primarily an instrument for business and the well-to-do was becoming a consumer durable for Mr and Mrs Everyman, who were perhaps keeping up with the Joneses. They installed the phone for somebody to ring them and it rested lonely and silent in the hall. A call was an event, the initial ring often worrying. Reluctance to make a call was not just fear of cost, although often an honesty box – typically a china pig with a slot in its back – was an adjacent reminder.

The phone was not as vital to most people as a TV set, which especially from the coronation of Queen Elizabeth I in 1953 rapidly became a focal point in more and more homes. No similar national event boosted the appeal of the phone, a convenience and symbol of the affluent society. Indeed, engaged lines could indicate the popularity of TV programmes. To avoid being disturbed, avid viewers would take the phone off the hook, causing congestion in the exchange. When a popular programme ended people rushed to make calls and the exchange switchboards lit up like Piccadilly Circus. It was a nationwide phenomenon previously only locally evident, in places such as the West End when theatres emptied. TV and the phone first came together in the UK on 1 July 1954, on a phone-in during a Conservative Party political broadcast.

Increasing demand caused problems. Waiting lists grew, ageing exchanges took more traffic, and quality deteriorated. The public complained about crossed lines, blocked calls and delays. Suffering from 40 years of underinvestment and afraid to stimulate an insatiable demand, the Post Office promoted its service cautiously. Sales staff spent more time explaining why service could not be provided than in winning business. Not until the latter 1950s were new services introduced: weather forecast, to take pressure off the Meteorological Office, and test match information (1956); road weather (1957); Teletourist (1958); Freefone nationwide and a radio-telephone service for drivers in South Lancashire (1959). That spring a new range of coloured phones became available, following the American lead of the early 1950s.

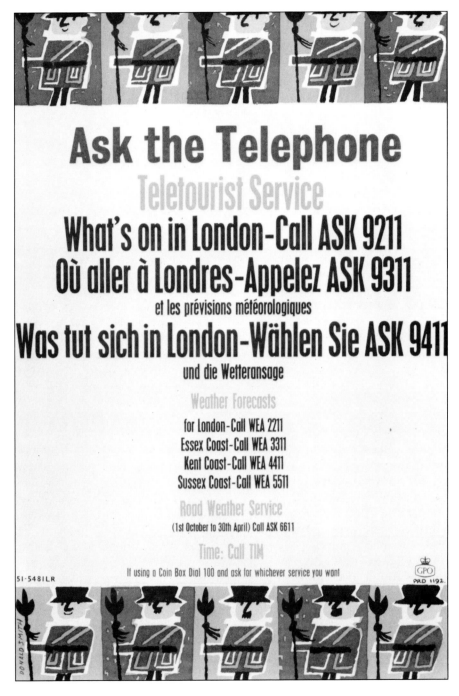

In the latter 1950s Britain introduced new phone services and recognized that foreigners existed. (BT Museum)

In the USA a mobile phone service began in 1946 in St Louis and within a month a driver called Honolulu, Hawaii. The next year an automobile was connected to an aeroplane, both moving. A regular phone service was also provided by two railroad companies, the Baltimore and Ohio on its Royal Blue and the Pennsylvania on the Congressional Limited between New York City and Washington DC. Between 1954 and 1956 West Germany followed suit on some long-distance routes, the connection being made by a train secretary. Switzerland introduced the weather forecast and winter avalanche bulletin (1948); the sports, pools results and news service (1950); and the road report (1957). Japan had a weather service (1954), a public radio-telephone service on Kinki Nippon express trains (1957), and on Japan National Railways (1960). Austria demonstrated its musicality by offering the standard tuning note A.

Popularity was marked by the use of cockney rhyming slang: dog and bone, and Molly Malone, similar to terms heard earlier in the US, Maggie Malone, and switch and bone. In Liverpool the scouse term remained 'blower', as in 'Give 'im ther griff on ther blower', meaning 'Phone the information to him'. Novelty and difficulties had their amusing sides. Practical jokers called users, asking them to put their phones in a bucket of water for testing. Students crammed themselves in record numbers into kiosks. In London, people unused to the phone called the BLAckfriars (Manchester) number of *The Guardian* and got the same number on ALBert Dock. Workmen rushed down the wharf to answer it. A Scottish freelance journalist was discussing the terms of a commission when his line crackled. 'Excuse me,' he said testily. 'What did you say?' He was told, somewhat apologetically: 'Well, we could raise it from 60 to 100 guineas an issue.'

The vicar of Upnor, Kent, the Reverend Michael Sims-Williams, who was also chaplain of the *TS Arethusa*, had a mooring chain to sell. He looked up a possible purchaser's number and lifted his receiver only to find that, before dialling, he was a third party to a conversation. Two men were discussing the sale of chains. Astonished, he listened for a few moments and then during a pause chipped in with: 'I've got a chain I want to sell.' A pregnant silence was followed by: 'Who the devil was that?... Get off the bloody line!' He said: 'I thought you might be interested'. The fluent reply was couched in terms unsuitable for a clergyman's ears or print. Twenty-five years later he still had the chain for sale.

It was easy to be abusive over the phone. Malcolm Muggeridge received several such calls after his *Saturday Evening Post* article 'Does England Really Need a Queen?' in October 1957. Tempers were not sweetened by frustrations. Gilbert Harding in his *Book of Manners* (1956) devoted a chapter to Telephone Tribulations, in which he commented:

I stood recently in the call-box of a provincial hotel waiting for somebody to speak to me… The box had not been redecorated for years and the walls were covered with scribbled numbers and messages – the dying messages, probably, of callers who had waited there hopelessly until rigor mortis had set in. Has it ever struck you, incidentally, how like most call-boxes are to an up-ended coffin?

William Plomer, poet and novelist, omitted the phone from *Electric Delights*, claiming in 1959 that he could 'still work and play, eat, breathe and sleep without it'. For Georges Duhamel it was one of the *Problèmes de Civilisation* (1962).

The critic Daniel George, reviewing a new edition of Lady Troubridge's *Book of Etiquette*, complained that she gave no guidance on phone use. His problem was to extricate himself with some elegance from a conversation in which he had become engaged. Some clear do's and don'ts were given in Judith Listowel's *Manual of Modern Manners* (1959). She recognized that, properly used, the phone can be a major asset, misused, a great hazard:

Do not visit without warning… if only you had telephoned to find out when it would be convenient for you to call…'callers' were Victorian characters who should have died out with their Victorian contemporaries.

Men in particular are apt to bring unexpected guests home for meals. Often, this is not entirely due to gay spirits… But first, they should telephone and make sure that there is food in the house for an extra guest…

The telephone has as many voices as a woman has hats and like a woman with her hats, there can be disastrous results.

Etiquette concerned most users less than the risk of infection from office and call-box phones used by so many other people. Finding several shreds of tobacco etc. in a mouthpiece aroused suspicions. For a re-assessment, R. E. O. Williams examined 153 instruments for the Ministry of Health and the Public Health Laboratory. His 1954 conclusion confirmed previous findings. That there was any particular risk of phones in ordinary use transmitting infection was improbable. On weekly 'disinfection', he found

that, while the disinfected telephones were cleaner than the others, there was no appreciable difference in the degree of bacterial contamination. Nor did the degree of contamination differ substantially between the day before and the day after disinfection… There was no clear justification for recommending regular disinfection (as distinct from cleaning) of telephones.

In short, if people heeded the scientific evidence, they could save themselves a weekly disinfection bill. Missing would be the nice smell left behind, temporarily. Kids helped put people off by amending Phonotas Girl adverts to read: 'She has come to sterilize you(r phone)'.

Contact between phone and user was avoided in offices with loud-speaking (or hands-free) phones, introduced in the late 1950s. Broadcasting a conversation, they allowed conferences between people at different locations. At first their use was restricted, for technical reasons, to internal systems.

There was an uneasy Cold War feeling that the authorities were being too suspicious, tapping phones unnecessarily in the name of security. Were there that many Reds under the bed? Card-carrying communists spoke carefully over the phone to their Covent Garden headquarters and to prominent party members. They did not know whether they were being bugged. The process was not as overt as in Argentina under Peron, where officials would interrupt, asking callers to speak more slowly. Far from being relaxed, peacetime surveillance was stepped up to combat nameless conspiracies. Much of UK tapping was done at a City office block, ostensibly a carpet company. Home Office vans collected samples.

The *Financial Times* political correspondent, Dr Paul Einzig, had his phone tapped following a May 1946 article giving 'the Cabinet's reasons for omitting from the White paper on the Iron and Steel Industry any justification of the Government's policy'. Like Frederick Kuh, London correspondent of the *Chicago Sun*, he had a foreign name and had been 'responsible for embarrassing disclosures in the past'. For doing a normal journalist's investigative job, both were monitored by MI5. This was known to the Prime Minister, Clement Attlee, and the Cabinet Secretary, Sir Norman Brook. Their concern was to find and plug the source of leaks. To do so, MI5 applied to the Home Secretary for the necessary warrants.

In the USA, amid a rising tide of anti-communist, anti-Soviet feeling, the atmosphere was even more suspicious. The menace seemed greater than during the Red scares after the First World War, when the authorities adopted tapping as a secret response to a situation they helped to create. To deal with espionage and subversion, the crusading J. Edgar Hoover secured broader FBI powers. University teachers, employees of government agencies, union officials, Hollywood actors, and many others of liberal views became suspect in the McCarthyite atmosphere, at its peak in 1953, the year that Julius and Ethel Rosenberg went to the electric chair in Sing Sing Prison for selling atomic secrets to the Soviet Union. Even the father of the atomic bomb, J. Robert Oppenheimer, was regarded as a security risk. The following year, after Senator McCarthy had been discredited, hysteria lessened, but by then tapping was thoroughly institutionalized. Perhaps though it was being misdirected. A more sinister threat to society came from the Mafia, whose growing heroin traffic was being run from Italy by the exiled Lucky Luciano over the transatlantic phone.

During the Korean War the Attlee and Churchill governments embarked on a rearmament programme, basically atomic. To protect the government machine against possible A- and later H-bomb attacks, the Whitehall tunnel network was made nuclear-proof. A 'hardened' (i.e. 'bombproof') exchange was installed under Holborn, and secret underground headquarters established at various sites, such as Cusworth Hall, a Georgian mansion near Doncaster, South Yorkshire, to house some form of administration after an atomic attack. From their bunkers and reinforced cellars, each of which had a communications room, senior civil and military personnel would in theory run local emergency services in spite of multi-megaton explosions, fall-out and radiation.

In protest against atomic weapons and to draw attention to the horrors of such warfare, in 1958 the newly formed Campaign for Nuclear Disarmament held its first Easter march, to the Aldermaston research establishment. So diametrically opposed to the government was the motley collection of marchers that the organizers had reason to suspect their phones were tapped. CND was the largest and most open band of nonconformists to have appeared since the war.

The Soviet spy Gordon Lonsdale, who was to be unmasked with the Krogers for obtaining information from the Admiralty underwater weapons base at Portland, claimed that when he came to London his

main task was to keep an eye on dangerous activities in Britain, especially those that might lead to a surprise nuclear attack against Socialist countries from British territory.

And, finally, I had to watch closely aggressive NATO activities, both military and political, directed against us and the uncommitted nations. I was soon making daily visits to a telephone kiosk on the Thames Embankment, near the back entrance to the Savoy Hotel. I pretended each time to use the telephone but in actual fact I felt beneath the wooden shelf holding the directories to see if a map-pin sign had been left for me.

At last, on one of my daily visits, I found the pin in its place. This meant that I had to visit a certain dead-letterbox which was described to me before I left USA.

Ironically, his contact kiosk was not a red one. It was outside the Institution of Electrical Engineers (phone number 1871, the year of its foundation), which between the wars wanted green to tone with the surrounding shrubbery.

In a world of manoeuvring superpowers and shifting allegiances, information on capabilities and intentions was worth gathering, by whatever means. 'Bugging' friends and enemies alike was fair game. In 1956, the year of the Suez Crisis, taps were found on two phones in the American military attache's residence in Israel, a state that depended for its very existence on US support. They had been installed by the Israeli intelligence service. Knowing where you stood was half the battle. Conversely, knocking out enemy communications helped. At 3 p.m. on 29 October 1956 four Israeli aircraft flew 12 feet above the Sinai Peninsula. The skilled pilots of the Second World War propellor-driven planes cut all the overhead lines serving the Egyptian forces, ready for the landing two hours later of 395 Israeli paratroopers in the Mitla Pass, Egypt's main supply route. Hostilities were halted on 7 November, largely through US pressure on Britain and France, which supported Israel. In a few transatlantic calls President Eisenhower, reportedly using 'cavalry barracks language', brought down the British Prime Minister, Eden, and destroyed British power in the Middle East. The Americans bugged the Russians – and *vice versa* – not just during the war. Commercial organizations did it to their competitors – Hazel Bishop Cosmetics lost $30 million in a year that way – and the precarious life of the industrial spy could be a profitable one.

The extent of authorized phone tapping in Britain was revealed 'as an exceptional measure' by the Birkett report in 1957. It showed that, following a brief post-war decrease in 'interceptions', their numbers had in general been rising. In contrast, fewer letters had been intercepted for police, customs, Post Office and security purposes. For security, no breakdown of categories was given. Instead, the report emphasized the importance of tapping in dealing with criminals. Information obtained for the police on the activities of Billy Hill, a 'notorious and self-confessed criminal', had been supplied to the Bar Council and raised parliamentary questions. These led to the report and, helped by the information, the Benchers of Lincoln's Inn found, among other things, that Mr P. A. Marrinan, 'in a manner unbecoming a gentleman and a barrister, had associated with persons of bad and disreputable character with criminal records'. Found guilty on this and other charges, he was disbarred. Some of Billy Hill's associates were arrested and convicted, and the police gave evidence of other successes from interception.

Escaped convicts had been recaptured and receivers of stolen property detected. During 1953–6, arrests made by the Metropolitan Police after direct interception had been 57 per cent of phones tapped, and up to the time of the Birkett Report in 1957 every interception but one had led to an arrest. Customs and Excise started using interceptions in 1946, when large-scale smugglers began circumventing exchange controls on capital exports. Such traffic was usually in diamonds. A smuggler believed to have illicitly exported £6 million in three years was convicted, and the overall success rate was high. Detection of major customs fraud through interception had been 80 per cent successful. MI5 said that it had identified major spies and detected communists operating in the Civil Service.

But was this a threat to civil liberties? *The Times* thundered in a first leader headed NOT FAR ENOUGH:

'Odious, invidious and obnoxious' was how a Home Secretary a hundred and fifty years ago branded the practice of intercepting and opening letters. The practice with its modern extension of telephone tapping is not less but more odious, invidious and obnoxious today. With good reason it is popularly associated with the worst excesses of the police state. It flies in the face of the free man's right to pursue his lawful affairs in privacy; and of all the means of detection it is the most open to sinister and corrupt abuse. It follows that before its use is sanctioned exceptionally strong justification must be advanced on the grounds of public advantage, and that if sufficient justification can in fact be found its use must be qualified by manifestly stringent safeguards.

The libertarian conclusion was:

One proposal that would enable the public to keep some track on what is going on they unaccountably reject. They were right, against departmental advice, to give with their report the figures of the number of warrants issued in years between 1937 and 1956. The very reasons which made that right make wrong their advice that no more should be published in the future. The figures should be issued annually so that the people may be given some clue to the extent of that threat to their liberties. Here, too, the Privy Councillors have not gone far enough in safeguarding the ordinary citizen.

There was little public disquiet, however, about what appeared an unattractive but necessary practice. *The Observer*, recovering from its vigorous stand against Eden's Suez venture, commented: 'to ban telephone tapping altogether would unfairly handicap the police in dealing with the more astute type of modern criminal, who himself takes every advantage of modern resources to outwit the law'. It went on to agree with Birkett's 'insistence that constant vigilance is necessary in a free society if the exercise of these powers is not to be abused'. Libertarians expressed reservations but theirs were the few voices of mild protest. For most people, 1984 and Big Brother watching them were far off.

Yet, after the Birkett Report was published, authorized tappings sharply increased. In 1958 the first national tapping centre was established in

Her Majesty Queen Elizabeth II enthusiastically inaugurated Subscriber Trunk Dialling (STD) in Britain in 1958. (BT Museum)

London, to centralize piecemeal operations in local exchanges. On a much grander scale was the Menwith Hill tapping centre in West Yorkshire, the main European base of the US Army Security Agency, planned in 1954 and opened in 1960. It was equipped to gather international political, military, and economic intelligence, with the secret co-operation of the British Post Office.

To the public at large, using the phone was becoming more do-it-yourself. Direct Distance Dialling (DDD), planned since 1944, started in 1951 in Englewood, New Jersey, to 12 US cities. Australia and Japan adopted the idea in 1956, and Canada in 1958. In the UK, in readiness, new local call areas were based on 'community of interest' instead of 'crow flight distance', greatly expanding most areas. On 5 December 1958 the Queen opened Subscriber Trunk Dialling (STD) by calling on a newly designed blue phone from Bristol the Lord Provost of Edinburgh. Some eighteen thousand Bristol subscribers could then dial about half the subscribers in Britain. As the system, based on the automatic GRACE (Group Routeing and Charging Equipment), was extended nationally, there were many local inaugurations. When GRACE failed, cub reporters had an obvious headline: GRACE IN DISGRACE. That acronym was overtaken by STD. Subscribers asked one another: 'Are you on STD yet?' Later, they had to be careful of the context. STD also stood for Sexually Transmitted Diseases: pox, clap, and genital herpes.

Subscriber Trunk Dialling was charged on a twopenny (less than 1p) unit. For the first time local calls were timed, the time bought decreasing with distance. The three-minute minimum on trunk calls ended, but so did 'pips' warning callers of the passage of time. They might need a pile of coins handy. A combination of the public still getting used to the system and old exchanges unfit to take the load increased the chances of misdialling or misrouteing. Dialling could feel like entering a lottery, and, on getting genuinely strange calls, several women screamed. A woman on Deeside, Scotland, had a number similar to one at Balmoral. One evening, on picking up the phone, she was asked 'Is that you, Gran?' She explained who she was and, after a short disbelieving silence, Prince Charles said: 'Good Lord, I've got a wrong number. So sorry.'

Recognizing that the service was becoming less personal, Ernest Marples, an energetic postmaster-general, encouraged a change in attitude:

> There will be more mechanization, fewer operators. But the people, many of them old and maybe a bit muddled, who cannot use the new mechanized services will need more help from personal operators. The intention is that the operators will lean over backwards to meet their wishes. Too long they have been inhibited by our own rules. In nine or 10 years three-quarters of trunk calls will be dialled. The remainder will call for more tact and skill than ever a Frankenstein machine can provide, and the remaining operators will have a more interesting job.

Immediately, he wanted them to be more friendly towards their customers. No longer restricted to stilted phrases such as 'Sorry you have been troubled' or 'If you will repeat the number I will change the line', they could give a brisk, cheerful greeting: 'Good morning, sir.'

More honeyed words of invitation were likely to be used by girls operating openly on pavements until the Street Offences Act 1959 forced them on to the phone. As media guru Marshall McLuhan put it: 'The phone puts the call girl at everybody's disposal.' Yet it could be hard to get a number or the number to suit a particular fancy. Some were available on carefully worded cards (e.g. 'Large chest for sale', 'Butterfly needs mounting', 'French lessons corrected') in places such as newsagents' windows, and *The Ladies' Directory* was clandestinely published, but probably most of those in need had appropriate numbers recommended.

The instrument was also being discovered for moving other goods. In

Italians latched on to the excuse of being engaged at the office.
(BT Museum)

In the early 1950s international communications could still be makeshift. From this hut, in which the operator wore Lapp boots to keep her feet warm, results in the Winter Olympics were relayed from Norefjell in Norway to the world.

(Norsk Teknisk Museum)

the US, market research methods were shaken up after the 1948 débâcle in which phone polling forecast Dewey to beat Truman for the presidency. The power of a number was shown in Germany in 1956 when the makers of 4711 eau de Cologne took Herr Koelsch of Siegen to court for damaging their interests by displaying the identical number prominently, and as he argued rightly, on his vehicle. His business was emptying cesspits, often an urgent service. In Britain, sexy voices kindled interest among local retailers lukewarm about stocking more frozen foods and other products. The regular call was welcomed and tripping through the list of items made the ordering routine a pleasure. That the participants never met helped preserve any illusions about their transactions. Busy in hiring and selling new and secondhand machinery, The 600 Group reckoned much of its success was due to one of the fastest switchboards in the south of England. It excelled because a general phone culture had not yet developed in Britain. It would come with the rising generation.

Answering calls when offices were unmanned could be worthwhile. Like the dial, the telephone answering machine was invented by a businessman who believed he was losing trade through the shortcomings of the existing service. In the USA Joseph L. Zimmerman developed the Electronic Secretary, and in 1949, with George W. Danner, incorporated a company including that name. His first machine simply answered, typically stating:

'Mr Smith is not in the office. He should be back at 3 o'clock. Could you please call again after then.' This was not enough. Many were unwilling to call back but wanted to leave a message. In the UK during the 1950s Ansafone Limited marketed and installed a Swiss telephone answering machine, the Ipsophone. Weighing $2\frac{1}{2}$ hundredweight, it took two men three days to install. Recording was on a wire and the opening announcement fixed. As smaller machines were developed they appealed outside business. Orthodox Jews, for example, could receive messages on the Sabbath without themselves activating electricity. Like a time switch, an answering machine was a convenient robot, a *shabbas goy*.

When phones were not available a walkie-talkie could sometimes be used, but it was as big as a large biscuit tin. An Extel employee had one suspended over his stomach under a raglan raincoat at Manchester and Aintree racecourses early in 1957. Extel, like other news agencies, refusing to accept the costs and terms demanded for phone facilities, especially during the Grand National, made its own arrangements. They worked. Newspapers and private subscribers got their normal racing service. After the last race the Extel employee was glad to get a weight off his stomach.

Through communications the world was becoming smaller. In 1956, 90 years after the first successful transatlantic telegraph cable and 80 years after the invention of the phone, the first transatlantic telephone cable was laid. Since 1927 transatlantic conversations had been by radio. In late 1946 waiting time for a UK–USA booked call was up to three hours. Then the call was limited to three minutes, but might in effect be shorter because reception quality varied. Such conditions made some GI brides, getting used to a strange land and separated from their families by an ocean, all the more lonely. Cable made all the difference. Users reckoned it was 'much better than a local call' or 'like talking in the same room'. Because they could talk naturally and be heard easily, people were glad to use the new link. Originally it was thought that 36 conversations at any one time would be ample, so the radio circuits were closed down. In the first year of the cable transatlantic calls doubled. Even so, international letter-writing would not decline as quickly as the inland habit. Most people did not even contemplate overseas calls.

Another means of bridging oceans and great distances was to become a reality. In *Wireless World* October 1945 Arthur C. Clarke, later better known for his science fiction, asked the question: 'Extra-Terrestrial Relays – Can Rocket Stations Give World-Wide Radio-Coverage?' He pointed out that, with powerful rockets, satellites could be placed in orbit over the equator. Synchronized with the earth's rotation, they would appear to remain stationary. Only three satellites would be needed for world-wide coverage of all possible types of service, including television:

In the first week of the first trans-atlantic telephone cable going into service in September 1956 UK calls to Canada were up by 85 per cent and those from Canada up 100 per cent. Many family calls were made during the night and Sunday reduced rate periods. (BT Museum)

In October 1945 Arthur C. Clarke brilliantly predicted in Wireless World *that transmitters could be carried on artificial satellites of the earth. He gave the exact conditions for putting a satellite into orbit so that it remained stationary over a given spot on the earth's surface.*

(Wireless World)

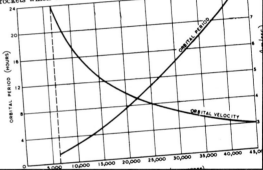

October 1945 **Wireless World**

305

EXTRA-TERRESTRIAL RELAYS
Can Rocket Stations Give World-wide Radio Coverage?

By ARTHUR C. CLARKE

ALTHOUGH it is possible, by a suitable choice of frequencies and routes, to provide telephony circuits between any two points or regions of the earth for a large part of the time, long-distance communication is greatly hampered by the peculiarities of the ionosphere, and there are even occasions when it may be impossible. A true broadcast service, giving constant field strength at all times over the whole globe would be invaluable, not to say indispensable, in a world society.

Unsatisfactory though the telephony and telegraph position is, that of television is far worse, since ionospheric transmission cannot be employed at all. The service area of a television station, even on a very good site, is only about a hundred miles across. To cover a small country such as Great Britain would require a network of transmitters, connected by coaxial lines, waveguides or VHF relay links. A recent theoretical study[1] has shown that such a system would require repeaters at intervals of fifty miles or less. A system of this kind could pro-

never return. This "orbital" velocity is 8 km per sec. (5 miles per sec), and a rocket which attained it would become an artificial satellite, circling the world for ever with no expenditure of power—a second moon, in fact. The German transatlantic rocket A10 would have reached more than half this velocity.

It will be possible in a few more years to build radio controlled rockets which can be steered into

fixed in the sky of a whole hemisphere and unlike all other heavenly bodies would neither rise nor set. A body in a smaller orbit would revolve more quickly than the earth and so would rise in the west, as indeed happens with the inner moon of Mars.

Using material ferried up by rockets, it would be possible to construct a "space-station" in such an orbit. The station could be provided with living quarters, laboratories and everything needed for the comfort of its crew

Many may consider the solution proposed in this discussion too far-fetched to be taken very seriously. Such an attitude is unreasonable, as everything envisaged here is a logical extension of developments in the last ten years – in particular the perfection of the long-range rocket of which V2 was the prototype. While this article was being written, it was announced that the Germans were considering a similar project, which they believed possible within fifty to a hundred years.

That time-scale proved pessimistic. German rocket engineers captured by the Americans and Russians were spurred into competition. On 4 October 1957 the Soviet Union successfully launched the 180lb Sputnik I, which circled the earth in 95 minutes. From Moscow the Russians rang the Cheshire village of Goostrey, checking Sputnik's progress with Bernard Lovell, director of Manchester University's radio telescope at Jodrell Bank. A month later Sputnik II carried an Eskimo dog, Laika, so that living conditions in space could be studied. In December an American satellite launch failed. World prestige and military advantage were the prize in the race to produce a successful satellite system.

Progress like this emphasized the enormous differences between nations and places. In 1948 Africa's most populous country, Nigeria, had only one place from which an overseas phone call could be made, a booth in Lagos. The service was indeed personal. The caller was summoned, by messenger if necessary, and the quality of his call personally monitored by an engineer for undue distortion and fading, the radio 'wow-wow' effect. This one phone was an improvement. Before 1948 the only overseas tele-communication was by telegraph, on an undersea cable.

In an Indian village the one place certain to be connected was the railway station, and an official often acted as go-between, perhaps between doctor and patient. The police station too might be able to help. A similar situation existed in remote Italian villages, as in Tuscany, and in the Abruzzi, not that far from Rome, where the one phone would typically be looked after by the literate person who wrote letters and read replies for people. Compulsory education after the age of 11 was introduced only in 1948 and many from large, poor families had never been to school, especially where travelling distances were long, the roads bad and transport expensive. There were *telefoni pubblici*, public phones in private houses, minded by an illiterate. When taking a message, such a person memorized the name and number to be called. Matching the numbers on a piece of paper to the numbers on a dial could be laborious. However cumbersome the facilities, they did lessen the demand for scribes and readers.

Across the Atlantic phones were an everyday convenience in all sorts of places. They were installed for example by parking slots at BAR-B-Qs so that customers could sit and order, having their meal delivered on a tray that clipped to the car door. There were drive-up phone booths. A gold-plated phone was an acceptable present for a head of state, such as Batista in Cuba. That 'thrice-accursed Judas', the Soviet police chief Beria, had a gold one on his desk, for making the most dreaded calls on behalf of his master, Stalin. Even under Khruschev's post-Stalinist thaw, however intense the competition in space, there was no eagerness to develop a public service rivalling the other superpower.

Although cable made transatlantic speech much clearer, people were still encouraged to send traditional telegrams, including greetings.

(BT Museum)

CHAPTER 15

MR AND MRS EVERYMAN

On 4 August 1962 the 36-year-old actress Marilyn Monroe was found dead in bed, face down, the phone under her. Normally, not to be disturbed, she never kept it in her bedroom. Nobody knew whether she had taken an overdose and was calling for help or had been killed for the secrets she might reveal. The controversy would last for years. She once said to a companion: 'Do you know who I've always depended on? Not strangers, not friends. The telephone! That's my best friend.' Its significance in her dying moments was caught by Ernesto Cardenal in his *Oración por Marilyn Monroe*:

A feature of the generation gap in the Swinging Sixties was young people using the phone as much as, if not more than, grown-ups. The mood is captured in Dodie Masterman's drawing. (ITU)

Lord, whoever it was that she was going to call up, she did not call (perhaps it was no one, perhaps it was Somebody whose name is not in the Los Angeles telephone directory) answer Thou the telephone!

The image of the dead Monroe summed up the sixties: the growth of international communications, leading to the rapid spread of ideas, instant reputations, and common cultures, good or bad; the need to make personal contact, especially reaching out for lifelines in emergencies, drug-related, political, or whatever; in the ferment of new ideas, authority protecting itself against possible subversive elements. TV and radio, which quickly became mass media, were largely soliloquies. The phone, which took almost a century to become a medium of the masses, offered a dialogue, with the potential to become a conference. It helped create new communities of interest, bringing together people of like mind. If you were not on the phone, you were poor or a recluse.

Its popularity was evident from various film roles. In *Midnight Lace* (1960) Rex Harrison terrorized his wife, Doris Day, with threatening calls on a small tape recorder. Elizabeth Taylor starred as the society call-girl in *BUtterfield 8*. More cheerfully, Judy Holliday appeared with Dean Martin in the film version of the Broadway musical *Bells Are Ringing*, in which a telephone answering service operator became passionately involved in her clients' lives. The screen version of *Bye Bye Birdie*, featuring the number 'The Telephone Hour', in which kids chat to one another after school, was less successful than on stage. In *The Slender Thread* (1966) a volunteer social worker had to cope with a would-be suicide while police tracked her down. The psychiatrist in the political-satirical farce *The President's Analyst* (1967) was pursued by spies of every nationality, the chief villain finally unmasked being the phone company. On the TV show *Laugh-In*, Lily Tomlin played Ernestine, the switchboard operator as petty bureaucrat with her catch-phrase: 'Is the party to whom I am speaking…?'

Increasingly, the party was likely to be overseas. The earth was being girdled with undersea cables, but a Commonwealth round-the-world phone system planned in 1958 was abandoned when South Africa declared itself a republic on 31 May 1961 and withdrew from the project. Global coverage was going to be politically easier to achieve with satellites in space. The first active telecommunications satellite, the 170lb Telstar, was launched from Cape Canaveral, Florida, on 10 July 1962, relaying phone calls and TV pictures to a 'dish' at Goonhilly, Cornwall, not far from Poldhu, whence Marconi had had the first transatlantic radio signal transmitted to him in Newfoundland in 1901.

An enemy might shoot down or disable a satellite but this new radio technique had arrived in time to save the peace. On Monday 22 October

Satellite ground stations like the UK's first one at Goonhilly in Cornwall were to help shrink the world to a global village. (BT Museum)

1962 President Kennedy announced that the Russians had installed in Cuba missiles capable of a first strike against American cities. For ten tense days it looked as though the great powers, in a trial of strength, were on the brink of nuclear war. *The Observer* conveyed the atmosphere:

> Everyone was watching the President. To his friends he seemed controlled and reasonably relaxed. But throughout the week he was never more than a few steps away from a telephone. Ever since the danger of sudden nuclear attack, the telephone had become the most crucial part of the President's equipment: whenever he moved, the switchboard moved with him, and even at the airport a wheeled trolley carried a telephone at his side.
>
> The 'situation room', just inside the west wing of the basement of the White House, was manned twenty-four hours a day by the President's aides, including McGeorge Bundy and his deputy, Carl Kaysen.
>
> Equally important was the telephone between Washington and General Norstad, the cool and sophisticated commander of Nato. After Kennedy's speech, he ordered American forces in Europe to a state of 'awareness' – the first of three pre-arranged stages of preparation for trouble in Europe which he had introduced about eighteen months before.

Meanwhile, at Plas Penrhyn, his rented home in North Wales, the 90-year old philosopher Bertrand Russell, an ardent campaigner for nuclear disarmament, after hearing Kennedy's broadcast had sent off telegrams. They were phoned through via Manchester to Kennedy; the Soviet leader Khrushchev; the British Prime Minister, Harold Macmillan; the leader of the opposition, Hugh Gaitskell; and the acting Secretary-General of the United Nations, U Thant. Copies of the texts were read to British newspapers, which showed no interest. Undeterred, Russell tried to mobilize mediators: in Africa the Nobel Peace Prize winner Albert Schweitzer, in Puerto Rico the Spanish cellist Pablo Casals, and in America the millionaire friend of Khrushchev, Cyrus Eaton. Russell also proposed that the scientists who had gathered at intervals since 1957 in Eaton's home village of Pugwash, Nova Scotia, hold an emergency meeting.

His pleas attracted no attention until the Tass news agency issued from Moscow Khrushchev's long, conciliatory reply. Russell's house was besieged. World-wide calls blocked the phone and, next morning, 36 journalists turned up. When a clash had been avoided but the missiles remained, Russell and his secretary sent further cables to Kennedy, the Cuban leader Castro, and Khrushchev. At Portmadoc exchange the night operator said: 'Don't you ever get any sleep, you two?' It was a striking demonstration of an individual exercising power on a world scale through modern communications, irrespective of his geographical position. A man such as Russell, whose phone bill for that quarter was over £400 but still a fraction of what world leaders spent on communications, did not need to be in the corridors of power to exert an international influence. In the event the crisis was solved through diplomatic channels, by Kennedy and Khrushchev corresponding secretly. When Khrushchev's opponents staged a coup in 1964, one of their ploys was changing Kremlin phone numbers.

There was no direct White House–Kremlin phone line, a war-preventive link once suggested by Sweden. The 'hot line' established in 1963 was a teleprinter link, not, as many supposed, an instant emergency line. Until 1984 messages in the originating language were encoded; transmitted between basements in the Pentagon and Moscow at about 66 words a minute; deciphered, translated and typed before being faxed to the other leader. The system was little used. To prevent a similar crisis recurring, even a peacemaker adopted an aggressive approach. Russell's secretary on his own initiative made transatlantic calls soliciting funds for the Atlantic Peace Foundation, using, as one potential campaigner put it, 'high-pressure tactics in money-raising that I do not like'.

In 1963 operators could dial UK–US calls direct and International Subscriber Dialling (ISD), later known as International Direct Dialling (IDD), was introduced between London and Paris. Distances between peoples were shrinking. 'The new electronic interdependence recreates the world in the image of a global village,' asserted Marshall McLuhan in *The Gutenberg Galaxy* (1962). At the time residents of Florence, which was not linked automatically to other Italian cities, complained they could not get out-of-town connections. The operator was busy helping children with their Latin and Greek homework.

Northern Europeans holidaying around the Mediterranean called home. To talk to family and friends, tourists queued at phone boxes in the evenings to use lines occupied by businessmen during the day. Characters such as Patricia Highsmith's talented psychopath Tom Ripley flourished in their intrigues without frontier. Easy, quality phone links helped the growth of multinational companies; individuals had to catch up with the new facilities. In the European headquarters of International Telephone and Telegraph Corporation in Brussels a British manager confessed to an American vice-president that he could not reach the man he wanted because he was in Puerto Rico, to which the American replied: 'Don't they have phones in Puerto Rico?' Later in the decade, a Brighton hotel waiter came into an international conference and announced: 'Excuse me Mr Chairman. There's a call for' – he garbled a foreign name – 'it's from the Continent!' With more of the world at their fingertips, many office workers had limits put on the distances over which they could call.

The rising generation had a broader horizon. In Britain it was growing

*London and New York, first con-
nected in 1927, in 1970 introduced
direct dialling between subscribers.*
(BT Museum)

up in the TV world of *Dr Who*, who from 1963 travelled to time warps simply by entering Tardis, a police public call box. Easy communications led to adventures. The American poet Howard Nemerov hymned 'The Dial Tone', and John Updike published a collection, *Telephone Poles*. A call I made from New York in 1969 to my 12-year old daughter led to my writing:

To promote use of the phones and equipment it made, ITT Austria commissioned cartoons.

(ITT Austria)

Dear Judy
When I phoned you transatlantic
You said: 'Hold on, daddy,
There's some Latin to check.'
Now here's the bill. *Et tu,* Judy?

There was a ready-made market for dial locks – which still permitted incoming calls – especially in homes with talkative teenagers or an overseas *au pair*.

In the USA enterprising youngsters dialled for free with home-made blue boxes that generated control tones. Their skills were to find even more profitable outlets in creating the personal computer industry in the late 1970s. Meanwhile, Phone Freaks such as Captain Marvel dialled around the world, revealing the backwardness and inefficiency of many overseas phone systems. In newly independent Ghana, for example, when the repairman arrived he was given the customary West African 'dash'. Realizing they had a profitable business in their hands, phone staff created faults for the best returns. No dash, no repairs. Soon subscribers felt that all faults were man-made.

In Britain the blame was laid on soaring demand, too much for the ageing equipment. Wrong numbers in the Chester area were caused by an 18-foot giraffe in the local zoo tangling the wires with its tongue. Criticisms were voiced in Parliament and Press. A one-day investigation reported by *The Sun* on 21 February 1966, showed a fault rate of 17 per 50 calls. Sometimes a call had more than one fault and there were faulty calls when reporting a fault. Small wonder there was little demand for musical phone rests, which played a tune to a caller when his party left temporarily. The main problem was getting through in the first place. Early in 1965 Ford estimated that call failures cost up to £750 a week in executives' wasted time. At the Paris Air Show that year exhibitors complained that several hours' delay on the London–Paris lines hampered sales. Unfavourable comparisons were drawn between the US private enterprise system and the UK public service. In the mid-1960s the percentage of British residential connections reached the 1927 US level. On paper some 90 per cent of UK service was automatic but not in practice.

Not that the US system was perfect. In 1965 a New York housewife, Rose Brown, who had a phone number the same as the White House and an area code almost identical, 212 for New York against 202 for Washington, got many of the President's calls. President Johnson wrote thanking her for her diplomacy in handling them and promised to be just as careful in receiving calls for the Brown family. In 1969–70 New York suffered service failures through a combination of factors: increased Wall Street trading, the inclusion of local phone service in welfare payments, more muggings keeping people indoors, and under-investment in equipment and service staff. Increased demand later caused snarl-ups in other cities such as Boston, Denver and Houston.

At the end of the decade call failure was still a key fact about the phone in a UK Consumers' Association survey. The situation seemed an impasse more prolonged than 'The day two phone robots crossed their lines', reported by the *Daily Express* in 1961:

> Faces are red in the GPO – almost puce in fact – because Robot George managed to dial Robot Charlie and each just went on talking.
>
> They were still talking hours later when someone realized something was wrong and order was restored.
>
> Robot George is an automatic device at an unmanned power station

somewhere in the provinces – officials will not say where. If there is a power failure George automatically dials 'operator' and says: There is a fault at — power station. Please send repair men.

There was a failure and George dialled O. No one had told him you now dial 100.

Robot Charlie's job, when someone dials O is to say: You no longer dial 'O' for operator. Please replace your receiver and dial '100'.

So George got Charlie, and their marathon backchat began.

Mr Ted Dollery, editor of *The Telephonist*, reveals the story in his current issue, and says: 'They were like statesmen at a peace conference – and with about the same effect.'

In its early days STD was not universally popular, especially among pay-phone users. There was scarcely time for the other party to identify himself or herself before an angry burst of pips demanded money. Having paid, you might be through to the wrong party. Time bought seemed all too short. 'Put in more money quickly' ran the stern notice. Occasionally, through a fault, a user might get more than the allotted time or distance. The canny used STD for signalling: a homecoming commuter would call from the station with an agreed number of rings for his wife to come and collect him.

Something else to get used to was the 1966 end of exchange names such as ABBey, TEMple Bar and VICtoria. Even if you didn't know exactly where the exchange was (FEDeral was an unlisted government one) you often knew its locality, which gave it a character. Changing to numbers made it less personal: 230 1212 did not seem the Scotland Yard of WHItehall 1212. Tom Stoppard wrote a 30-minute verse play *If You're Glad I'll Be Frank* (1968) about the TIM voice, but nobody was likely to be similarly inspired by 123. Dialling CHICKEN for a delivery was much easier than trying to remember seven digits. Young pop fans found it fun to dial BEATLES, though it distressed a housewife on a BECkenham number. Numbers were not only difficult to remember; in the expanding service they grew longer, increasing the chances of error.

To administrations, the change-over was logical and necessary. *General News* in the USA set out to explain All Number Calling (ANC) in 1960:

Disadvantages to the two-letter, five-digit telephone numbers include: confusion between the letter O and the numerical zero, and the letter I and the number 1; with many names, such as MUrryhill, and MErcury there is frequently confusion between the prefixes which use different letters for identical sounds; others such as ENdicott seem to begin with the second letter of the prefix; also, a limited number of prefixes are available since the names

HAI - I and FAR - ewell !

Must we forever say goodbye to you
Poetic KEAts and WORdsworth — BYRon too?
Majestic ELGar, stirring IVAnhoe,
Immortal DICkens, GIBbon (the scholar's woe);
ARNold (of Rugby?), DRYden the classicist,
ALBert the Good and GLAdstone the moralist:
CLIssold and DUNcan (who on earth were they?),
PRImrose the pretty, VALentine the gay;
Audacious ACOrn, leafy PERivale,
Sleepy LAGoon and pastoral IVYdale;
Mysterious EMBerbrook, stern COPpermill,
Crafty FOX Lane, seductive GIPsy Hill;

Alas! Your days are numbered and perforce
The past must yield and progress run its course.
Time marches on and calls us to pursue;
Tomorrow to fresh dials and systems new!

ALL·FIGURE TELEPHONE NUMBERS

01-846 4905

an essential step in expanding the telephone service

Losing familiar exchange names was resented in many countries and phone administrations had to make the case for the change to all-number calling.
(BT Museum)

are based on a combination of two digits. This explains such inappropriate names as YUkon and KLondike in Florida.

Additionally, there are no appropriate names which could be used with such combinations as XY, JK, PS, WX, eliminating their availability. The use of seven-digit numbers will make available many more central office codes, since numbers can be used in any combination. This situation will eliminate the need for numbers of more than seven digits in the foreseeable future.

Nationally, conversion to ANC seemed to proceed without opposition. Small and medium-sized communities accepted it without demur. The Hyatt hotel chain paid $40,000 and $5,000 in hotel credits for 243 2546

(CHECK IN). Opposition erupted in San Francisco, a capital for radicals and odd-balls, but by no means the only objectors to 'the cult of technology'. Conservatives joined the Anti Digit Dialling League, founded by a freelance public relations operator Carl May, a Quaker peacenik, to retain exchange names such as KLondike and YUkon. New Yorkers wanted to keep their famous names such as SPring, the city's first exchange just three years younger than the phone itself, and BUtterfield 8. In Washington the Committee of Ten Million to Oppose All Number Calling was optimistically formed. All the protest achieved was a delay in converting some cities entirely to ANC. New Yorkers and San Franciscans could speak of some exchanges as personal institutions a while longer.

To the public, the new system seemed to benefit the administration more than them. They saw all-figure dialling causing so many problems. Anne Hare, a housewife living near Gatwick Airport, had her fair share. At first she was given the former number of an office-cleaning company. Still appearing in Yellow Pages, it produced enquiries. Through a fault, she then got calls for an airline. When that was put right she received Gatwick flight enquiries, the number for which had all but two digits close to hers. Either through misdialling or faults she was getting unanswerable queries in the small hours. To end her misery the Post Office wanted to delete the number, but it went to a call box, which people dialled. Getting no reply, they thought she was always out.

Subscribers going straight from manual to STD experienced the biggest shock. Instead of calling the operator, who might well know them personally, they suddenly had to dial. Post Office supervisors such as Cicely Hammond in rural Kent tried to sort out problems:

> I remember going round to one old girl who was crying. She said 'I don't think I'll ever be able to work this thing.' She was a cripple. She said 'What shall I do?' When she felt ill she used to call the operator and say 'I want the doctor'. We knew who her doctor was and we'd ring him. We had to explain the new system to her.

As STD spread, fewer operators were needed, to everybody's relief especially in unsocial, unpopular working hours. Staff who left were not always replaced and jobs were not necessarily secure, long-serving employees sometimes becoming redundant on more than one occasion. Annual 'Hello Girl' competitions were held both to boost flagging morale and to improve customer relations. The character of the work changed. With the routine calls fully automated, operators were left to deal with transferred charges, credit-card calls, freephone, emergency calls, difficulties and the awkward squad: niggly people who couldn't deal with

Telephonists were encouraged to project a friendly personality to subscribers. (BT Museum)

the system, who'd been upset by it, or who were furious because it didn't work.

Nor was it always the old style operator – in the Ministry of Housing they still wore white cotton gloves, which kept hands clean, plugs grease-free and protected them against shocks – who was dealing with them. Towards the end of her career Cecily Hammond saw attitudes towards respected Post Office training change:

> The younger girls – the telephone generation, who took the instrument for granted – had been so used to kicking authority (e.g. answering teachers back, which we never dreamt of doing) that they didn't take easily to this. I had one girl when I was a supervisor who was a long time before she could bring herself to say 'sorry' because she wasn't. She'd done what she could and she wasn't going to adopt the almost bowing and scraping attitude that we'd grown up with. To us the public was always right. Even though they were wrong they were right. If you got a chap in a call box who was drunk and swearing at you you never swore back. We were always told to put a smile in our voice. We were not to sound bored, fed up. You could cope with the odd one but a string of them, which is what you got on STD, was a bit much. I once had a chap on for a quarter of an hour bitching about the postcode system when that started. It was nothing to do with me but I had to listen. I couldn't tell him to buzz off.
>
> You might feel that people at the other end were stupid but you couldn't imply it. People don't read directories, don't know how to look up numbers. I asked the girls how often they would ask a porter or somebody on a London station for reassurance about where and when their train left. The old girl at the other end may sound silly but she probably only makes one call in six years. She doesn't understand what you're talking about. Directory enquiries I enjoyed. People were grateful for what you'd done. Of course we used to get teenagers asking us for pop stars' phone numbers.

Another difficulty was the increasing number of foreigners – immigrants, tourists and people in business, such as continental lorry drivers – wanting directions:

> They could be a problem to understand. Chinese, Pakistanis, and Jamaicans tended to be soft spoken or to slide their words. Some operators got impatient with foreigners and put them on to the supervisor: 'I can't understand this bloke'. You sometimes had to connect foreigners to the international exchange so that they could be understood.

Lacking customary English and local knowledge, immigrants were not necessarily ideal operators, even when they were badly needed and turnover was high:

> In a sense operators have to be more highly trained than ever because the routine's been taken out of the job. No more easy calls. The ongoing personal relationship has gone. Also the Post Office found by the sixties that giving too much help was uneconomic. If you haven't got a certain amount of information the Post Office won't help, e.g. name and initials of somebody you want. It's all timed and costed for staffing levels. Ticketing was largely taken over by metering.

Occasional lighter moments relieved the monotony, as at Chatham, Kent, where operators got a spate of mildly obscene calls. The caller always asked what colour bra they were wearing and went on to discuss its size and features: 'Is it trimmed with lace? Do you like lace?' Kept talking and traced, he proved to be a lingerie firm representative for whom dialling 100 from a call box was cheap market research. The chances were that he would get a different operator each time he called. At least it was more straightforward than pinching directories from kiosks, a way some commercial travellers obtained a ready-made guide to their territory. It was also an example of intimate questions being asked and answered over the phone, questions that might not be posed face to face.

In an age of shifting standards, etiquette writers upheld good phone manners. 'When they are away from each other a man should write or telephone his wife every day,' stated Barbara Cartland, adding firmly, 'The same applies to his wife.' She went on to advise: 'Telephone calls in other people's houses must always be paid for and, when making the call, be careful to ask how much it is.' For her part she chose 'secretaries with soft, charming voices because they represent me'. In *The Complete Guide to Etiquette* Betty Messenger prescribed the correct form for secretaries when answering, stiltedly pointing out: '"OK," "Hang on a minute," "He'll be with you in a minute," etc., are naturally not representative of ideal telephonic manners for a secretary.'

Anne Edwards and Drusilla Beyfus devoted nearly four pages to the subject in *Lady Behave* (1969), dealing with topics such as calling up for a long gossip, phoning department stores and ministries, and how to dodge the unwanted caller. They reckoned 'to give expert advice on freezing off the Bores, Bullies and Belligerent Boy Friends who badger you on the telephone'. A monumental untruth reserved for impossible pesterers was to be out of phone distance. Another stratagem was:

> Putting Granny on the telephone. Most elderly grannies are guaranteed not

New designs like this lightweight Trimphone gave the instrument a sexier image, but its 'warble' could be mistaken for a blackbird.

(BT Museum)

to hear properly the name asked for, and to say emphatically and with complete honesty that no one of that name lives here, when in fact they do. The cleverness of this technique is that the quavery sincerity of Granny's voice leaves no suspicion in the mind of the caller.

Less subtly, advantage could be taken of foreign helps whose English was extremely limited.

They omitted advice on dealing with obscene callers, a growing menace. From late 1965 American Bell offered subscribers a 'called-party holding' device which, at the push of a button, signalled the exchange and locked the caller's number for tracing even after the call was finished. It led to arrests and convictions but did not stamp out the problem.

Certainly the phone was becoming more intrusive, penetrating into people's lives because of techniques such as opinion polling and direct selling. As it became less an option and more a necessary item, so pollsters could reach representative groups. The dwindling number of phone-less were less important anyway, either for their opinions or their buying power. Some callers deliberately blurred the distinction, pretending to be on a survey when in fact they were sounding out prospects' needs, ready for a sales approach. In the USA they were unflatteringly known as 'telephone solicitors'.

Salesmen to industry and commerce could save the time and effort of travelling. Their customers were being dispersed. Whereas communities were thought of as belonging to a particular place, sociologists now talked about non-place communities and emphasized the importance of being able to reach other people rather than being next door to them. The Location of Offices Bureau used the argument in its efforts to move employment out of London. Consulting engineers did not have to cluster in Victoria Street and jobs such as insurance administration could just as easily be done in suburbia or out in the countryside. Direct dialling enabled people who were physically separated to keep in easy contact. You did not always have to be there to make the sale, especially in repeat business for established, tangible products.

Persuasion techniques were becoming more sophisticated, and apparently simple conversations were in fact carefully structured and scripted in favour of the caller. A telesales trainer reveals a little:

> There is a difference between what can be done when you can see somebody and when you're on the phone. You can achieve as much but you must know the rules of the game. Don't let anyone pull your strings. You've got to learn how to use theirs.
>
> You must give the person a choice to make them feel important, to make them feel that they are controlling the situation. By giving a choice you actually bring it round to your side... you can feel a clinical puppeteer using the wires to manipulate the person at the other end. It's a game. You can see reflex actions.
>
> No body language can be transmitted over the telephone. You have only two things, words and tone. It's amazing how you can feel reactions along a telephone line. You're using your instincts because you're blind, like the

other senses of blind people being sharpened. It's not so much what is said so much as the manner. You can't put your finger on what it is but you've picked it up. It's a soul feeling more than a simple gut feeling. Although you hold the phone to your ear you feel down in your stomach with it. The thing that creates that feeling isn't the words that are spoken but those that aren't.

Practical psychology works in telesales and there are many tricks to the trade, apparently self-evident truths that take time to learn and put into practice. Quick reactions are essential. Karen Seary, a management and training adviser at the Industrial Society:

I once phoned a chap to fix an appointment and I soon realized he knew the technique. We played about for a bit and then I asked 'Where were you trained?'. We'd been trained by the same person.

Books have been written on the techniques but the perfect manual does not exist:

There is no high priest, no Dale Carnegie of telephone selling. If there were it's more likely to be a priestess. Somebody who could put down in writing how to do it so that anybody in any industry could pick it up and do it would earn a fortune.

Far from public ken, phone tapping was increasing, mainly for 'security' purposes. For instance, the lawyer William Rees-Davis knew his phone was tapped when he was acting in 1963 for Stephen Ward, a central figure in the Profumo affair. Through his association with a call-girl, Profumo, the war minister, appeared to be endangering national security and several phones must have been tapped in an alleged search for the truth. When Lord Gardiner, a pacifist who had appeared for prominent political figures, became Lord Chancellor in 1964, he discussed some matters with the Attorney-General, Sir Elwyn Jones, in his car because he feared that MI5 was bugging his phone. The US Attorney–General, Robert Kennedy, authorized wire tapping of the civil rights leader Dr Martin Luther King.

By the mid-1960s the UK national tapping centre had 300 lines, and a training unit had been established. In 1968, when 333 tapping warrants were signed, more than twice the 1956 number, new systems were brought together at a centre nicknamed 'Tinkerbell'. Its curtains were always drawn and the building manned 24 hours a day. Exactly what went on behind its locked doors – it moved in 1980 – remained secret. Informed guesses suggested that computers enabled specified connections to be logged automatically, contents of calls transcribed quickly, and 'voice-prints' recorded, as unique to individuals as fingerprints. Perhaps the tappers could also interpret scrambled conversations. Increased surveillance promoted sales of simple £50–£100 scramblers. They were worth it, compared with the value of the information they protected.

The most spectacular example of phone tapping was in the Middle East, where it was widely believed that Israeli intelligence eavesdropped on an Egyptian–Jordanian conversation suggesting that Israel was vulnerable and would succumb to the surrounding Arab armies. Forewarned, the Israeli Defence Minister Moshe Dayan staged a preventive war in June 1967, during which the Arab forces were trounced in six days.

Security companies saw the advantages of radio-telephones. Securicor started installing them in patrol vans in mid-1960, soon adding them to cash-carrying vehicles as well. Communications became an effective weapon in the haulage industry battle against hijackers. A driver of a high-value load such as alcohol, cigarettes, cosmetics, or hi-fi equipment became less vulnerable if, from his cab or through an unmarked escort vehicle, he could be in regular touch with a radio control room. Several local and national private mobile radio-telephone services developed. Local taxis were natural users; in 1961 a service from aircraft was introduced; and in 1965 the Post Office radio-telephone service for vehicle users, which had started in South Lancashire, was extended to the London area.

All the services were based on a radio control room handling messages, acting as a link between the traveller and the other party. Executives out of the office were not out of reach; many service staff kept contact with their base. Typical users were vending machine operators and service engineers for computers, lifts, traffic light systems and the like. Individual subscribers such as doctors, or vets shuttling between all creatures great and small, did not want to lose time in an emergency. The self-employed appreciated that time was money. No longer need messages be received too late for action. As in an office, users could be abreast of events. On the move, they could re-assess priorities, change arrangements and tell others. When Securicor started its parcels service in 1968, it equipped the vehicles with radios. Private users quickly appreciated facilities essential to ambulances and the police. Their value to the police was dramatized in the BBC TV series *Z Cars*, first seen in January 1962.

In emergencies speedy communications were vital. When thieves broke in through the roof of Brussels Museum of Ancient Art in February 1964 and stole Rubens' famous picture *Negro Heads*, there was widespread concern. Reproduced on the Belgian 500 franc note and described by the museum curator as 'priceless', the picture was almost impossible to sell but he valued it at $1 million (£357,000). The 19-year-old thief, André Beugnies, underestimated what he could get and the resources of the police. When demanding the equivalent of about $14,000, he was traced to a call box and arrested.

That same year Mrs Addie McCormick, a 64-year-old operator in the Beacon Arms Hotel, Ottawa, stayed at her switchboard to warn guests that a fire had broken out. It gutted the 300-room building but only two of the 60 guests were killed. Addie died in the blaze and was posthumously awarded the Royal Canadian Humane Association's gold medal for her 'heroic devotion to duty'. When student demonstrations spread after the May 1968 riots in Paris, rumour control centres were opened in the USA to reassure callers worried about social upheaval.

To many, society seemed less stable. Wanton damage to phone kiosks was only one example of disregard for public property and others' needs. Vandalism was an international problem, the motive often theft. Addicts desperate for drug money found coin boxes a worthwhile target, though in some poor areas drug dealers protected them so that they could conduct their business. In New York boxes were reinforced with stainless-steel jackets, but these could be exploded by a fire-cracker stuffed into the coin-return slot. Narrowing the slot made it difficult for the large-fingered to get their change. Cords on public phones had an armoured sheath and an inside steel strand. Theft of the takings, which could be over $100, did not necessarily cut off the operator, but damage to the handset, dial and cords all too often did. Damage to public call boxes and those of the motoring organizations was an argument quietly used by promoters of radio-telephone services. A solution demonstrated in West Germany was sockets for personal portable phones. That was to come about in the 1990s, preceded by the partial solution of the prepaid cardphone.

By 1969 General Telephone Company of Florida was losing over $100,000 a year to kiosk thieves – not including the cost of equipment damaged or destroyed. To combat the rising loss, the company's security department and local law enforcement agencies got together. Training sessions were held and special alarms installed in key locations, leading to the arrest and conviction of more pay-phone burglars. In Japan it was reputed that the only vandalized phone booth was on an American army base. The situation worsened in Northern Ireland, where phone boxes were wrecked and burned out. Republican residents might be cutting off lines for their community but they had the satisfaction of destroying a symbol of Brit authority.

A partial solution to vandalism was making a kiosk less like a box, more an open but sheltered spot. It took up less space, was easier to maintain, and altogether cheaper. Virtues could be made of necessity: access for wheelchairs was easier; in hot spots such as the US Sun Belt you were not in a sweat-box; in cold spots such as the Mid-West drifting snow could not jam doors; it did not shelter obnoxious creatures such as skunks; there was no carbon steel to be corroded by the urine of dogs outside and humans inside; salesmen were less inclined to use it as a temporary office. The only other person inconvenienced was Superman. From the mid-1960s fewer kiosks were installed; instead there were more pay phones on premises, where they could be supervised.

That vandalism could cause serious loss of life was demonstrated at Aberfan, South Wales, on 21 October 1966. Gwyn Brown, a crane driver, arriving at the top of the colliery tip just before 7.30 a.m., noticed that it had sunk about nine or ten feet and that part of the crane track had fallen into the depression. Apprehensive, he suggested that David Jones, the slinger, should go down and report it to the charge-hand, Leslie Davies. David Jones had to go down the mountain because, although there had been a phone on the top of the tip, it had been removed after the wire down to the mine had been repeatedly stolen. His message stopped the tipping.

About an hour and a half after he had first noticed the depression, Gwyn Brown was standing on the edge:

> I was looking down into it, and what I saw I couldn't believe my eyes. It was starting to come back up. It started to rise slowly at first, I still did not believe it, I thought I was seeing things. Then it rose up after pretty fast, at a tremendous speed. Then it sort of came up out of the depression and turned itself into a wave – that is the only way I can describe it – down towards the mountain… towards Aberfan village… into the mist.

His shout brought the rest of the tipping gang out of their cabin. Leslie Davies gave further evidence to the tribunal inquiring into the disaster:

> When he shouted, we all got to the top of the tip and all I can tell you is it was going down at a hell of a speed in waves. I myself ran down the side of No.3 tip all the way down towards No.2 and No.1 tip on the side. As I was running down, I heard another roar behind me and trees cracking and a tram passing me. I stopped – I fell down in fact. All I could see was waves of muck, slush and water. I still kept running… I kept going down shouting. I couldn't see, nobody could. And I heard a voice answer me and he shouted, 'Come out of there, for God's sake'. That man was Trevor Steed… I went with Trevor Steed down on to the old railway line. By that time my mates had come down with me, behind me. We went along the line as far we could towards the school, which we could see. All the houses were down. We could not pass that way because there was too much water rushing down… we could not go the way we wanted to go.

The tribunal report noted:

> There can be no doubt that Mr Leslie Davies was himself for some time in the gravest danger. Indeed, it is little short of miraculous that he and all his workmates did not suffer the same fate as that which befell the 144 whose lives were so tragically terminated by this disaster.

Among the 144 were 116 children, mainly aged between seven and ten, 109 of them from Pantglas Junior School, where five teachers also lost their lives. Had there been a phone line from the tip to the mine, the outcome might have been less tragic. The thieves of the vital length of copper wire were never discovered. Their punishment had to be their own conscience.

Meanwhile the movement against self-slaughter had grown, internationally. For example, the Reverend Berndt Bäcklund and other clergymen started an emergency service on the last day of 1956 in Örebro, Sweden, a country with a high suicide rate. The specifically Christian and initially night-only service spread to major southern centres, leading to a national organization by 1965. Modelled on centres in Australia and New Zealand, an international Christian movement, Life Line, started in 1966. In Dallas, Texas, Life Line was called Contact because oil billionaire H. L. Hunt already used the name for his reactionary radio programme. In Canada, where it began in Sudbury, Ontario, it was called Telecare. There was also a separate network of Crisis Centres.

Most callers said that loneliness was their great problem. Close behind was stress in personal relationships. Psychotherapists discovered that phone contact was often more effective than face-to-face meetings for those unable to establish intense emotional relationships without great anxiety. They might be adults who were intellectually superior, or adolescents. In rural Ontario the suicide rate was higher than in urban areas, especially during long winter nights. The same was true in the Netherlands, although the attempt rate was higher in cities. There, a correlation was discovered between the number of suicidal calls and the actual suicides in the ensuing month. Graphically, the curves were almost identical. Once or twice a year, at different times and not necessarily every year, there was a sudden eruption of calls. They lasted for about seven to nine days and tended to be about one type of problem such as sex or money. Calls could be over 40 per cent above average, so not only the quantity but also the pattern was upset. Robert Louis, national secretary of the SOS Telephonic Help Service, observed: 'No satisfactory explanation has been found so far for these unpredictable outbursts of human misery.' Correspondingly, he noted periods of very few calls. Neither preceding nor following an eruption of calls, they occurred unexpectedly at different times of the year. The fall in number was slightly less significant, about 35 per cent, and the period shorter, from five to seven days, with the relative proportion of problems remaining constant.

'She finds it difficult to show her feelings, especially on the telephone', remarked a character in David Mercer's play *Ride a Cock Horse*. For people like that, perhaps more content to listen, there were more dial-a-message services. This form of Christian ministry appealed to the aged, the ill, the housebound, the depressed, and the bereaved. Anonymously, they could lift the phone and hear a simple message, often based on a familiar Bible verse; it was committed, the same approach, although the text might be changed weekly, and the caller made it effective. Such messages could be heard much as one might read comforting lines by Patience Strong.

The success of any helpline depended on an ability to listen sympathetically, to show an understanding of the problem, and build a one-to-one relationship with the caller. Preaching at callers with a problem was unlikely to be helpful. Helping them realize that they were individuals with their own future but whose problem was not unique was much more constructive. For this the phone was ideal. Callers were anonymous, unseen, and less likely to feel shame over their problem. Having this security, they were more inclined to be open, unburdening themselves to a stranger. If the conversation did not go well, they could always put the phone down and nobody would be any the wiser. Gamblers Anonymous was founded in the USA in 1957 and in the UK in 1964 as a voluntary fellowship to help compulsive gamblers kick the habit from which they got their kicks. In the UK first contacts by phone and letter were in the rough proportion 60:40. The organization Release began in London in 1967 to help people in trouble through cannabis use. Whereas its phone was in constant use, the number of letters received was typically in single figures. 'If we got as many letters as we do calls I don't think we could cope at all,' said one drugs worker. 'It takes longer to write.'

'Live' information of all kinds was being sent over phone lines. Hospitals were distributing electro-cardiograms to medical centres while patients' hearts were being monitored. International publishers were sending copy at high speed between offices. Facsimile, hitherto a form of communication for fixed installations such as newspaper offices and weather forecasting centres, was becoming – at least in theory – portable. A salesman could fix an acoustic coupler to his or her home/hotel phone and send orders to base. In the water industry, to run more sophisticated distribution systems, computers monitored reservoirs and water towers and then automatically started and stopped combinations of pumps to meet demand most economically. Computers in places such as bank and insurance company branches were beginning to 'talk' to one another, taking advantage of cheap overnight rates to be up-to-date for the opening of business next morning.

Even imprecise 'mood' information could be transmitted. H. Owens, an American dentist, induced over the phone mild hypnosis in patients, who felt more relaxed and suffered less pain after treatment. For the hard of hearing, transistorized devices were now available. Much smaller, they were easier and more comfortable to wear or could be incorporated in a phone itself. In many ways the phone was becoming easier to use. Push buttons, sometimes designed by 'human-factor engineers', reappeared as a 'new' and quicker way of dialling. Harder to lock than dials though, buttons could tempt like an open cash box. Hotels introduced single-digit calls for room service, laundry and other services. Mobile exchanges served events such as sports meetings and shows. They could also be deployed in emergencies, as when a tornado and a hurricane ripped through Florida in 1966, disrupting services. Florida, which also operated a special seasonal service for the influx of winter visitors, introduced in 1969 the Chatterbox, a family booth 10 feet by 12 feet. In public gardens by a lake, it was heated in winter and air-cooled in summer. It had no dial, no handset and no coin slots. You pressed a button to summon the long-distance operator and spoke through hidden microphones and loudspeakers, great fun for kids of all ages. Charging was to a phone credit card, to a home number, or call collect.

Phone credit cards, for inland and overseas calls, avoided the bother of coins, and appealed particularly to businessmen. Unauthorized possession of such cards could be even more profitable than blue-box entry to the system. Bill Mayhugh, a Washington disc jockey, lost his card at a New York railway station on 18 December 1983. Although he reported the loss to the Chesapeake and Potomac Telephone Company the next day, his card was not invalidated until 15 February 1984. Meanwhile, 15,000 long-distance calls had been made throughout the USA and to 47 foreign countries, many to places he had never heard of. Fortunately he did not have to pay the $194,656 bill. Nor did housewife Jane Landenberger, whose bill totalled $109,504 instead of $47. They were just two examples of fraud costing Ma Bell $100 million a year.

The British Post Office introduced its card in 1960. A variety of popular services followed: the recipe service, started in Birmingham in 1961; dial-a-disc, launched in Leeds in 1966 (in 1972 in Walthamstow, through 'an exchange fault', it promoted the services of local prostitutes); and the *Financial Times* index in London in 1969. In 1961, under the Betting and Gaming Act, street betting shops were legalized and there was a greatly increased demand from bookmakers for the Extel-PA racing service.

Visible evidence of the new importance of communications was the 620-

Telecom towers became new land-marks. This one in London is 620 ft (189 metres) high. (BT Museum)

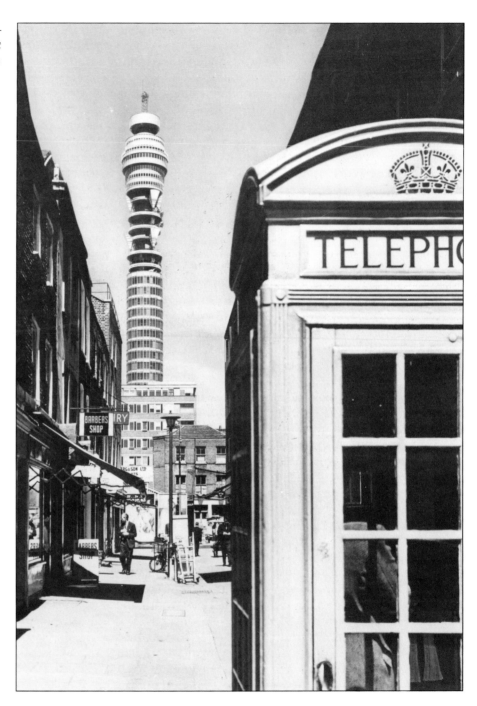

foot Post Office tower, opened in London to the public in 1966, affording panoramic views in the smoke-free air. At last it seemed that the phone could be used without fear. On 7 October 1961 Toby O'Brien, the public relations officer of the Post Office, had a letter in *The Lancet* reiterating that there was no danger of infection. It looked like the last word on a much-covered subject, but citing another study did not prevent the well-meaning but less well-informed continuing to use disinfecting companies.

Moral hygiene was the concern of BBC Radio when it started a listeners' phone-in programme *It's Your Line*. 'Aunty' was worried that, when asking questions of a panel chaired by Robin Day, listeners would abuse being live on the air. After trailers inviting participation, some 30 to 40 secretaries marshalled calls and rang back the safe ones. Moral pollution of the airwaves was no greater risk than catching a disease from the phone. Phone-ins, cheap in that listeners entertained one another, were to become a staple item on local radio stations, the first of which the BBC opened in Leicester on 8 November 1967. Previously, permission for phone-ins had to be secured *ad hoc* from the GPO through the BBC Communications Department.

As always, in North America further advances had been made. In 1965 Bell opened its first commercial electronic exchange, at Succasunna, New Jersey, offering quicker connections and a greater range of subscriber services. The military also used electronic equipment in AUTOVON, its global *Auto*matic *Vo*ice *N*etwork. AUTOVON facilities included conference calls to link parties internationally, automatic take-over of lines for high precedence calls, and hot lines that caused a predetermined phone to ring as soon as the caller picked up his own phone. The private system linked more than a million phones, typewriters and data sets at two thousand military bases around the world. Military leaders could get through in seconds.

Bell Canada installed its first electronic exchange at Expo 67, the big exhibition in Montreal. That year, 14 years after the 50-million mark was reached, the USA installed its 100 millionth telephone, a gold one in the White House office of President Johnson, who seemed to live with the phone at his ear. Most people were talking longer. By the end of the decade the average conversation was almost twice as long as at the end of the Second World War.

In 1969 a call was made out of this world. On 20 July, President Richard Nixon from a six-button telephone on his White House desk made a two-minute call to the Apollo 11 astronauts, Neil Armstrong, Edward Aldrin Jr, and Michael Collins, when man first landed on the moon. They were 240,000 miles away. Not long after, 3,000 miles away in Britain, the Post Office became a public corporation. It had a long way to go to catch up with the USA in customer attitudes. More so France, where General de Gaulle, who had dismissed the phone as 'un gadget', had resigned as President and retired. Half the French were supposed to be waiting for a phone and the other half for a dial tone.

CHAPTER 16

INTO THE SECOND CENTURY

To mark the centenary in 1976 of Bell's invention, various events were staged. Places from Aitutaki Atoll to Yemen issued commemorative stamps. There were centennial weeks, displays and exhibitions. Specialized magazines looked back and traced progress since pioneer days. A few books appeared. New Zealand introduced direct dialling and Singapore international direct dialling. Yet, in retrospect, the centenary was a muted event. The eloquent tribute was paid by the mass of people in their daily use of the simple instrument, in essence little changed over a hundred years. Its environment, though, had. No longer was it possible, as during Bell's funeral service, to observe a minute's silence.

The British Post Office marked the occasion by closing its last manual exchange, at Portree, on the Isle of Skye. Now the UK system was entirely automatic, though it was not till three years later, the same year as Japan, that direct dialling was complete. The UK was thus ahead of the USA, where the last hand-cranked system, in the corner of a living room at Bryant Pond, Maine, was replaced in 1982. Personal service survived at sea, over radio-telephones to yachtsmen, who were able to get in friendly fashion weather and other news reports.

In the 1970s phone ownership among UK manual workers more than doubled. Whereas one-third of households had an installation in 1970, by 1979 it was two-thirds. When mail halted for nearly seven weeks in the 1971 strike, people turned to the phone. The strike presaged the day when the postman would disappear, replaced by electronic mail carried invisibly. The 1970s were years of expansion, in the number of new customers, in home extensions, in the facilities and services offered. In offices 'doll's eye' switchboards were giving way to cordless boards on which operators simply flicked keys instead of handling plugs. Automatic diallers speeded frequently wanted numbers. Recognizing the importance of operators, 'the company's first contact with the outside world', Robert Townsend asserted in *Up the Organisation* that, if he were designing a head office, he would

Canada anticipated the centenary of the invention of the phone by two years because it was on his summer holidays in 1874 in Brantford, Ontario, that Bell evolved the basic concept of the phone. His first phone to transmit recognizable voice sounds – not words – was the 'gallows' model in the centre of the stamp (top right).

Bell was featured on many centenary stamps, such as these from Grenada, Ireland and Malawi.

(Stanley Gibbons Ltd/Tom Gillespie)

'spend money to make the switchboard girls comfortable... Executives row will look like the cubicles of a Trappist monastery, and the telephone-switchboard area like a Turkish harem. Money spent on offices for management is largely wasted.'

There was a wider range of instruments, colourfully intended for modern environments but also drawing on the past. Besides fun phones with Mickey Mouse and Snoopy holding handsets, on which children could hear bedtime stories, there were 'space-saving' versions of the original wall sets, turn-of-the-century desk sets, the 'candlestick', and modern 'warbling' phones. Some had jack plugs for removal from room to room.

It had taken a century for the phone to have a general impact on the way of life, and then only in developed countries. The instrument was part of what was being regarded as the information society. Moreover, it was not the only thing that could be attached to the line. Computers could 'talk' to one another over the network. Communications and computers were converging into information technology. Future emphasis would be on the importance of the network rather than the simple instrument at the end.

When growth slowed during the middle years of the decade, following the sharp increase in oil prices in 1973, the phone was promoted as an energy-efficient instrument. It was more economical to move information than people. People on the move could be paged, as they had been in Tokyo since 1968 and were in London from 1977. It was not always necessary to move. Inspectors with the International Atomic Energy Agency did not have to leave Vienna to check seals they had put on nuclear equipment. Sites from Bulgaria to Canada and Japan could be instantly monitored by Recover (remote continual verification) for compliance with the Non-Proliferation Treaty. More modestly, security companies carried out surveillance on industrial and commercial premises, checking boilers, refrigerators and locks from central control rooms.

The idea of business meetings over permanent TV links was slow to catch on and the person-to-person videophone had little appeal. In North America, where it was promoted during the early 1970s as Picturephone, it failed commercially. A customer objection was that it was difficult to tell lies. Its success was over short distances and in special circumstances such as hospital operating theatre to pathology lab, and building entrance surveillance. It used an expensive number of circuits – and was it worth it? To most people though an advantage of the ordinary phone was that voice

Defying long-made predictions, videophones like this Bigfon on trial in Berlin from 1983 to 1986, remained largely experimental. Fifty years earlier, the world's first public service was opened, on 1 March 1936 between Berlin and Leipzig, but was short-lived. (Siemens)

and vision could be separated. You did not always want your caller to be able to see you.

Towards the end of the seventies customers showed more interest in audio conference systems, by which people in various places, including overseas, attended a meeting over the phone. Experience showed that in exchanging information and solving problems, the absence of vision had no measurable effect on the outcome. The phone was not inferior to face-to-face contact and the time and expense of travelling were saved. A 1979 study suggested this was so for up to 60 per cent of business meetings. Members of Lloyds Bank offshore island chess league enjoyed their annual tournament this way, without leaving Jersey, Guernsey, the Isle of Wight, the Isle of Man, the Shetlands, or wherever they were based.

In the next decade transactions in city financial and commodity markets were to move from trading floors, where buyers and sellers bargained in person, to phones and computer screens. Electronic trading became global. For good or ill, it was one world and one market around the clock. Decisions worth millions and affecting the prosperity of companies and countries were made in split seconds by young traders who never saw their commodities and were distant from the consequences of their decisions. The only thing they were close to was the phone. Away from the dealing desk, they relied on a portable one. Remote from the real action, they believed they were in the cut and thrust of events. 'In 10 minutes it's history,' yells a dealer in the film *Wall Street*. On days like Black Monday, 19 October 1987, when stock markets inexplicably crashed, it seemed a self-contained world, divorced from the reality of making things or just scratching a living. Dealers lived by the phone in a fantasy, cut off from the world of doers and the growing groups of non-doers, the underclass of unemployed. So hectic was the pace that they usually had to move on to something else by the age of 40, the beneficiaries and victims of instant information.

To ordinary and not so ordinary users, except in places such as Hong Kong and Macao, where local calls were free to subscribers, the phone seemed increasingly expensive. Sir Patrick Wall, MP for the appropriately named constituency of Haltemprice, pointed out that the cost of the division bell in his Westminster Gardens home summoning him to a late-night vote in the House of Commons was less than £40 a year in 1979. Three increases took it to nearly £133 by 1982.

So frequent were the rises in this inflationary period that there were jokes based on the speaking clock ('... at the third stroke it will be time for another price rise, precisely...'). Increases were a considerable shock to great users like the hermit novelist William Gerhardi, who seldom left his flat and kept in touch with friends by long calls. One to the biographer

Michael Holroyd lasted seven hours, during which Holroyd played Mozart and Wagner to the old man, who had no TV, no record player and an ageing radio. With employees regarding personal calls as a perk, companies installed devices for logging their destination and length. Instruments could be programmed to reach only certain numbers or limited in their calling distances. It added a new status symbol: how much phone have you got?

Particularly concerned about charges were people in rural communities. The phone began mainly as an urban instrument and was a minor factor in encouraging drift from country to town. Main contacts were within and between towns. The people least likely to have or be near a phone were agricultural workers. In Wales, for example, most subscribers were on the

Although provided with the latest computer terminals, many of the dealers on the new Hong Kong stock exchange preferred to keep their old black dial phones 'for good luck'.

(South China Morning Post)

coastal fringes, leaving inland rural communities comparatively isolated. Their public transport declined in competition with the private car, making the least mobile members of society the elderly, the semi-skilled and unskilled in country areas. They were the most likely to feel distant from public services, which were concentrated in larger centres, and from services such as courts, schools, planning, fire and ambulance, gas and electricity authorities, driving test centres, and local administration. Supermarkets were taking trade from small shops. So country folk felt farther away both from useful information, not always easily gathered on the phone ('If you'll hold on I'll put you through to the department that should be able to help'), and from the goods they saw advertised on TV.

To make matters worse, remote areas were in greater danger of losing their kiosks through rising costs of maintenance. Most urban boxes never fell below break-even revenue but, it was argued, economies could be made in country areas. Local inhabitants quickly sprang to the defence, pointing out that call boxes in remote parts were the only convenient link with the outside world, especially in emergencies and hard winters. In the village of Kersall, Notts, Mrs Hemsley dutifully kept the inside – including ashtray, carpets and doormat – clean, while Mrs Wood tended the pot plants. Why should the good work of these two ladies and others like them subsidize the costs of abuse and vandalism in big towns and cities? Some rural boxes were removed and others subsidized by bodies such as parish councils. At Beachy Head, Britain's most famous suicide site, which had had a lonely kiosk since 1909, the Samaritans of Eastbourne underwrote its upkeep.

The trend was turning by the early 1980s. Till then, telecommunications had reflected the patterns of physical communications such as main roads and railways, the same centres and similar routes being prominent. Different in kind, telecommunications offered instant connections, according to the needs of the moment. Subscriber dialling made nationwide and international contact easy, overcoming some of the barriers that isolated people geographically. It helped make up for the decline of rural transport, caught in the trap of rising fuel costs, declining numbers of passengers, and less frequent services. A trend discernible in the UK 1981 census was a reversal of population drift from country to town. Companies large and small were leaving London, which although it had in the City the densest concentration of telecommunications, was no longer the great place of all the action. Geographical position was no longer so important as having access to information. In the developed world communications put power where the information was, not necessarily in the traditional centre. They helped to decentralize and diffuse power and influence. Whereas inner cities were decaying, more people found it possible and desirable to live in the country.

*Ferrying a new kiosk to a remote
Scottish island, where half the 200
residents rely on the public pay phone.*
(BT Museum)

There the quality of life was better. You could be remote yet in touch. It was possible to live out on the Norfolk wetlands, unspoilt by poles carrying overhead lines but connected to the network by underground cables armoured against wild coypus' sharp teeth. In remote Inverness-shire solar panels used as battery chargers maintained radio links with the back of beyond. Being a personal, one-to-one instrument, the phone helped to preserve individual cultures, like those of the Western Isles, where through local initiative directories were published in English and Gaelic.

Divided up on a village basis, the directories were most distinctive in their use of traditional Gaelic patronymics and nicknames. As these are much more frequently used than the conventional English christian name and surname, people found the books easier to consult. In Fearann Eilean Iarmain, with a population of one thousand, the directory, Leabhar nam Fon, listed the names of all the residents over the age of 18 in each house with a phone. It was not necessary to know the first name of the householder, important in an area where there is a relatively small number of common surnames. Through the efforts of the Welsh Language Society, Cymdeithas yr Iaith, more concerned about the cultural impact of the broadcast media rather than the *ffôn*, instructions in kiosks were usually bilingual and there were some recorded announcements in Welsh. Even so, there were people glad to escape the instrument. When the jobs of warden and cook on the windswept island of Skokholm, a bird sanctuary off Pembrokeshire, were advertised in 1981, hundreds of people applied to be marooned for eight months without electricity or phone.

There were those in business who agreed with them: shops, such as those selling poorly made fashion shoes, that received frequent complaints were ex-directory. Encouraging individuals to complain could be commercially useful. In the USA, a domestic appliance maker, Whirlpool Corporation, launched in 1967 a Cool Line service for customers to call repair staff free of charge. By 1980 there were two hundred thousand calls a year, with 95 per cent of problems being resolved on the first call. Similarly, when customers complained that the Polaroid camera did not work, they were asked to check the battery. Many did not know it existed. On this evidence, the camera was redesigned.

During the 1970s the notion of renting grew, including almost anything from characters and crowds to mink coats and do-it-yourself tools. Best known were Hertz and Avis rent-a-car, which helped the growth of competitors large and small, including Rent-a-Convertible, Renta-Wreck, Rent-a-Klunker and Lease-a-Lemon, all in the Los Angeles directory. In an age of do-it-yourself and serve-yourself, the phone was helping to bring back personal service. Fast food such as pizzas could be delivered. Teleshopping services relieved shoppers from pushing a trolley round, queueing at the checkout and then loading all their items into a parked car. Many businesses were able to grow by restoring personal service, based initially on phone contact. You could quote your credit card number over the phone, which could in turn be verified by phone, and in the fullness of time (usually 28 days) your goods would be delivered.

New 'telecottage' industries were created by bringing together skills in informal networks linked by the phone. A successful example was F International, a dispersed group of computer programmers, mostly women. The F stands for 'freelance', but there were career prospects. Started in the UK, it initially branched out to Benelux, Scandinavia and the USA. Like graphics, translation and may other skilled occupations, computer programming can be carried on at home in flexible hours. Working for such organizations, people can pace themselves. There are not the instant pressures and office distractions encountered in formal networks. Productivity and quality of output is higher, and home-workers are not exploited. Decentralized organization keeps down overheads. Phone costs can be reduced by making calls in cheap rate periods and from the country with lower phone charges.

Efficient communications were essential to such dispersed and one-person businesses. In the 1970s they acquired answering machines, which could perhaps be interrogated from any distance, so that opportunities were not lost. Fun tapes carrying answering messages from well-known voices removed some of the impersonality. In the 1980s mobile phones kept the office on the move and fax provided instant correspondence. With so many points of contact, business cards began to look like phone directories. Less successful was the marriage of the phone and television in viewdata. Fewer people than expected wanted to call up information and have it displayed on a screen. In the UK it remained a limited and specialized business service, the largest single user being the travel industry. Mr and Mrs Everyman were not yet ready for electronic publishing, but in France the virtual gift of Minitel terminals in large numbers overcame this reluctance. Managing one's bank account from home was also in its infancy by the early 1990s.

People were more accessible to salesmen though. Phone selling was made easier by Yellow Pages ('Let your fingers do the walking'), introduced in the UK in 1965, and local commercial directories. There were plenty of courses on sales techniques to control a conversation. Video Arts produced three amusing short training films: *When I'm Calling You, Will You Answer True?*, and *The Cold Call*, the last two featuring John Cleese, showing how orders could be lost – or won. This form of direct selling, even for large items such as cranes, became attractive as a salesman's costs went up. More people could be contacted simply by sitting still and letting your fingers do the hawking. At the very least, hopeless prospects could be eliminated. In the USA – where else? – a robot salesman had been devised. When plugged in, it could ring a set of numbers, make its sales pitch and record replies.

Companies staged phone-in contests among telesales staff, with motivating prizes and managers encouraging the staff to boost turnover and strengthen customer loyalty. Jingles and other promotional aids helped people remember individual numbers to call for service. Securing a grave plot or fixing a cremation was a different matter. American undertakers had changed their attitude towards the phone since one of them, Almon B. Strowger, invented the automatic exchange. By the 1970s they purposely did not discuss their services and charges over the phone, preferring to lure the bereaved into the soft-sell atmosphere of the funeral parlour, where it was easier to sell embalming, expensive caskets and extras. In mid-1981 a new set of Federal Trade Commission rules obliged them to discuss terms over the phone.

Commercial information of all kinds was becoming readily available by

Electronic fraternity – in the ten years since 1981 the number of French citizens using Minitel terminals to tap into thousands of information services grew to 5,000,000.

SIC PTE (France)

dialling. Responding to phone-booth graffiti, especially at railway stations, the lonely could find out what variations Kim, Lisa, Susie and other attractively pseudonymed girls had to offer. The old-style telegram was partly replaced by singing telegrams and kissograms delivered by girls in suspender belts and fishnet tights, or by a variety of animals, including ducks, bears and gorillas. The medium was more important and probably more embarrassing than the message. More respectably, you could, among other things, commission a troupe of actors to perform in your own home, consult leisure lists, travel schedules and horoscopes, check seasonable fruits and vegetables at the nearest pick-your-own. Information was a commodity that boosted phone traffic.

The phone was being used increasingly in education. As long ago as 1939, intercom equipment was installed in Iowa for the hospitalized and the homebound to hear lectures at the same time as classroom students. Having textbooks, participants found it as good as being in the classroom. In 1947 the College of Dentistry at the University of Illinois staged six lectures simultaneously in Chicago and Scranton, Pennsylvania, with slides being shown at both sites. It was a way of making wider use of intellectual capital. A class gathered in Boston was taught from a phone booth on New York Taconic State Parkway. Commercially, you could learn a language.

In the 1970s phone conferencing systems were tried in places such as the University of Quebec and in the UK the Open University, founded in 1969 to teach by TV and radio, essentially one-way media. Contact between tutors and students one-to-one over the phone was common and the aim was to extend this by creating tutorials in which, say, eight people in scattered locations took part. Studies showed that students could learn as much or more than in face-to-face groups, though it was useful for the members to have met. In phone tutorials the atmosphere was more formal and businesslike, with shorter and more efficient meetings. Where a simultaneous link was necessary, a 'remote blackboard' could be provided by a slow-scan TV system operating over a phone line. Diagrams a tutor drew on a special pad could be seen in black and white on a student's set. A development from that was drawing on a TV screen with a light-pen and amending the drawing as the tutorial proceeded.

Sharing of experience was important to people isolated by what they felt was their unique problem. Hilary Prentice, a drugs worker:

> I was taken on to deal with prescribed drugs, which Release hadn't dealt with before. There was one mention in *The Sun* on the problem page that Release was interested in people trying to get off tranquillizers and would put people in touch with others going through the same thing. We had an incredible flood of calls for about two weeks, literally hundreds of calls and still some. A

lot of those people probably hadn't had anybody to ring before because their problem hadn't been recognized as a problem. Somehow they had carried on living – or not.

They think they are barmy, especially on tranquillizers. They can't come off. People around them don't understand because they think tranquillizers aren't addictive. The messages they're getting from people around them is that they're pretty weak, pathetic and barmy. To talk to somebody who responds normally and says that the pills are addictive and that I've spoken to hundreds of people who have those symptoms of withdrawal comes as a revelation. 'Oh, goodness!' It comes as a new experience to them, one shared over the phone. They are not alone. We are putting people in touch with other people and getting local groups going. Quite a lot of the tranquillizer callers were interested in getting in touch with somebody else. That tends to be at the end of a call, when you've won their trust.

That was the essence of dealing with disturbed and desperate people such as hijackers. On Independence Day 1977 Louis Robinson hijacked a coach bound from New York to Maine, murdered two passengers and held another 21 hostage, as well as bringing Kennedy Airport to a standstill. To persuade him to surrender, while he had his gun trained on a passenger, two New York policemen, Frank Bolz and Julio Vasquez, negotiated with him by radio-phone. It was the only way to establish a dialogue. Terrorists too, like those in the IRA, used the phone for their own purposes, giving warnings of bombs about to explode, or messages preceded by their code that established their bona fides, no matter how misguided their purpose. Kiosks in public buildings were likely places in which explosives could be planted so doors were removed and open booths became the norm. In any event, there was less to vandalize.

Enraged members of the public were able to vent their spleen. After John Hinckley Jnr, infatuated with the teenage actress Jodie Foster, shot President Reagan on 30 March 1981 outside the Washington Hilton, his father's office in Denver was besieged by bomb threats and menacing calls. The phone could be an instrument of mass protest, generally to no avail. Just before Christmas a Tory peer, Lord Morris, took the unusual step of issuing the phone number of three Foreign Office diplomats responsible for the Falkland Islands. He urged the public to ring them and protest about government plans to sell *HMS Endurance*, the ice patrol ship that was the only regular Royal Navy presence in the area. When it finished its last tour in March, Lord Morris argued, the Falklands would be cut off from Britain. His campaign – 'Having debates in Parliament is pretty useless as far as I can see' – was unsuccessful but within months he was proved right. On 2 April 1982 the Falklands were invaded and Britain and Argentina were at an expensive war. During the invasion the besieged governor, Rex Hunt, kept up a running commentary over the islands' radio by phone from under his desk, with lead flying around outside. It was the first invasion phone-in. During the war a Welsh housewife gave vent to her patriotism by dialling Buenos Aires and singing 'Rule Britannia'.

In more routine ways emergencies could be handled by phone: breakdowns and crashes on motorways, the availability of human organs for transplant, incidents involving divers in the gas and oil industry. Time though had overtaken the UK underground emergency control posts set up in the 1950s for use after The Bomb dropped. By the early 1980s, when popular support for nuclear disarmament revived, these secret centres were looking distinctly dated. Left-wing councils, such as that in South Yorkshire, were glad to open them to the public, revealing how inadequate the old-fashioned switchboards and other equipment would be after an atomic holocaust. A more sinister part of civil defence was the phone preference scheme, whereby access to the remains of the network would be restricted to designated officials, including lock-keepers and ice-makers but not clergymen.

It was the kind of serio-comic set-up that lent itself to hoax calls, if such were possible. Usually these were in poor taste, as when people received calls asking them to identify the body of a relative killed in a road accident. Their number was said to have been found on the corpse. Emergency services were always at risk. Probably the cruellest hoaxer was the man with the Wearside accent who pretended to be the Yorkshire Ripper and put the police on a false trail in the five-year hunt for the multiple killer.

Mogens Listrup, the lawyer who founded the anti-tax Progressive Party in Denmark in 1972, however, was being entirely serious when as an economy measure he suggested abolishing the Ministry of Defence and substituting an answering machine with the message in Russian: 'We surrender'. When convicted in mid-1983 for tax evasion he was able to lead his party from his gaol near Elsinore by countless phone calls. On the lighter side, it was possible to buy an alibi, a cassette tape for husbands or wives staying out late. The tape contained authentic background noises – airport, railway station, busy street, keyboards clacking away – to support a range of otherwise tired excuses.

Fantasies could be indulged in, legitimately. In Toronto, for example, an organization called Tele-Fantasy provided a 24-hour service whereby subscribers could solicit a $35 call indulging their particular kink. Payment was by credit card and within an hour you could be discussing your sexual tastes with a man or woman who was perhaps an unemployed teacher or secretary working from home and glad of the opportunity to earn perhaps $400 or $500 a week. The rapid success of Tele-Fantasy, launched in Canada in September 1982 after the formula was shown to be successful in the USA, quickly produced local competitors. A police spokesman commented: 'There are statutes in the Criminal Code and Telephone Act which speak about obscene phone calls and the harassment aspects, but this is different. The way these services are set up, it is the customer who solicits the service and, as far as obscenity laws go, because both parties agree, nothing said between them is obscene, so it's legal.' In Denmark, when the sex magazine *Ugens Rapport* used a three-minute recording of 'Eva' giving a stimulating account of her tastes, the promotion had to be cut off. The Copenhagen exchange was jammed by 40,000 calls in three hours, with four callers per second trying to get through.

The phone as a link between two worlds was a strong theme in films. Antonio Mercero's *La Cabina* was a piece of Spanish Surrealism in which entering a kiosk meant stepping into an inescapable nightmare. In Clint Eastwood's *Play Misty for Me* (1971), he was a radio disc jockey pestered by a homicidally jealous woman caller. Francis Ford Coppola's *The Conversation* (1974) depicted the amoral world of the bugging expert, a timely subject following the real-life Watergate affair. In mid-1972, members of the Republican Party organization had been caught with bugging devices in their opponents' campaign headquarters in Watergate, a Washington apartment block. Although the affair was hushed up until President Nixon had been re-elected in the November, it was his ultimate undoing. In 1974 he had to admit that he had been party to the cover-up and became the first US President to resign. In Bill Forsyth's *Local Hero* (1983), the link between the two worlds of the aggressive Texan oil millionaire and the not-so-simple people of a northern Scottish village was the ordinary red kiosk on the end of the jetty. The comic/cosmic mood was caught when an oilman anxiously fed 10p pieces into the box, trying to reach his star-crazed boss in Houston as the northern lights were visible outside.

Popular with children of all ages were science fiction fantasies, many involving space. *Superman* was successfully revived (1978). When E.T. (1982), the strange but lovable creature from another planet, in the film of the same name, was left alone in an American home he was inspired by the comic strip of Buck Rogers sending messages to outer space and somebody on TV making a call. The extra-terrestrial's first words in English were: 'E.T. phone home.' On a makeshift ground station, he tried. Later, when he came to life after

In Britain, Buzby was a chirpy campaign character stimulating calls.
(BT Museum)

This labrador is not straining to reach the telephone pole for the usual dog's purpose. Trained to sniff out decay, he is one of a team saving the Swedish telecommunications administration 10 million crowns ($1.8 million) a year. (Televerket, Sweden)

he was thought to be dead, he repeated: 'E.T. phone home.' That he had been successful was revealed when his fellow creatures descended in their spaceship and collected him.

Phone-ins had become an established part of radio broadcasting, chat often being interspersed with records. There were plenty of appropriate ones: 'Telephone Line' and 'Calling America' by the Electric Light Orchestra; Meri Wilson's 'Telephone Man'; 'Hanging on the Telephone' and 'Call Me' sung by Blondie; Pete Shelley's 'Telephone Operator'; and Manhattan Transfer's 'Operator, Give Me Jesus on the Line'. On phone-ins callers were becoming more forthright in their opinions, airing their views about authorities such as the local council and the police. In theory, the governed were getting access to the governors. The BBC called its first network phone-in outside London *Voice of the People*. Local radio stations could see themselves as performing a community service, creating 'a psychological neighbourhood'. Professional presenters were listeners' friends. They helped the novice caller express a point of view. In reply, the authorities tended to use the bromide of public relations prose – 'putting it in perspective' and 'looking at the situation overall' – to smooth things over. There was no real meeting of minds because those in power were

more interested in defending than in listening. Occasionally you could feel that somebody had broken through and managed to get a hearing but it was most likely to be in some stark emotional/sexual situation revealing genuine personal stress beneath the apparently calm surface of society. It took somebody like a crying 17-year-old girl, pregnant and on drugs, to stir feelings and get something done. On a wider scale, the phone became a medium for charitable giving. In the UK, for the 1988 Telethon, 10,000 volunteers, working shifts over 27 hours, took almost 1,000,000 calls pledging money.

By 1983 the phone-in had become a diplomatic weapon. On 30 October Mrs Thatcher, the British Prime Minister, conducted an unprecedented programme on the BBC World Service, answering questions from New York and Barbados about President Reagan's invasion of the Caribbean island of Grenada. The invasion of the Commonwealth territory had been launched without consulting the British government and she was able to repudiate the action strongly to an international audience. Other world leaders such as King Hussein of Jordan, the Irish and New Zealand Prime Ministers, joined a series that followed in 1984.

A disadvantaged group that attracted attention in several countries was the disabled. In the UK the 1970 Chronically Sick and Disabled Persons Act gave local authorities the power to provide or help in obtaining a phone and any special equipment necessary for its use by the handicapped. The power was not always used. Concern grew internationally and the United Nations proclaimed 1981 the year of the disabled. In phone terms there were four categories: the hard of hearing, those with speech problems, the blind and visually handicapped, those with impaired mobility.

For the hard of hearing, a term preferred to 'the deaf', there were amplifying handsets with a volume control (of which normal users had to be aware), handsets that flashed to indicate an incoming call, extension bells, and a bone conduction receiver that transmitted sound vibrations directly to the skull. Calls could be visualized on displays, also important to the dumb. Greyhound, the US coach operator, installed a Silent Information Service on which, by means of a keypad and screen, a handicapped person 'talked' to operators in the centre at Allentown, Pennsylvania. Bell Canada donated reconditioned teletype machines to the Canadian Hearing Society so that the deaf could communicate, perhaps by fast two-finger typing. In Cherry Hill, New Jersey, a similar installation was made for deaf would-be suicides. For those with weak speech there were various amplifying devices, including an artificial larynx that, when placed against the throat, substituted electronic vibrations for the natural ups and downs of the voice. In speech therapy clinics the phone was used both as a means of assessing degrees of stuttering and monitoring progress after treatment.

If they had problems locating the correct finger holes or buttons, for which instructions were issued in Braille, the blind could use automatic callmakers. Switchboards for blind operators were adapted with tactile indicators, buzzing probes and Braille markings. Those with impaired mobility who found handsets too heavy to hold could have headsets or handsets on flexible stalks. There were guides to help trembling fingers operate push buttons and for coins in pay phones operated from a wheelchair. For the severely disabled there were loudspeaking phones controlled by simple suck/blow or gentle pressure on a switch. To the disabled, the elderly and the infirm, as for agoraphobics and those isolated by AIDS, the phone was a responsive link to the outside world, available for companionship and emergencies. It was undoubtedly a factor in reducing the number of fatal accidents in the home.

In December 1980 Sharon Smylie, a 12-year-old schoolgirl in Ballymena, Northern Ireland, dialled what she thought was her school but instead heard an elderly woman gasp down the phone: 'I'm dying... get help.' Managing to establish that the woman lived at '45 Something Galgorm', Sharon dialled 999 and the police were in time to get 86-year-old Miss Wilson, living alone and suffering from hypothermia, into hospital. Some countries have a system whereby pushing a button sends a prerecorded message to a registered helper. On the other hand, still active elderly people sometimes like to demonstrate their independence and exercise themselves by keeping the phone away from their easy chair. Celia Fremlin wrote a chilling short story, *A Case of Maximum Need*, about an 87-year-old spinster, rejected by a man in her youth, who refused her social worker's offer of a phone. When it was routinely installed she used her siren's voice to lure a heavy breather to her sheltered housing unit, where she sat waiting with her ever-ready carving knife.

To cater for the lonely of all ages Chatline was introduced in London just before Christmas 1982, bringing as many as nine people together. Advertised in the capital's evening paper, *The Standard*, available from midday, by the evening it had become a forum for bad language, blue jokes, and lewd suggestions. Ten hours after it was started the plug was pulled. The service was tried again, after Easter, in Bristol, this time with only five people participating at a time and a separate number for under-18s. Called Talkabout, it fulfilled a social need, the ten groups of five lines attracting half a million calls in four months. Some callers were happy to just listen, others to flirt, talk about money, jobs, pets, music, fashion, what was going on around town. Night-owls continued into the small hours. Charged at premium rates, like its French equivalent Téléconvivialité, this service too fell into disrepute, largely through the high bills run up by addicted youngsters. It was suspended in 1989. An alternative, also at premium rates, was a one-to-one call, the content of which often did not live up to the titillating promise. An independent body dealt with complaints. In France by 1990 the novelty of *messageries roses*, pink messages of soft-porn and dating services carried on the Minitel videotex network, had worn off.

Helplines proliferated like charity Christmas cards. Not all were seen as good causes. Gay Switchboard, found about one-third of its calls were abusive or a hoax. Such specialist services though provided a discreet, unashaming consultation for the individual and helped reveal the extent of problems in society at large. In New York during the recession of the later

For the lonely, all sorts of personal services are just a phone call away. In the UK, stickers led to prosecutions for criminal damage to kiosks and the use of loose cards, which were a litter offence.

1970s the Food and Hunger Hotline was established as a private organization to find food for the stream of callers, not all badly spoken. A helpline could help a deprived or abused person, even a child, as in the Netherlands and Sweden, find a voice to express a grievance or fight back. On ChildLine, a British child could be assured of a free and confidential hearing at any time of the night or day.

Or the phone could be intimidating. The disadvantaged, for example the unemployed wanting to be first in applying for a job, needed quick access to a phone, even though some of them, such as long-term prisoners coming out, could shake with dread at using it. The tone of the rebuff expected at the other end was something to be feared. Blue collars had always been at a disadvantage against white collars at work and, when they were out of work, their phone could be one of the first items queried by social security officials. Racial equality also was not easily made a practical reality. Indeed, racialists were able to turn the phone into a weapon against immigrants, using it to disturb them at night and drive them out of the neighbourhood with messages of hate.

According to mid-1982 Samaritan statistics, the main person in despair in the UK was the retired male. He was more likely to be a successful suicide than somebody who was redundant or unemployed. Women tended to inflict injury on themselves, without causing death. The Samaritans claimed that the suicide rate had declined in England, Wales and Western Australia, largely because of their work and in spite of the voluntary euthanasia movement gaining ground. National differences made direct statistical comparisons invalid. For instance, in Catholic countries such as Ireland and Italy some suicides may be recorded as accidental deaths to spare family feelings. In Norway, coroners can consider the distress of relatives when recording a verdict. In Japan, where there are tremendous pressures on young people to succeed in university entrance exams, suicide is not culturally condemned. It tends to occur when the results are known. When the Life Telephone was started in Tokyo in 1971 it was second only to the New York equivalent in the number of calls received.

Cities offered immediate facilities for phone counselling. In rural areas connections had to be made to a common emergency number – in Sweden, 90000. In remote places in Ontario, long-distance calls are accepted by Telecare virtually without charge to the caller. This highlights problems in the Third World, where the cost of phones is almost prohibitive, especially for the long calls necessary in counselling. In Papua-New Guinea, with a typically low phone density, most calls occur during working hours, especially lunchtimes, from places of work.

Even death was no reason to remain incommunicado. In Anthony

Whatever message these Chinese girls have just got on the phone in a Hong Kong restaurant, there is no mystery about the cost. Subscribers pay a flat monthly rental and are not charged for local calls. So shop owners do not mind customers using their phones.

(South China Morning Post)

Burgess's novel *Beard's Roman Women* (1977), one comic element was the widower getting phone calls from his dead wife. Nature soon caught up with art. In 1979 two American researchers, D. Scott Rogo and Raymond Bayless, published *Phone Calls from the Dead*, in which they detailed the manifestations of psychokinetic (PK) forces:

> It is therefore also plausible that PK force might also be able to set up and manipulate electrical impulses sent over telephone wires. Thus these 'phone calls from the dead' cases might actually be a very bizarre form of PK function – either carrying out the dead agent's wishes to contact us or being the projection of our own minds.

The two researchers discussed mechanics:

> Are the dead contacting us by manipulating electrical currents, or are they literally 'speaking' directly to us during the course of these mysterious calls? We think we have some tentative answers to these questions, and it could well be that the dead can contact us either way... We were a bit amazed when we realized that some phone calls from the dead are placed through long-distance operators.

The possibility was always there – after Constant Lambert's death in 1951, the novelist Anthony Powell received an inarticulate call at the time the composer regularly rang him – but most people were sceptical. During 1981 a dentist in Regensburg, Bavaria, claimed he was haunted by a voice coming out of his phone. His poltergeist proved to be a self-perpetrated hoax. People receiving phone calls from God were cases for psychiatric treatment.

Several education and counselling services were available to the public by phone, mainly concerned with the feared disease of cancer, sexually transmitted diseases, AIDS, and what to do in the event of an occurrence such as pesticide poisoning. These services tended to be more developed in North America, where there was a stronger phone culture, medical expenses could be high, and where home visiting was less frequent, possibly because distances were greater. Wherever they were, patients with heart conditions could be monitored over the phone, having direct contact with the doctor, who could advise and reassure. Relatively inexpensive in manpower and equipment, remote monitoring enabled easy contact to be made, for example, by patients with implanted pacemakers, either at a time of concern or as a routine during long-term treatment. Cardiopet, a Brooklyn-based service, did the same for birds, cats (including tigers), and a Central Park carriage horse hooked up to a pay phone on Fifth Avenue.

Foetal information could also be transmitted. The idea mooted in *The Lancet* soon after Bell's invention had taken almost a century to become an everyday reality.

The phone itself could be a form of therapy, as in teaching stroke patients to dial or as an exercise for the retarded. A 1973 medical paper was headed: 'Experiences with frog breathing tetraplegic polio victims as telephone operators'. The instrument also had its dangers, as reported by a plastic surgery journal: 'Tearing of an earlobe by weight of a telephone earpiece on an earring'. In 1989 the *British Medical Journal* reported a case of 'Yuppie Ear': 'A 28-year-old journalist tried to answer his portable cellular telephone in the dark. Unfortunately, in his haste he thrust its antenna in his ear, perforating his ear drum.' An American psychiatrist was awarded $300,000 damages for hearing loss from an early cordless phone with a loud ringer. Attention was still being paid to the occupational hazards of being an operator, particularly the effects of posture and on hearing. An extensive 1969 American study found only borderline evidence of increased hearing loss in older linesmen, most at risk because of their exposure to repeated high intensive clicks, and none in the switchboard operators. Twenty years later linesmen were shown to have a higher rate of cancer, possibly from low-frequency electromagnetic radiation.

Public concern on the subject of phones and disease could still erupt. In 1976 the German magazine *Quick* claimed that an examination of 250 pay phones revealed germs that could cause bone and kidney inflammations, and fatal fungi. In 1978 *The Sunday Post* published the results of an investigation in Glasgow city centre, entitled 'Filthy Phones!' Dr Tom McAllister, the bacteriologist who analysed the swabs taken from mouth- and earpieces, described his findings as 'outrageous and potentially dangerous'. The phones were 'nasty and grubby. They obviously had not been cleaned for some time. Although the bugs we found won't kill, they could cause serious illness'. One phone showed traces of excreta. 'There definitely is a danger of cross-infection,' he continued. 'If your fingers touch a contaminated handset, then you rub your mouth, you could contract a disease. In the case of earpieces, it's worse. Remember, they're in contact with the skin'. It seemed more a comment on the users of Glasgow phones and the failure to clean up after them than a cause for general alarm. Some of the boxes stank, had stains spattered on the walls and rubbish on the floors. They could well have been used as refuges by down-and-outs. In quieter spots teenagers found booths useful for stand-up sex, and they were also handover points for drugs.

Privacy was something to be guarded – against anonymous callers, heavy breathers, obscene callers. Various protective measures could be taken: using only initials and not status (Mr, Miss or Ms) in directories; having

HANG UP ON OBSCENE PHONE CALLS

Hang up immediately. That's the best advice for handling an obscene or nuisance telephone call. Don't say one word and don't make any noises. Most annoyance calls are placed at random to see what the response will be. If the callers get no such satisfaction, they usually will stop.

If these calls continue, report them to your telephone company's business office. If you are threatened or fear personal harm, call the police.

Other helpful safety tips for you:

• Teach children and babysitters to be cautious with unknown callers. Instruct that a message be taken—with no indication that you are away.

• Leave the phone number where your sitter can call you, and also leave emergency numbers. Provide a pencil and paper for messages.

• Don't identify yourself to unfamiliar callers, and don't tell them you are alone.

• Don't provide your number if someone calls you by mistake. Simply ask what number the caller is trying to reach, and then either say that the wrong number has been reached or suggest checking the directory for the correct number.

• Teach children how to use the phone in emergencies. Demonstrate with a toy phone, or use your own phone while holding down the on off switch.

Provided As a Public Service By Your Local Telephone Company

This advice from the US Independent Telephone Association applies anywhere. (US Independent Telephone Association)

calls monitored; changing a number; blowing a police whistle; outdoing a caller in his own sickness. The US Independent Telephone Association published *Hang Up on Obscene Phone Calls – Brief Tips for Everyone* and British Telecom produced *Nuisance Callers.*

Victims wondered why these crackpot cowardly callers could not be trapped by phone-tappers, who seemed to be busy intruding on privacy elsewhere. When British Telecom installed surveillance bugs in kiosks in Newcastle to detect vandalism, fears were immediately expressed that it was a short step to overhearing conversations. For its part, the company saw the devices as a means of reducing the rising costs of vandalism and of protecting instruments for legitimate use, especially in emergencies.

Public fears were not unfounded. Whereas people could understand the reasons behind intercepting calls to jurors who might be nobbled, this was much more suspect. Earlier in 1982, following the chance observation of a pocket radio set being installed in a public kiosk in Snowdonia, where Welsh patriots were setting fire to English-owned cottages, new evidence on bugging emerged. In accordance with secret Home Office guidelines, chief police officers were empowered to use such devices. This was a new kind of surveillance, never officially reported upon, and quite distinct from the kind of tapping unsuccessfully challenged in 1979 in the High Court by James Malone, an antiques dealer who had been acquitted on a charge of handling stolen goods. Unable to get any redress because the police had not broken the law, he took his case to the European Court of Human Rights, where 18 judges unanimously supported him. To clarify the law, the British government passed the 1985 Interception of Communications Act, but in essence little changed. The cloak of secrecy remained, accountability was no greater and advancing technology seemed to be on the side of the security-obsessed.

In this atmosphere there were doubts about itemized phone bills, long wanted by some customers, on the grounds that listing the time, duration, cost and destination of calls could provide evidence of intensely personal calls, say, to helplines, and police and security forces with yet more information about an individual's activities. There were cases of people pretending to be policemen and obtaining information held on police computer and intelligence files: arrest records, private addresses, occupations, sexual orientation. With so much more information moving between computers, they were sources worth tapping. Key words or names could be correlated, not necessarily accurately.

Tapping for information seemed to be almost accepted. It had moved out of the realms of big business, where rooms were 'swept' before important meetings, and crime fiction, as in Paul Ferris's *The Detective* (1976), into the everyday acceptance of comedy. In early 1981 an episode of the popular TV series *Yes Minister* was based on The Death List, discovered through phone tapping. Yet shortly before that an investigative edition of the BBC programme *Panorama* dealing with the security services was weakened after large portions of it had been suppressed internally. Nevertheless, one of them showed a former agent who claimed to have carried out dozens of 'black bag jobs', illegal phone taps, for MI6. What had been a threat to written records was now becoming a source of them, at least among selected people.

According to Lord Diplock, chairman of the Security Commission, who reported in March 1981 on the interception of phone calls and the post, existing procedures worked satisfactorily 'with the minimum of interference with the individual's rights of privacy in the interests of the public weal'. That fine-sounding verdict seemed far from the disquiet in various quarters, especially as technical advances since the Birkett Report of 1957 had made tapping on a much wider scale so much easier. The Canadian High Commissioner suggested that Britain tapped transatlantic phones to monitor the Canadian constitutional crisis. The National Council for Civil Liberties, Campaign for Nuclear Disarmament activitists and trades unionists in dispute felt they were under political surveillance, like citizens of South Africa or just as prominent protesters against the Vietnam War, such as Jane Fonda and Dr Spock, or Karen Silkwood the whistle-blower on safety in the nuclear industry, had been in the USA. Arthur Scargill, elected president of the National Union of Mineworkers at the end of 1981, believed his phone was tapped because the Home Secretary declined an invitation to send a letter assuring him that it was not. Certainly Scargill had made effective earlier use of the phone in deploying thousands of flying pickets during the 1972 strike.

In fact Lord Diplock looked at random cases from only four of the nine organizations in Britain officially engaged in phone tapping: MI5, which called it Source Towrope; the Special Branch counter-terrorist section; Customs and Excise; and the police. Omitted were: MI6, involved in spying and undercover political work; Government Communications Headquarters (GCHQ), which was involved in worldwide eavesdropping in conjunction with the American National Security Agency (NSA), whose 'watch lists' included former attorneys-general, civil rights and black activists; NSA's own bases in the UK, gathering among other things economic intelligence about Arab oil and Russian grain; the British Army, operating mainly in Northern Ireland; and the Northern Ireland authorities themselves.

There, both sides used it. The IRA had help in tapping from sympathetic phone engineers, and stole scramblers to decode conversations. In August 1971 it intercepted a phone conversation between Sir Howard Smith, the UK representative in the province, and Philip Woodfield of the Home Office, which probably gave the republicans the tip that internment without trial was starting the next day. In 1979 the Special Air Service (SAS) found an IRA centre that was eavesdropping on several lines, including that of Lieutenant General Timothy Creasey, the commanding officer of the Army in Northern Ireland. In 1983 a Dublin couple who were founder members of the Irish Republican Socialist Party claimed that they were lured on a free week's holiday in Torremolinos on the Costa Brava by British Intelligence and then offered £10,000 to grass on members of the Irish National Liberation Army. Casure Holidays, the firm that told them they had been picked by computer, operated from an accommodation address and had an MI6 phone number. Nor did Diplock get into the subject of private bugging operations for purposes such as industrial espionage. Altogether it seemed a bland report that dodged the issues of proper parliamentary accountability.

Britons lived in a less accountable society than citizens of other Western nations. In West Germany, people were notified when taps were removed and could sue the government if they could prove there was no valid reason for such surveillance. Portugal suspended security police operations after the 1974 socialist overthrow of the dictatorship until terrorist activities became a menace ten years later. In the USA, the Attorney-General annually gave Congress details of all applications and authorizations, as well as of arrests and convictions. The new socialist government in France introduced stricter safeguards. When the 'Liffeygate' scandal broke in Dublin over the bugging of two journalists' phones, it led to the resignation of two influential policemen and the removal of two politicians from the opposition front bench. In 1983 the British government had some reason to be annoyed with the practice. When Mrs Thatcher visited the Falklands, a call from her Press secretary to the assistant Director–General of the BBC was intercepted by a radio ham, tape-recorded and broadcast on a rival TV channel.

Well might an ordinary British citizen write to *The Guardian* wishing that somebody would tap his calls and listen to his views on current events. So suspicious were the public that there was a ready sale for devices claiming

During the 1980s phone cards were adopted in over 60 countries. Cards relieved callers of the need to carry small change, removed a great source of temptation from potential thieves, and became collectors' items.

(Stanley Gibbons Ltd)

to alert users to bugs on the line. Unapproved, they were more a smart gimmick than a reliable indicator that somebody was definitely listening in. They could be triggered by something innocent – such as damp weather. Paranoid executives could buy briefcases containing computer-controlled scramblers, a voice distorter was available, and a device for registering the tremors – indicating stress – in the voice at the other end of the line. That such devices might have some value was demonstrated in a £780,000 gold fraud perpetrated in the City of London in 1983. Thieves ordered kruggerands from two bullion dealers, payment to be made on banker's drafts. A member of the gang intercepted calls at the bank branch and, when authenticity of the drafts was sought, pretended to be the manager.

A wider variety of phones was becoming available, many of them based on the microchip, which brought facilities such as timing calls, calculating, diverting calls to another extension, and remembering frequently used numbers, which could be dialled by keying two digits. More intelligence was being put into what were becoming information terminals that incorporated directories, acted as diaries and notebooks, sent messages by telex or delivered them to an electronic postbox, displayed news and statistics from public and private viewdata sources, and provided urgent reminders. At the same time computers were being supplied with built-in phones.

You need never be far from a phone, even in a shower, where you could use a water-resistant model. During the 1980s the great growth was in car phones, which became a yuppie symbol. There was fun, and possibly profit, in eavesdropping on conversations with a radio scanner. Coin-box phones were installed on high-speed trains. In the 1990s satellite communications made possible the international in-flight office, already an earthly reality with business systems in a briefcase. Similar technology can be used for a global messaging service, sending bleeps to pagers in trucks on the move. Pagers in a wristwatch are available. As an alternative to being sent to prison, offenders can be put under house arrest, being electronically tagged and their presence monitored. Pioneer experience in the USA pointed to lower recidivism rates. More than one line could be provided on a single phone and pocket radio-phones were expected to provide personal portable communications for the masses by the mid-1990s. To some people this heralded a new form of pollution, the prospect of loud-mouths demonstrating their social superiority by making calls in all sorts of public places. That put a premium on places that barred such traffic and, even better, on silence. Proprietors of some exclusive restaurants relieved patrons of cellphones and pagers on entry. There were further fears about invasions of privacy by unwanted callers. These could be screened out by their numbers being displayed or by the calls being diverted to a message centre.

Through technology the phone had become a more pervasive instrument. Comparing the number of calls and the number of employees in the Bell System in 1910 and 1981 revealed the enormous increase in productivity in the service. Had there been no such increase, by 1981 the Bell System would have needed nearly four billion employees, or about the estimated population of the world, to deal with the volume of traffic.

CHAPTER 17

TERMINALS

The international phone system is the biggest automatic machine that man has ever created, and it is still growing. For example, the few inhabitants of Pitcairn Island, the tiny Pacific island originally colonized by Fletcher Christian and mutineers from the *Bounty*, joined the network in 1983. Till then they had had a radio station and had issued two postage stamps on telecommunications. Over three decades, the development of International Direct Dialling has linked most of the world's subscribers. Yet their call signals are no more universal than numbers for the operator or emergencies. Even in the European Community tones are different and new callers are not always sure whether the line is engaged or nobody is answering. Yet through a simple instrument each subscriber, in theory, has direct access to some 700 million others. Within seconds, via equipment of which they are unconscious, two people – perhaps strangers – can be talking. People who have never left their own countries talk to relatives and friends abroad, finding it surprisingly easy to get through and the quality often better than on local lines. By making and keeping in contact they may be encouraged to travel.

In what has been called the new science of 'telegeography', the number of minutes of international telecom traffic has been suggested as a rapid, reliable indicator of patterns of economic activity, much as the number of railway cars moving around the USA at the end of the nineteenth century was studied by Wall Street. They could, for example, indicate the growth of drug traffic to various destinations as well as pointing to relative demand in other service activities. The problems are that patterns can be distorted by individual nations' charges for international calls and, although phone administrations are in a position to be economic consultants, they do not readily divulge data commercially valuable to them. Within countries, phones reflect national characteristics. The USA is phone-conscious, with the world's largest number of phones, while Sweden has the greatest density in relation to population.

Differences in national attitudes were appreciated by an immigrant Irish doctor:

> In 1970 I was a locum in a one-horse town in Co. Longford, where the phones were hand cranked. The woman in the exchange took messages for me when I was out on call and gave them to me with her own diagnosis: 'Mary O'Malley's had that pain in her tummy for years. She just wants a bit o' sympathy'. In Ireland the doctor and the priest were usually the only two people with a phone, perhaps the policeman. There was no phone service 11 p.m. to 7 a.m., when the telephonist went to bed.

Ten years later he was working in a 360-bed private hospital in Baltimore, which had 960 incoming lines:

> Each patient has his own phone, costing a dollar a day, which includes free local calls. As soon as a patient gets to hospital he phones his friends and they phone him, often instead of visiting. When a doctor makes his rounds the patient will put a caller on hold. I probably call the hospital about ten times a day from home.
>
> The hospital phones to fix and confirm appointments, especially for out-patient operations. When a patient has returned home we can check whether he's OK by phone. If the appointment is not kept we can also check. The hospital checks a patient's insurance status, valid or invalid, computer to computer on a phone line. It saves the cost of writing a letter, which is about five dollars.

His home was a veritable communications centre:

> We have three incoming lines, of which one is unlisted so that it's free for outgoing calls. There are nine phones in the house. The kids share a line and have a phone each. Seven year olds phone next door before going to play. My wife calls the store to check that items are in stock before she goes.

Back in the old country things were changing. In 1984 the manual exchange in the hamlet of Glenade, County Leitrim, which had one subscriber, gave way to an impersonal electronic system. The last subscriber praised the service, which had always been 'very friendly, very efficient, prompt!'. He got 'personal attention'. There were those who could remember the party line with eight subscribers – in true Irish fashion Glenade 6 had four rings – and the joys of listening in, especially when the priest had a call.

Meanwhile American satellites were monitoring some of the long-distance phone traffic in the Soviet Union, which was in turn doubtless being monitored by the authorities internally. Although Khruschev had formally abolished censorship, people inside and outside the Soviet Union were resigned to calls being monitored. It was well known that the KGB used tapes of alleged tappings as a means of spreading disinformation about prominent people and the policies of other nations. The tapes were carefully spliced recordings. Monitoring did not inhibit dissident Jews, 'refuseniks' wanting to emigrate to Israel, from keeping in touch with the Promised Land, even conducting informal seminars in a 'university of the air'. Internally, bureaucracy was an obstacle to communication. Phone directories were produced infrequently and in limited editions. In some Eastern European countries the wait for a phone could be as long as 20 years. One of the more entrepreneurial countries, Hungary, hit on the novel idea of promoting a bond issue by promising subscribers a phone within three years. The situation began to improve, legally if not technically, with Gorbachev's perestroika embracing the privacy of phone calls as a human right and the 1989 revolutions in Eastern Europe creating a climate in which communications could flourish. A further massive change was necessary though. Systems that had restricted the flow of information, to the advantage of centralized regimes, were to prove a handicap in the transition to free market economies, where success depended largely on the ease and speed of contacts, internally and externally.

The other great communist power, China, initially seemed to take a more open view than the Soviet Union, although it was just as adept at restricting the issue of directories and at monitoring calls. Post-Mao, as part of the drive towards national unity and modernization, the People's Government wanted to popularize 'common speech', a standard form that would enable different parts of the country to understand one another. Like the Soviet Union, China was a multi-national country, with 56 nationalities speaking eight families of dialects. The aim was not to eliminate dialects, which would remain for home use, but to promote cultural unity and hence technological advancement through communication. In this, the phone, an infrequent and unreliable instrument, would have a small role. Most phones were public, looked after by minders who served a neighbourhood, typically of some 400 households. The minders, often women, made pin money from a share in the revenues from outgoing calls and running messages, perhaps on a bicycle.

Modern communications, especially TV, radio, fax and computers, were used to rush information in and out of China during the pro-democracy student demonstrations in Tiananmen Square, Beijing, in May–June 1989. The world received graphic eye-witness reports of events, and local people's accounts that evaded official censorship. Chinese-language newspapers outside China produced news summaries in a format for cutting out and faxing. In a country with a low phone density – about eight million in a population of over one billion – and a very uneven distribution, instant communications were a striking challenge to an authoritarian regime. In the short term the students were crushed but their thoughts, news of their actions and repression had been authoritatively and widely disseminated. Unlike most news, it was not a perishable commodity.

Internationally, the Chinese wanted a greater role. Their delegate pointed out at the International Telecommunication Union conference in Nairobi in 1982:

> The developing countries make up 75 per cent of the present 157 member countries of the union. However, owing to historical and other reasons, huge gaps exist between developing countries and the technically advanced developed countries in sharing the benefit of scientific and technological progress in telecommunications. By the end of 1981, more than 2,700 satellites and spacecraft have been launched in the world, of which over 90 per cent belong to two countries.

China got itself into the space business, but bringing developing nations into the space age was fraught with bribery and corruption. Publicly, satellite ground stations looked good *in situ* and on the postage stamps and, privately, in the bank balance of a local agent, who could get a commission of as much as 10 or 15 per cent on the contract. Many African and Middle Eastern governments were all too ready to invest in communications projects for some vague prestige and definite personal profit. When the technology was explained to one sheikh in terms of 'the big dish' he was curious to know about 'the big spoon' that went with it. 'The result', according to Dr Murray Watson, a consultant ecologist who had worked in Africa for 15 years, 'is that aid is really the movement of money from the poor people in rich countries to the rich in poor countries'.

Such prestige facilities could be used by the few for international transactions, as in the electronic transfer of funds in bidding at major art auctions, but they offered little to the mass of the people. Often, not far beneath the prestige, there was a ramshackle communications system, inadequate, overloaded, and unreliable. Getting a line could take years or a considerable payment. In places such as Argentina, Brazil and India a phone was a major asset of a company, perhaps enough to redeem its liabilities when it was in liquidation. Custody of the phone could be a contentious issue in a divorce suit. In such constrained circumstances it was not an instrument of social change.

Nowhere was the combination of old and new better seen than in the structured society of Japan. On a push button phone you could reserve your seat on the *Shinkansen*, the bullet train, and when you were on board there was a phone at your disposal. In the nation the service was unbelievably efficient and polite. Even when the operators were on strike they were still at their switchboards, explaining to users why they were on strike and apologizing. Users bowed on the phone and it was considered bad form to thank somebody over it. Much better to go in person or send a present to show that you were taking time and valued the personal bond. There was an etiquette associated with the phone that the Japanese tried to export through their training centres for operators that they set up in various parts of Asia. They also had some concern for the environment in that they put plastic caps on hollow steel poles so that wild birds did not get trapped inside when nesting.

At the other extreme were the Italians, voluble Latins who made a public performance of using the phone, holding long conversations in bars, oblivious of the noise around them and gesticulating the while. They were able to go on at length because in off-peak periods *un gettone*, one phone token, gave them unlimited time. During weekdays the service was still cheap and woebetide any politician who wanted to raise charges unduly. The Italians had taken the instrument to their hearts. It occurred in the recipe *il telefono*, a short fat sausage consisting of meat and soft cheese, which together resembled wires, that was dipped in beaten egg, deep-fried, and served piping hot. It began as a winter snack in Rome bars, sometimes being ordered by phone for picking up. Human pick-ups, call-girls and - boys, were called *squilli*, from the harsh, squeaky screams sometimes made by Italian phones. Consumers were also quick to protest when they received their bills, claiming that the phone meters gave false readings. Neighbours in blocks of flats could have interfered with them and those located in streets jerked up – always up – when juggernauts and other heavy traffic rumbled past. They were not above recording peals of thunder and bolts of lightning, all at the expense of the consumer. No mention of the TV shows in which consumers phoned in their complaints or tried to win large sums by answering simple questions. Some 70 per cent of Sunday afternoon/ evening calls in Rome were directed to competitions.

Apart from charges, the thing that made the phlegmatic British raise their voices was changing their red phone boxes. When British Telecom 'experimented' with yellow on its kiosks, a livery that was widely regarded as in line with the colour of Buzby its canary mascot, or some attempt at Euro-uniformity, there was a public outcry. New booths, of simpler design in modern materials and easier to maintain, replaced most of the traditional boxes, some of which were saved by ardent conservationists. Foreigners

Yoko Terauchi from Japan has produced a series of sculptures, Hot-line, using single lengths of cable to demonstrate continuum and harmony. This is Hot-line 6, Split-ends.
(Victoria Miro Gallery)

were prepared to pay good money for them and, with the British, joined a queue for redundant ones.

The realities of the early 1990s seem a far remove from the predictions of the futurologists. Some see voice recognition in general use by the end of the century. We shall simply speak the number we require and be put through, rapidly. It might even be possible to return to the level of service at the beginning of the century when you asked the operator to get somebody for you. In the future, a machine will translate the name into a number. The possibilities of error are enormous. Not to worry. Our conversations will be routed via electronic exchanges that translate simultaneously and any misunderstanding will soon be sorted out. It will not be like getting a wrong number in France today, when the only English the woman seems to know is 'Allo? Allo?...' Cost won't be a concern either. By the year 2000, a phone call to anywhere in the world will cost about 50

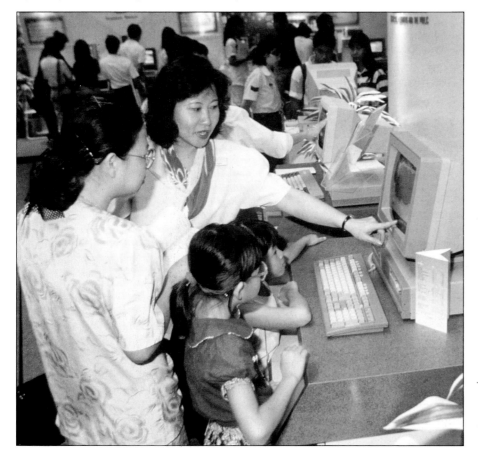

In 1990 Singapore, which proclaims itself The Intelligent Island, launched Teleview, which provides on-line access via rented home terminals to electronic information services. Children can learn from images with photographic quality, play games and get career advice. Among other things, adults can make bank enquiries, plan and book holidays, and send greetings to friends. With Teleview and other developments, Singapore aims to be the world's first 'on-line' society by the end of the century.

(Singapore Telecom)

While keeping an eye on the blackjack table in a Seychelles casino you can be in touch with the world via a satellite over the Indian Ocean.

(Cable and Wireless)

cents. Why not have the world's copy-typing done in South East Asia, faxed from technological city-states such as Hong Kong and Singapore? Within the early decades of the 21st century we may see the direct connection of man and machine with bio-electronic components.

This kind of future is science fiction to the mass of the world's population. Instantaneous universal communication is a long way off. At present there is an enormous imbalance between the industrialized nations, the top eight of which account for about 80 per cent of all phones, and the less developed struggling to attain some basic level of service. In 'telegeographic' terms they are off the map, as was Iraq after the few weeks' aerial bombardment in the six-week 1991 Gulf War. Over half the world's population is more than two hours walking distance from a phone. In theory they are at an advantage and, not burdened with a mass of obsolescent equipment, can go straight to modern technology. In practice, they may not need that amount of sophistication and perhaps cannot really afford it. They may have more pressing priorities. A Swedish equation such as 100 kilometres of motorway costing as much as 100,000 phone channels is meaningless because it presents an unreal choice. The mass of the people will go on cooking their simple meals, marvelling at stories of people who can switch on an oven with a phone call.

In the depths of the Hong Kong countryside an emergency phone is at hand. (Cable and Wireless)

As in other aspects of North/South relations, the gap between rich and poor is growing. In the poorer nations the majority of people will live their lives unaffected by the phone. 'A hungry man has no ears.' In the richer nations it will become a more sophisticated device, an intelligent terminal capable of doing so much more. Combined with computers and TV screens, it will be a key instrument in expanding the world of information technology. Masses of digital information – representing speech, data, still and moving pictures, music – will be stored in computer databases, called up by phone, carried on optical fibres, and presented for eye and ear.

Messages will be cheaper and more convenient than messengers. Plodding postmen could disappear, at least from business districts. People will find it easier to work at home with terminals rather than commuting to an office. A daily newspaper will not be left at the front door but displayed on a TV screen or printed out on a low-cost fax machine. Gas and electric meters will be read down the line. It will be possible to shop and bank from an armchair, to offer opinions to pollsters, to vote. People in different parts of the world with a common interest will be able to communicate via electronic mail boxes. In this way new forms of instant specialist publishing

– 'narrowcasting' – could be created. People from different continents interested in, say, the early Hungarian film industry, advice on keeping tortoises, or discussing some new piece of design could soon be in touch with one another. Researching the detail of a book like this could become much easier.

All these are possibilities. Certainly more information will become more easily available. Will we want so much? The means of communicating information are expanding at a greater rate than man can receive and absorb it. His faculties do not increase in proportion. Do we want to be followed around with messages? There are times when it is pleasant to be selectively deaf or simply unavailable, like the man in Ray Bradbury's story *The Murderer*, who disables the insistent communications devices surrounding him.

The means of communication are unlikely to determine our ways of life as much as Marshall McLuhan predicted. Technological advance does not necessarily change society immediately nor always in the expected direction. However big an extension of our faculties the phone becomes, it will remain a neutral instrument, to be used for good or ill. As always, the choice will be ours.

ACKNOWLEDGEMENTS

Whereas there are several books and papers on the influence of the press, the telegraph, radio and TV, comparatively little has been written about the telephone. It is the largely neglected communications medium. After initial curiosity, people have taken it for granted. References to it are not easy to come by and I acknowledge help from several sources, not all of which are evident in the text.

Particularly, I should like to thank three enthusiasts for their support: Miss Laurie Dennett, former archivist of STC; Eric Clayton, formerly curator of the Norwich Telephone Area Museum; and Neil Johannessen, manager of BT Museum.

Among other sources were: Jean Adams, curator of Easdale Island Folk Museum, Argyllshire; Kathleen Adams of the George Eliot Fellowship; Alcoholics Anonymous; Jim Ally; Ansafone; The Duke of Argyll; Arundel Castle Trustees; AT&T; BBC; Bank of England; The Marquess of Bath; Sir Brian Batsford; Bell Canada; Quentin Bell; Bell Telephone Manufacturing Company; Bentalls; Andrew Birkin; Tony Boyes; British Coal; The British Library; Sidney Burdfield; The Burton Group; Cable and Wireless; The Castle Museum, York; Catholic Central Library; Central Lenin Museum; Centre National d'Etudes des Télécommunications; Chubb; Contact Teleministries USA; F. Palmer Cook; Mrs M. Corbould; Crawley Library; Judith & Roy Dalton; Shirley Davy; Deutsche Bundesbahn; Distress Centre, Toronto; Leon Edel; English China Clays; L. M. Ericsson; David Finch, honorary editor, Arnold Bennett Literary Society; Mrs Felicity Firth; Bryan Forbes; Gamblers Anonymous; Cecil Gegg; Richard Perceval Graves; Edwin Green, archivist of Midland Bank; GTE Automatic Electric Inc; Richard Hall; Major A. G. Harfield, historical officer, Royal Signals Museum; Brian Harrison; Evelyn Heath; Health and Safety Executive; HongKong Telephone; Imperial War Museum; The Industrial Society; Institut Français; Institute of Economic Affairs; Institution of Electrical Engineers; Institution of Post Office Electrical Engineers; ITT Austria; Dom Philip Jebb; H.

Russell Jones; Kingston upon Hull Telephone Department; The Kipling Society; Leicestershire Trade Protection Society Ltd; Library of Congress; Liverpool Record Office; Roger Longrigg; Phillipa Lord; L. J. McDonald, archivist of the Pilkington Group; Bill McNair; The Earl of March; Metropolitan Police Forensic Science Laboratory; Michael Meyer; Michael Millgate; Mitchell Library, New South Wales; Dr Jerrold Moore; Mrs M. More; Dominique Moussu; National Film Archive; National Railway Museum; Mrs Robert Nesham; Netherlands PTT; Netherlands State Institute for War Documentation; New Zealand Post Office; Hermann Neumuller; New Scotland Yard; The Northumberland Estates; The Open University; Dr M. J. Orbell, archivist, Baring Brothers; The Overseas Telecommunications Commission (Australia); Mrs Nancy Papantoniou; Mrs Pleydell-Bouverie; Robert S. W. Pollard; Post Office; John Randle; Release; Royal Geographical Society; Royal National Lifeboat Institution; Royal National Throat Nose and Ear Hospital; Jean Salvarelli; The Samaritans; The Savoy; Pina Scalera; Philip Scowcroft; Securicor; Denis Sevenoaks; Brocard Sewell; Anthony Shadrake, history librarian, King's College, London; R. Shingles; Siebe Gorman & Co; The 600 Group; Barbara Smoker; Social Science Research Council; South African Post Office Museum; Commander P. J. Stickland, HMS Vernon; Strindbergsmuseet; Swiss Posts and Telecommunications; Telecom Australia; Telecom Singapore; Televerket; John Thaxter; Marquess Townshend; E. S. Turner; Alison Turton, archivist, House of Fraser; US Independent Telephone Association; University College of Wales; University of Essex; University of New South Wales; University of Sussex; University of Texas; Roger Voeller; Penny Wallace; Mariko Watanabe; The Wellcome Institute for the History of Medicine; Welsh Miners Museum; Welsh Water Authority; D. E. Wickham, archivist of The Clothworkers' Company; K. V. Wilkinson; E. S. Wilks; Walter G. Wright; Dick Young.

Written sources included: Andrew, Christopher, Secret Service (Heinemann, 1985); Anstey, F., The Man from Blankley's (1893); Aronson, Sidney H., The Sociology of the Telephone, International Journal of Comparative Sociology, Sept 1971 and The Lancet on the Telephone 1876-1975, Med. Hist., 1977, 21; Associated Newspapers; Golden Milestone (Automobile Association, 1955); Barty-King, Hugh, The Baltic Exchange (Hutchinson Benham, 1977); Bell Telephone Quarterly; Bierce, Ambrose, The Devil's Dictionary; Boettinger, H. M., The Telephone Book (Riverwood, 1977); Boorstin, Daniel J., The Americans, 1965; Brighton Evening Argus; British Journal of Audiology; British Medical Journal; Brooks, John, Telephone (Harper & Row, 1975); Cartwright, F.C., G-Men of the GPO (Sampson Low); The Children's Encyclopaedia; Clark, D., Communications and the Urban Future, Regional Studies, Vol 7, 1973; Clark,

Ronald W., The Life of Bertrand Russell (Cape/Weidenfeld & Nicolson, 1975); Clarke, Thurston, By Blood and Fire: The Attack on the King David Hotel (Hutchinson, 1981); Coates, Austin, Quick Tidings of Hong Kong (Oxford University Press, 1990); Collins, Robert, A Voice From Afar (McGraw Hill-Ryerson, 1977); Cooper, Dennis, The People Machine (GTE Florida, 1977); Country Life; Country Quest; Dagens Nyheter; Daily Express; Daily Telegraph; Detroit Free Press; Eastern Daily Press; Duhamel, Georges, Problèmes de Civilisation (Mercure de France, 1962); The Electrician; Electronics and Power; Every Woman's Encyclopaedia; Financial Times; Franklyn, Julian, A Dictionary of Rhyming Slang (Routledge, 1961); Fraser, Ronald, Blood of Spain (Allen Lane, 1979); Frost, Robert, The Poetry of Robert Frost (Cape, 1971); The Girl's Own Paper; The Guardian; Haffner, Sebastian, Failure of a Revolution (André Deutsch, 1973); Haight, Gordon S., The Yale Edition of the George Eliot Letters, Vol 7 1978–80 (1955); Harding, Gilbert, Book of Manners (Putnam, 1956); Harman, Nicholas, Dunkirk: The Necessary Myth (Hodder & Stoughton, 1980); Harper's Magazine; Hasek, Jaroslav, The Good Soldier Schweik (1930); Herbert, A. P., Uncommon Law (Methuen, 1935); Hughes, M. V., A London Family Between The Wars (OUP, 1940); Independent Telephony in New England (Independent Telephone Pioneer Association, 1976); Jackson, Brian, The Black Flag (Routledge, 1981); Jennings, Paul, The Jenguin Pennings (Penguin, 1963); Journal of the Liverpool Telephone Area; Journal of Science and Technology; Journal of the Society of Arts; Keesing's Contemporary Archives; Keynes, Margaret, A House by the River: Newnham Grange to Darwin College (Darwin College, Cambridge, 1976); Kingsbury, J. E., The Telephone and Telephone Exchanges (Longmans, 1915); Lewis, Sinclair, The Job (1916), Main Street (1920); Libois, L-J., Genese et Croissance des Télécommunications (Masson, 1983); The Listener; The Magnet; Nalder, Major-General R.F.H., The Royal Corps of Signals (1958); The National Geographic Magazine; The National Telephone Journal; Nemerov, Howard, Collected Poems (University of Chicago, 1977); New Scientist; New Statesman; North Wales Chronicle; Oban Times; The Observer; Pakenham, Thomas, The Boer War (Weidenfeld & Nicolson, 1979); Paul, Elliot, A Narrow Street (Penguin, 1942); Pool, Ithiel de Sola (ed), The Social Impact of the Telephone (MIT, 1977); Pope, W. McQueen, The Melodies Linger On (W. H. Allen, 1950); Post Office Magazine; Proust, M., Remembrance of Things Past Vol III, trs C. K. Scott-Moncrieff and Terence Kilmartin (Chatto & Windus, 1981); Punch; Reader, W. J., Hard Roads and Highways (Batsford, 1969); Revue Français des Télécommunications; Roskill, Stephen, Hankey (Collins, 1972); Ruffin, Raymond, Résistance PTT (Presse de la Cite, 1983); Rush, Michael, The House of Commons: Services and Facilities (Allen & Unwin,

1974); Scott, J. M., Extel 100 (Benn, 1972); Siemens, Georg, History of the House of Siemens (Arno Press, 1977); The Sketch; Standard News; Storey, Graham, Reuter's Century (Max Parrish, 1951); Strand Magazine; The Sun; Sunday Post; Sunday Times; Surgeon-General's Catalogue; The Telcon Story (Telcon, 1950); Telecom Heritage; Telecom Journal (Australia); Telephone Engineer & Management; Telephony; Theoharis, Athan G., The Boss (Harrap, 1989); Thomas, Hugh, The Spanish Civil War (Hamish Hamilton, 1977); Three Victorian Telephone Directories (1884/85) (David & Charles); The Times; The Times History of the War in South Africa (Hurst and Blackett, 1905–09); Victorian Studies; Volk, Conrad, Magnus Volk of Brighton (Phillimore, 1971); Warley Independent News; Western Electric News; Wireless World; Yarmouth Independent.

For permission to reproduce copyright extracts, acknowledgements are due to the following:

Kingsley Amis, *Lucky Jim* (1954), Gollancz Ltd and Doubleday, a division of Bantam, Doubleday, Dell Publishing Group, Inc.;

Vera Brittain, *Chronicle Of Youth* (1981), her war diary 1913–17, are included with the permission of Alan Bishop, the editor, and Paul Berry, her literary executor, published by Victor Gollancz Ltd and Wm Morrow & Co Inc.;

George Eliot, *The George Eliot Letters* (1955), ed. G. S. Haight, Yale University Press;

Richard Le Gallienne, *Vanishing Roads And Other Essays* (1915), The Society of Authors as the literary representative of the Estate of Richard Le Gallienne;

Gilbert Harding, *Book Of Manners* (1956), The Bodley Head as publishers for Putnam;

F. Tennyson Jesse, *A Pin To See The Peepshow*, Virago Press, 1979. The Public Trustee Harwood Will Trust;

G. H. Lewes' diary, Gabriel Woolf;

Gordon Lonsdale, *Spy* (1965), Neville Spearman Publishers;

W. Somerset Maugham, *The Summing Up* (1938), reprinted by permission of William Heinemann Ltd and A. P. Watt on behalf of The Royal Literary Fund;

George Orwell, *Tribune* article 25 February 1944, the estate of the late Sonia Brownell Orwell, Martin Secker and Warburg Limited, and Harcourt, Brace, Jovanovich;

Margaret Powell, *My Children And I* (1978), Michael Joseph Limited;

D. Scott Rogo and Raymond Bayless, *Phone Calls From The Dead* (1979), reprinted by permission of the publisher, Prentice-Hall, Inc., New Jersey, USA;

Bernard Shaw, *A Village Wooing*, The Society of Authors on behalf of the
Bernard Shaw Estate;
Angela Thirkell, *Growing Up* (1943), Hamish Hamilton Limited.

INDEX

Figures in bold refer to illustrations

167, 171, 202, 204, **210**, 211, 256

rural 83–7, 104, 119, 126–7, 140–1, 148–51, 194, 198, 235, 245–8

Russell, Bertrand 198–9, 218–19

Russia 91–2, 127–8, 206–8, 214, 215, 218–19, 264, 269

sabotage 172, **173**, 180, 185

Sacco and Vanzetti 127

saint 198

San Francisco 105, 106, 135, 159, 225

satellites 213–15, 217, 266, 268, 270

Savoy, The 45, 66, 207

Sayers, D. L. 110, 112–13, 151

Scalia, L. 107–9, 129–30, 137–8, 142, 160, 175–6, 179, 187

Scotland 5, 15, 54, 142, 151, 156, 193, 204, 241, 244, **247**, 253

security 95–6, 120, 128, 182, 185, 206, 208, 210, 231–2, 236, 243, 263

Selfridge, G. 67, 104–5, 109, 156, 172

selling 125, 126, 141, 146, 193, 212, 228, 230–1, 234, 236, 244, 249

servants 3, 11, 13, 14, 118–19, 120, **134**

services 29, 49, 135, 146, 149, 194, 198, 202–4, 232, 236, 237, 241, 253, **258**

Shakespeare, W. 2, 9, 11, 90

Shaw, G. B. 13, 18, 48, 114, 149

ships 2, 14, 39–40, 41, 49, 52, 69, 96–7, 123, 128, 145,

160, 180, 184, 241

shopping 33, 43–4, 60, 62, 66–8, 104–5, 119, 121, 143, 147, 149–50, 155, 190, 191, 193, 228, 246, 248, **259**, 268

Simenon, G. 197

Singapore 100, 180, 187, 195, 241, **273**

Skinner, B. 176, 177

slang 107, 204

solicitors 19, 110, 112, 174, 178

songs 10, 11, 15, 24, 29, 32, 74, 88, 105, 117, 118, 128–9, 162, 195–6, 252, 254

South Africa 17, 34, 83, 86, 100, 119, 132, 138, 140, 217, 263

South America 138, 159, 174, **242**

Spain 110, 119, 138, 159, 168, 218, 253

speaking clock 147, 154, 223, 244

speaking tubes 2–3, 34, 39

spies 51, 71–2, 172, **173**, 206–9, 217, 264

Stalin 127–8, 215

stamps **5**, 33, 241, **242**, 270

Stevenson, R. L. 54

storms 33, 63–4, 70, **84**, 88, 109

stress 34, 62–4, 130, 235, 265

Strindberg, A. 48

submarines 40

Sweden 22, **48**, 60, 81, 136–7, 156–7, 219, 235, 248, 254, 258, 267, 274

switchboards 15, **20**, 25–31, 37, 60–5, 67, 76, 95, 99, 104, 129, 130, 141, 154, 179–80, 190, 202, 212, 217, 218, 241, 242, 252, 256, 271

Switzerland 11, 14, 19, 45, 52, 60, 62, 88, 106, 138, 145, 147, **152**, 156, 204, 213

tapping 51, 112, 126–8, 169, 174–5, 183–5, 206–10, 231–2, 253, 262–5, 269

telegrams 19, 41, 78, 101–3, 107, 120, 121, 126, 179, 190, 194, **215**, 218, 250

telegraph 1, 2, 6, 9, 12, 14, 15, 17, 23, 31, 33, 39, 40, 41, 51, 52, 72, 125, 126, 128, **157**, 165, 182, 197–8, 213, 215

television 2, 167, 196–7, 202, 217, 221, 232, 243, 245, 246, 250, 253, 263, 269, 275

terrorists 190, 217, 251, 264

theatre 11, 19, 45–8, 55, 73, 105, 109, 113, 114, 117, 147, 149, 155, 156, 159, 162, 164, 165, 195–6, 202, 223, 236

thieves 37, 66, 74, 104, 132, 151–4, 233–5, 265

Thurber, J. 88

Toronto 27, 36, 44, 62, 68, 252

toys 3–4, 10, 13, 19, 81

transatlantic 58, 137, 145, 156–7, 160, 172–4, 187, 207, 208, **213**, **215**, 217, 219, 221, 261

Trotsky 101, 127

Troubridge, Lady 118–19, 205

Turkey 59, 138, 242

Twain, M. 26, 54

undertakers 55, 82, 249

USA 8, 11, 12, 15, 32, 51, 54, 59, 62, 64, 75, 81, 96, 99,

128, 135, 138, 140, 141, **157**, 159, 164, 170, 177, 179, 194, 204, 206, 210, 214–15, 218–19, 221, 222, 223–5, 230, 233–4, 237, 239, 241, 248, 249, 253, 260, 263, 264, 266, 267

Ustinov, P. 135

Vancouver 104, 106

vandalism 58, 132, 233–5, 246, 251, 262

Victoria, Queen 10, 49, 62

videophone **21**, 114, 144, **243**

Volk, M. 13, 14

waiting lists 202

Wales 15, 75, 86, 112, 150–1, 192, 218, 234–5, 245–6, 248, 252, 258, 262

Wallace, E. 74–5, 113, 117, 156

Wall Street 126, 140, **157**, 222, 244, 267

Washington 16, 38, 40, 105, 172, 204, 218, 222, 225, 251, 253

Watson, T. 5, 9, 10, 26, 32, 33, 105

Waugh, E. 148, 165, 182

weather 94, 110, 127, 148, 202, 204, 236, 241

Welles, O. 164

Western Union 9, 17

White House 55, 82, 174, 218, 222, 239

Wodehouse, P. J. 14, 107

women 26–31, 58–65, 76, 85, 100–1, 114–19, 130, 140, 177–8, 211, 248

Woolf, L. 148

Yellow Pages 32, 225, 249